Riviera Na

Lost and Found Series

*Classic Travel
Writing*

Riviera Nature Notes

*A Popular Account of the More Conspicuous Plants and
Animals of the Riviera and the Maritime Alps*

Signal Books
Oxford
2004

This edition published in 2004 by
Signal Books Limited
36 Minster Road
Oxford
OX4 1LY
www.signalbooks.co.uk

First published in 1903
Introduction and Notes © Rob Cassy, 2004

A catalogue record for this book is available from the British Library

ISBN 1-902669-82-7 Cloth
ISBN 1-902669-83-5 Paper

Cover Design: Baseline Arts
Art & Production: Devdan Sen
Cover Image: Courtesy Daniela Guglielmi, Giardini Botanici Hanbury
alla Mortola

Printed in Canada by Webcom

Contents

To

Sir Thomas Hanbury, K.C.V.O., F.L.S., etc,
of La Mortola, Italy,
the munificent patron of education,
of science, and of natural history,
these nature notes
are dedicated with much esteem.

"J'observe et je suis la Nature:
C'est mon secret pour être heureux."
FLORIAN

FOREWORD
by Rob Cassy

> *Knowest thou the land where the lemon trees bloom,*
> *Where the gold orange blows in the deep thicket's gloom,*
> *Where a wind ever soft from the blue heaven blows,*
> *And the groves are of laurel, and myrtle, and rose?*

Goethe

SOME of the best things in life come to us by happy accident. Several years ago I was in Paris for a couple of days, staying as usual in the Latin Quarter. Walking by the Seine one evening on my way to dinner I had time to kill, and passing the bouquinistes I looked idly through the stock of one particular second-hand dealer I'd bought books from in the past. I picked up and thumbed a small black clothbound volume from 1898, called *Riviera Nature Notes*. "A popular account of the more striking plants and animals of the Riviera and the Maritime Alps", it seemed interesting enough, but what really struck me, and what closed the deal, was the dedication: "To Commendatore Thomas Hanbury, F. L. S. of La Mortola, Italy, the munificent patron of education, of science, and of natural history I dedicate with much esteem this book, which has been published through his kindness."

Hanbury (1832-1907) was a man of many parts. The second son of a well-to-do London Quaker family in the pharmaceutical business, he became an unpaid clerk to a firm of City tea brokers at the age of 17. He learned his trade well, and was soon augmenting a small allowance from his parents with profits from his own import/export investments. Come 1853 he set sail to Shanghai in partnership with a cousin, a friend and two older, more experienced hands. Over the next twenty years he amassed a fortune and travelled widely, but neither his money nor his time were ever idly spent. Good Quaker businessman that he was, he is remembered in China, Great Britain and throughout the Riviera as a philanthropist who looked after the working man; the gardening world still looks on him as one of the great plant collectors and horticulturalists. In 1867 he bought the derelict Palazzo Orengo at La Mortola with the aim of restoring it to its former glory and of creating a botanical garden in the grounds; he was elected a Fellow of the Linnaean Society in 1878; in 1892 he presented a Botanical Institute to the University of Genoa; he was awarded the Victoria Medal of Honour in 1903—thanks in part for buying Wisley in Surrey for the benefit of the Royal Horticultural Society. If Hanbury had a hand in anything it was bound to be of interest. This book, published at Hanbury's expense by the Labour Press in Manchester, by an author mysteriously signing himself only C.C. in the modest preface, was clearly worth closer inspection.

It would be too much of a cliché—and not quite the truth—to say that I sat up all night reading. After a long meal and countless drinks on the Île de la Cité it was already morning when I returned to my hotel. I took the slim little book from my jacket pocket intending only to skim the surface for a few moments before falling asleep. By dawn I'd read the damn thing from cover to cover. It's informative; it's incredibly incisive; sheer intelligence and wit keep you turning page after page. Back home in England, in the course of tracking down the author's identity, I acquired a copy of the second, revised edition of *Riviera Nature Notes*. This is the book you are shortly to read.

Published by Bernard Quaritch in 1903, the chapters reorganised and expanded, almost twice as thick as the original, with a rather handsome embossed pictorial cover, and including numerous photographs by the controversial Ellen Willmott, it is a testament not only to the rather grand connections of C.C. but to how well the original, very limited edition was received by its small circle of admirers: seasoned travellers, ladies and gentlemen with a moderate interest in gardening and natural history, or simply tourists after more information on their holiday destination, many would have come across the book by personal recommendation. In those days members of the international leisured class occupied a small social world; they would have known who the author was and what his profession. Out of time and out of place, later commentators have made rather a muddle. I will shortly put the record as straight as possible, but let us first look at the text itself, and meet C.C. through his very own words. Travel is now within everyone's financial grasp; the French and Italian Riviera is still a popular destination—in fact, one of *the* popular destinations—and I'm sure you'll find that *Riviera Nature Notes* is as fresh and relevant today as it was a whole century ago. As the man himself says, "there will always be much to observe and much to study in so favoured a region."

Observation and study are two keys to the book's readability. C.C. knew the region well, he was eager to share his findings with others, and he sought wherever possible to augment them with the opinions of fellow botanists and travellers, with the folklore of the region, and with extracts from Classical and European literature. His ability to convey hard information in an amiable, quickly assimilated way is no less astonishing than his intellectual range and we realise straightaway that he is an earnest teacher and a trustworthy guide. In his discourse on the date palm (*Phoenix dactylifera*) the traveller in us learns how the fronds at Bordighera are tied up and blanched before being woven into Easter decorations (to this day, the town supplies the Vatican with all its palmureli). The budding etymologist realises that the plant's Phoenician origins could have been guessed from the name. The botanist learns of an important observation by Goethe. There is a statement from John Lindley that will be of interest to all gardeners. In describing how the Arabs propagate palms using shoots from the base of fruit-bearing trees, the author cleverly introduces the necessary concept of flowers and flower parts that are staminate (male) and pistillate (female) while avoiding any direct mention of sexual reproduction.

Clearly, *Riviera Nature Notes* is intended for people of all backgrounds, all ages and all sensibilities. The master and mistress of the house could read it, and their children could read it. Even their servants could read it. Today's cooks might be surprised to read about fashionable ingredients like pine kernels and wall rocket—"The leaf is very pungent; it is used to flavour salad. I should think that a little would suffice."

Gardeners from Northern Europe and North America will encounter species currently deemed rare and fashionable yet which are in fact as old as the Mediterranean hills. To name just a few, these include *Cerinthe major, Convolvulus cneorum, Melianthus major* and *Teucrium chamædrys*. Some spellings have changed back and forth a little over the years, but that is all. (A few invisible corrections have been made in this present edition.) No species is at all hard to identify, and the notes on their natural habitats and their patterns of growth remain invaluable.

A quiet, scrupulous authority pervades the work. When C.C. has seen a thing in the flesh, where facts are beyond refute, he tells us so. If he quotes a learned authority or a secondary source, then all credit (and not occasionally a caveat) is given. Nothing whatsoever is taken for granted: "The peasants say that when the Great Reed waves its plumes aloft the winter will be sharp. I have not made up my mind about this saying, whether it holds good or not." When engaging in speculation, he tells us so, if he is mystified or at a loss he elicits our advice. But woe betide *anyone* speaking outright nonsense. Intellectual dishonesty is never allowed to pass unremarked—"The latest Bible commentaries give the astonishing piece of information that the Blood Orange is produced by grafting a branch of Orange on the stem of a pomegranate!" In C.C.'s hands the exclamation mark becomes a lethal weapon. And pity the poor fool who isn't prepared to listen and learn: the chap who insists that olive trees are colzas (oilseed rape) is given very short shrift indeed.

Only one aspect of the book might worry the modern reader: at first sight there seems an awful lot of Latin, French and German to translate. Fear not! This is where C.C.'s genius for education really shines. If a quotation has any serious bearing on your understanding of the text, you will find that he either gives a straightforward crib or discreetly conveys its meaning in the surrounding sentences. If you don't catch the drift of the odd phrase or two there's no need to worry, they're simply flies thrown for the benefit of really bright pupils. "Look it up if you must, boy!" I can almost hear him say.

C.C. often shocks, challenges and surprises the reader. He has strong opinions (especially where religion is concerned), a roving mind, a dry wit combined with a strong social conscience, and (when we look back over the hundred or so years that have elapsed since he first penned his words) extraordinary prescience.

Nothing is too simple or mundane to be mentioned, and nothing is too difficult to be explained clearly. Above all else, he likes making connections. For example, he segues perfectly from the "peculiar scent, insipid juice and flaccid rind" of a tangerine, to explaining how three different perfumes are extracted from the orange, to interrupting botanical descriptions of citrus fruit with a summary of his wife's recipe for marmalade—and that's barely the half of it. But he also likes stirring things up. Joy! Describing how farmers protect their grapes from theft with the purgative juice of the squirting gourd, he explains how gourds have been used to make water bottles, ladles, musical instruments and pipes for tobacco, then gives the correct time for sowing the seeds: "Here is a piece of information for amateur gardeners: the right moment for planting Gourd seeds is while the church bells are ringing on Easter eve… I suppose a chapel bell would do just as well. Some chapels make noise enough on a Sunday morning to start any Gourd seed germinating. Still one could hardly expect the jangling of schismatical bells to have the same effect as the orthodox carillon."

Nonconformists, Scotch metaphysicians and mumbling priests all come in for good-natured professional ribbing; pompous tourists are reminded to respect the peasantry; unwary visitors are apprised of the local shopkeepers' wiles. He also takes regular pot shots at the Germans, a universal pastime among holidaymakers to this day. At other times, though, C.C.'s digressions raise serious concerns. Without ever sermonising or unnecessarily labouring a point he takes advantage of the natural flow of his book to raise moral, social and political issues that worry him, and in this way *Riviera Nature Notes* has a broader mission than you might at first imagine.

Consider this. "There was held in Nice, a few years ago, a 'Concours de Beauté'. Ladies from different parts of Europe submitted themselves to be stared at, and prizes were awarded to those Professional Beauties who obtained most votes. The thing was hardly in good taste, not to say anything stronger about it."

Or this, on the grubbing up of olives groves in order to plant roses for the perfume industry: "Shall a valuable food-plant be destroyed to provide roses, and purely ornamental plants? There is beauty in the eglantine that clambers on the cottage porch; but to grow flowers by the acre is to invite famine and to insult Providence. O sacred laws of supply and demand! O vile commercialism!"

C.C. speaks out strongly against vivisection. "There is probably no new experiment which could be tried upon a Frog, this never-failing resource of the physical experimenter. It would take long indeed... to tell the sufferings of much-enduring frogs 'in the cause of science'. We have tried what Frogs can do without their heads; what their legs can do without their bodies; what their arms can do without either head or trunk; what is the effect of the removal of their brains; how they can manage without their eyes and without their ears; what results follow all kinds of local irritations, chokings, poisonings, and mutilations the most varied. And each of these experiments is repeated a hundred thousand times."

He deadpans on the evils of gambling: "Though reduced (by the bill-hook and chopper?) to a shrub on the Riviera, the Terebinth must grow to the size of a tree in Palestine, for Judas is said to have hanged himself on a Terebinth. There is no specimen anywhere near Nice on which a man could hang himself with any hope of keeping his toes off the ground. Those persons who are unfortunate at Monte Carlo find out a great many different ways of ending their lives, but they never attempt to make use of a Terebinth for this purpose."

C.C. loves Mankind, he loves Nature, he has great respect for the traditional ways of the countryside, and he wants all three to get along side by side. It's just that every now and again he has to shake someone by the shoulders to get his point across. I applaud him for this. What I admire most though, and what makes this such a wonderful book, is his powerful evocation of the plants and animals around him, their natural communities, the Riviera scenery, even the evanescent quality of light: "We must wander often and long... in these ancient olive groves, in order to become acquainted with the charms that are peculiar to the tree. The venerable trunks which have bestowed food and fuel upon generation after generation should be viewed in the diffused sunlight, with glimpses here and there of the deep blue Midland Sea."

To describe the date palm he quotes the following:

The Palm depends in a great measure upon the atmosphere for its beauty; the leaf plucked off has no brilliance of colour to boast; it has not the rich green of the Oak or the Beech, nor does it change to gorgeous hues in Autumn like European forest trees. On a dull day it looks dull, actually grey and sombre like the clouds above; and the peculiarity of the Palm is that it varies with the colouring of the atmosphere. Now a deep purple seems the hue of those fronds which scarcely move in the calm evening air; now again they are of a golden green; a little later of a bluish tint; then rose or crimson, as the setting sun casts its glow over the distant grove.

When talking about the chestnut tree he first locates it in the landscape: "As you advance inland, the Olive is gradually replaced by the Chestnut: pass up higher still through the pleasant Chestnut groves of Bollena, Berthemont, Valdeblore, and St. Martin Vesubia, and you reach the Alpine region where the Chestnut gives way to the pine, the larch, and the birch." You might look through a conventional guidebook, flora or sylva till the cows come home but you'd never get as clear a picture of the Riviera hinterland as this. Next, he brushes in the "large round soft eyes" of a dormouse peering down from above and describes the butterfly most commonly associated with Chestnut groves. Then a little social commentary: "They say that if a Corsican obtains possession of two or three Chestnut trees and a goat, he will never do another stroke of work. What, plough and sow and reap and toil, when you can lie under a Chestnut tree, and pick up the fruits as they fall!" Surely, these are the kind of nature notes travellers *really* want!

And what about notes on the travellers themselves? The book provides a fascinating insight into the social mores of the time. A discourse on pine trees leads to the curious habits of the procession caterpillar that feeds on the needles. "I have observed them as early as the second week in February. They form long lines upon the road, the head of one insect close to the tail of another. I believe that the not strictly scientific experiment has been tried of placing the procession caterpillars in a circle; but it is not on record for what length of time they continued to crawl round and round. Possibly the spell was broken by the wheel of some passing carriage. Perchance, driven by fate, they are still describing their circle on the hill-side." Then C.C. simply can't resist: "Exactly so the swarm of travellers behave: from London to Paris they go; then down to Nice or Cannes by the 'train de luxe'; the more disreputable of them turn up at Monaco. Next they appear at Florence or at Rome, each following his neighbour, he knows not and he cares not why. Back then to the Italian lakes, or Switzerland, or Aix, and on to London, where the round begins again. From hotel to station, from station to hotel, the great procession moves year in year out."

Now, *who* was C.C. and where was he from? From the book itself we infer that he was a clergyman and schoolmaster, that there was a Midlands connection, that he was married with children, and that Irish blood probably ran in his veins: "It seems to me that certain plants, of which the Arbutus is one, have a perception of the picturesque. Mark well the spot where this tree loves to grow, and you will find it has a special charm. Name the most lovely scenery in the British Isles: is it not where the evergreen foliage and the waxen bells of the Arbutus are reflected in the crystal waters of Killarney?" Research bears all this out.

The eldest son of George Casey and Mercy Bourcicault Casey, he was born in 1845 at Wavetree, West Derby, and christened George Edwards Casey. He took a BA followed by an MA at Lincoln College, Oxford, and was later elected both a Fellow of the Geographical Society (1878) and of the Linnaean Society (1879). Before marrying Ellen Georgina Alvina Bertram in 1874 he was curate of St Mary-le-Wigford in Lincoln. He was subsequently Assistant Master in the High School, Nottingham. By now his name was recorded variously as George Edwards Comerfield Casey, George Edward Comerford-Casey and George Edward Comerford Casey. The couple had three children: Olive Bourcicault (1875), Alvina Bertram (1877) and Edward (1880). Since Mrs Comerford Casey generally went as Alvina, little Alvina soon became Bertie.

Before completing his masterpiece our author wrote three other books: *Outlines of Latin Mood Construction* (1882), *Die Urzeit; or, Kindergarten German, Old Testament Tales in German and English* (1888), and *The Broad Churchman, a Catechism of Christian Pantheism* (1891). It is assumed that *Riviera Nature Notes* (such a frivolous thing!) was published anonymously in deference to his liturgical works. C.C.'s family helped with the illustrations to the second edition, and you will find Alvina credited as A.C., Olive as O.C., and Bertie as B.C. In 1906, at Sir Thomas Hanbury's suggestion, Olive and Bertie translated Eduard Strasburger's *Rambles on the Riviera* from the German.

C.C. died in Dorset in 1912. (On his death certificate and in his obituary he is George Edwards Comerford Casey—perhaps he'd finally made up his mind). Europe was in turmoil and the Great War was in sight. An era had vanished, and it was not until the Twenties and Thirties that the Riviera became an international playground once more. C.C.'s book was long out of print by then, and long forgotten.

Their fascination being in part a delight in the natural world as an expression of the divine, there is an eminently respectable history of English clergymen contributing to the layman's understanding and appreciation of the countryside. Think back to William Turner and his *Herball,* to John Ray and the *Historia Plantarum Generalis.* Think of Gilbert White and *The Natural History of Selbourne,* of Charles Kingsley and *The Water Babies.* Think now of C.C. and *Riviera Nature Notes.* He belongs in their ranks.

R.C.

The Hanbury Botanic Gardens

The gardens of La Mortola are now in the permanent care of the University of Genoa. Under its many careful hands they are flourishing as never before. Visitors today, from all around the world, continue the pilgrimage that began more than a century before.

Giardini Botanici Hanbury alla Mortola
C.so Montecarlo 43
La Mortola 18030
Ventimiglia
Tel ++39 0184 229507

PREFACE

THESE Natural History Notes were written at different times and in different moods during a long residence on the Riviera. My first stay in the South was before the annexation of Nice to France, when railways were as yet unknown in this part of the world. Having spent as many as twelve summers in the mountain and subalpine villages of the Maritime Alps, these higher regions are as familiar to me as the narrow strip of land along the coast where strangers congregate.

Some fifty of the chapters were written without any thought of publication, and with no other aim than to occupy the scanty leisure of a hard-worked schoolmaster. The few remaining articles were added in order to make the series more complete.

As the book is intended for those to whom Natural History is a recreation, I have not thought it necessary to affect the sober style of a scientific treatise. Nor have I confined myself to remarks about the structure and affinities of the different species. For many of the plants which surround us here have an interest other than botanical. They are connected with history, with mythology, and with the outward symbolism of religion: they are enshrined in the literatures of Rome and Greece and Palestine, and associated with the progress of mankind. To lose sight of this would be to do scanty justice to the subject.

Fault has been found with these little sketches on the score of unconventionality and naïveté. It is a curious coincidence that Alphonse Karr, a classic (I must not say another classic) of the Riviera, was also somewhat unconventional and not quite free from naïveté. Possibly the climate may have something to do with it! In order that the reader may know the worst, I will mention one or two other shortcomings. Some plants (Castanea, for instance) are worthy of a longer account than I have given of them: others I have been compelled to omit altogether. Instead of one chapter, I should have liked to write half-a-dozen about the butterflies. But, whatever may be its imperfections, this is, I believe, the only book dealing in a general way with the Natural History of the Riviera. Of course I have but touched on a very small part of a vast field. The Geology alone would form an interesting volume: and much might be written about the beetles, spiders, dragon-flies, land-shells, &c.

The district is changing rapidly. The spread of the towns, the disforesting of the hills, and other causes are conspiring to destroy many of the conditions which made the Riviera of former days so happy a resort for lovers of Nature. But there will always be much to observe and much to study in so favoured a region. In the last Chapter I mention a few of the problems which have interested me, and which I recommend to the attention of naturalists.

I am pleased to find that these Nature Notes have been useful to Riviera visitors. From distinguished botanists the book has had a reception more flattering than I could possibly have expected.

In the present edition I have corrected a few mistakes, supplied some omissions, and inserted a large number of illustrations. For the convenience of foreign botanists I have given the scientific as well as the English names of plants. Indeed, I am disposed to regard popular plant names as an unnecessary evil.

In order to facilitate reference, the Index has been made very complete.

My friend Mr. W. Dubois Duddell has placed at my disposal his magnificent collection of Riviera photographs, from which I have selected some excellent illustrations of the mountain scenery.

Miss E. Willmott has been good enough to contribute some beautiful pictures, coast views and vegetation of the littoral zone.

Acknowledgments are also due to Mr. Stanley Lane Poole; Messrs. Lovell Reeve & Co., Frederick Warne & Co., of London; Firmin-Didot & Co., Vilmorin-Andrieux & Co., of Paris; and E. Schweizerhart'sche Verhandlung, Stuttgart; for permission to produce certain illustrations.

To Sir Thomas Hanbury, at whose expense the book was originally printed, I am indebted for the foot-notes which are followed by the initials T. H.

Some of my friends have blamed me for wasting my time over a book which has brought me no profit, and in which I have no pecuniary interest. But I may, perhaps, venture to plead that there are many recreations even less profitable than writing notes upon the Natural History of the Riviera.

C. C.

Parkstone,
September, 1903

1

Date Palm and Chamærops

"Quel cachet oriental ces palmiers, qui se balancent, donnent à la colline: on se croirait en Asie."

Doctor Antonio

THE Date Palm (*Phoenix dactylifera*) adorns the gardens and open places all along the Riviera; but Bordighera is the palmiest spot. Here thousands of palms are grown to make ornaments for Easter. The Bordighera palms are very badly treated; they tie up the outer fronds with hazel twigs, so as to etiolate the inner ones. These straw or cream-coloured leaves are plaited and woven into the most complicated and wonderful patterns. In this, as in other cases, says Hehn ("Wanderings of Plants and Animals"), the Christian Church has faithfully retained the imagery of Hellenism and Judaism, and the palm frond which figured at the feast of Osiris in Egypt; which adorned the solemn entry of kings and heroes into Jerusalem; which was worn as a badge of victory at the Olympic games, and embroidered on the garments of Roman emperors, is now consecrated at Rome on Palm Sunday by the Head of Christendom, and distributed to all the churches of the eternal city.

The Palm was from ancient times a symbol of Palestine. Thus on the coins of Vespasian and Titus, struck to commemorate the conquest of Juda, a female figure sits weeping beneath a Palm tree, with the legend JUDAEA CAPTA.

PLAITED PALM FROND

The Date Palm loves to grow, as the Arabs say, with its foot in water and its head in fire. It is fiery enough here on the Riviera, one would think, yet many of the trees do not succeed perfectly; perhaps the gardeners do not quite understand them. Some are little more than stem, with a wisp of ragged fronds protruding at the top, like a pellitory on a gate post. In contrast with these meagre and stalky specimens we see other palms almost devoid of trunk: the dense growth of foliage spreads outwards from the ground, so that they look like Cycads. Others again have spindle-shaped trunks growing thicker and thicker towards the top, and so slender at the base that one is surprised they can remain erect. *P. Canariensis*, the Canary Date Palm, is stronger and hardier. It promises to be one of the chief ornaments of the Riviera; but the fruit is small and worthless.

In order that the fruit of the Date Palm may come to perfect maturity, the temperature should rise daily for some months in the year above 40°C. (about 105° F.). Nevertheless the tree can endure without injury five or even seven Centigrade degrees of frost.

It is remarkable that although the dates do not ripen in this district, yet the seeds will sometimes germinate in favourable spots. At Elche, near Alicante, in Valencia, five degrees farther south, the fruit is said to ripen. The Date groves there number about a hundred thousand trees. But the home of this Palm, the "Date Country," as it is called, lies to the south of the Atlas range, stretching between Morocco and Tunis. The origin of the tree is not known.

Phoenix has the staminate and carpellary flowers on separate plants. It follows that from a single Date Palm you can obtain no fruit. The Koran speaks of this plant as the only one which is not fertile by itself; but Mohammed is mistaken. A great prophet may be a very poor botanist. There are plenty of diœcious plants; Bryony, for instance, and Smilax, and the Pistacias and Hemp. I have read of a carpellary palm tree which grew under glass in the Botanic gardens in Paris, but never fruited, as it was the only specimen in Europe. A staminate plant of the same species was brought to Berlin, and the year after that the Paris palm tree bore some fruit. If a flower had been sent by post from Berlin, the thing would be easy to understand; otherwise I should be inclined to suspect a cross from some allied species growing near.

LANDSCAPE WITH DATE PALM

The Arabs propagate the Date Palm by shoots from the base of the fruit-bearing trees. A seedling would not flower earlier than ten years old, and, as the half of these young palms would be staminate, the ground would be cumbered during all this time with unprofitable trees. One staminate plant suffices to pollinate some hundreds of the carpellary ones. (Professor Massart, "Voyage au Sahara.")

Dr. E. B. Tylor, F. R. S., seeks to show in an interesting article, which appeared in the proceedings of the Society of Biblical Archæology, for June, 1890, that the cone-like object in the hand of the winged human figures of the Assyrian sculptures represents, not a pine-cone, but the staminate inflorescence of the Date Palm. The basket or bucket held in the left hand corresponds with the basket carried at present in the East by the cultivator to hold his supply of pollen-bearing inflorescences when he climbs the fruit-bearing palms to fertilize them. Thus the winged figure would be a genius of agriculture.

The Date Palm will reach water if there be any within reach. Dr. Bennet showed me in his garden near Mentone a row of palms one of which was twice as big as any other. Yet they were all of the same age,

and had received equal attention from the gardener. But the roots of this particular tree had found, or made, a leakage in a water-pipe.

Like the great majority of Palms, the Date tree is unbranched. It grows only by a terminal bud; if this is destroyed, the tree dies, for it has no power to throw out lateral shoots as a Dragon tree will do. Xenophon notices this fact in his Anabasis. It

GENIUS OF AGRICULTURE FERTILIZING A DATE PALM

follows also that if the trunk of a palm is badly injured, there is no saving the plant; whereas many exogenous trees would branch out below the injured part. I have seen a fine specimen so weakened by the attacks of some wood-boring larva, probably that of the Goat-moth (*Cossus*), that it was brought down by a gale of wind. In the case of another palm which became unhealthy and perished, the gardener attributed the mischief to a snail, *Bulimus decollatus*. The base of the stem was completely eaten away. This destructive species of snail has an elongate many-whorled shell of which the tip is invariably wanting. Thus the Date Palm, admired by all nations for its beauty, and so productive that one single tree will almost support a family—this tree which surpasses all others both in elegance and in utility—is yet most easily destroyed. Like the most valuable plants, the finest and most attractive human characters lack that repulsive hardness which enables others less highly organized to repel all attacks, to resist every encroachment, and to turn each circumstance to their own account.

I have seen it stated that when a Date Palm reaches a certain age, the circulation of the sap becomes impeded by the constriction of the hard outer wood. If cracks are naturally formed in this, the tree revives; otherwise the Arabs relieve the tension by making vertical clefts with a hatchet.

Can you guess from which end a date stone germinates?—It grows from neither end, but from a little scar which you may notice on the back. The seed-leaf of a Date Palm does not rise towards the light, as do those of most other plants; it plunges downwards, carrying with it the rootlet, and also the stem-bud; so that the young tree grows, not as an Oak does, from the spot where the acorn is lying, but from far below. At the same time the plantlet, though it has established itself beneath the burning surface of the sand, does not abandon the store of food which the parent tree has provided for its sustenance, for a communication is kept up with the seed until the albumen is exhausted. Thus Nature attains the same end by various means; the acorn, they say, is buried by a provident squirrel; the winged fruit of a Maple or an Ash is dragged underground by a hungry worm; but the young Date tree has the power to plant itself.

We read that in certain parts of Egypt date stones are boiled to soften them, and the camels and cattle are fed upon them. In Spain they are burnt and used for a dentifrice. The text-books tell us that cellulose is stored in the seed of the date.

As the name "Phoenix" testifies, the Date Palm was carried westward by the Phœnicians. On the Syrian coast, the Cornice of the Levant, the Greek sailors first saw the sacred tree. Thence they took it to the island of Delos to adorn the temple of the Sun God. The earlier Greeks knew nothing of the Palm, for the Iliad makes no mention it; but in the Odyssey the shipwrecked hero likens Nausicaa to the stately tree which he had seen at Delos. Some people never lose their self-possession, nothing can possibly take them aback. Brought quite suddenly, naked and dripping as he was, face to face with a remarkably good-looking princess, Odysseus has a pretty compliment ready to hand. "You are as beautiful as a Palm Tree!" Nausicaa is propitiated at once.

These same Phœnicians must have brought either drawings or descriptions of the Palm to the distant west at a very early date. For this tree gives its name to the first letter of the Irish alphabet.

The name *Tamar*, that is "Palm tree," was common among Hebrew maidens; we find it again in *Tadmor* or Palmyra, the palm-crowned city of the desert.

Contrast the loosely hanging sickle-shaped leaves of the Eucalyptus, swayed by the gentlest breath of wind, with the great palm fronds which remain undisturbed until startled by a ruder shock; for even the storm-wind does not easily overcome the strength of the firm woody petioles.

No one has questioned the beauty of the Date Palm; but the following passage shows that this grace does not lie merely in the outline, for there is in some trees, as in some human characters, a subtle charm not easily expressed in words. I quote from Whateley's "Among the Huts in Egypt." The Palm depends in a great measure on the atmosphere for its beauty; the leaf plucked off has no brilliance of colour to boast; it has not the rich green of the Oak or the Beech, nor does it change to gorgeous hues in Autumn like European forest trees. On a dull day it looks dull, actually grey and sombre like the clouds above; and the peculiarity of the Palm is that it varies with the colouring of the atmosphere. Now a deep purple seems the hue of those fronds which scarcely move in the calm evening air; now again they are of a golden green; a little later of a bluish tint; then rose or crimson, as the setting sun casts its glow over the distant grove.

The little Fan Palm, *Chamærops humilis*, is the only European representative of the Palmaceæ.

It is indigenous on the Riviera, but the wild specimens have gradually disappeared, having been dug up and carried away. Native botanists believe that some of these dwarf palms still remain in their original habitat, clinging to the inaccessible precipices of Petite Afrique. The plant spreads by suckers, and forms dense tufts. Lindley states that if these suckers are not permitted to grow, *Chamærops humilis* will rise to the height of twenty or thirty feet. In Sicily and elsewhere the leaves are used for a variety of purposes, and it is said that the roots have been eaten in time of famine.

On this palm Goethe made the first observations which led to his famous discovery of the law that all the organs of a plant are modifications of the leaf. He noticed the gradual transition from the narrow primordial leaves to the perfect radiating fan, but he was puzzled to find out how the spathe, so different in appearance, could harmonize with the theory which was slowly forming in his mind.

Goethe's palm is still carefully preserved in Padua, a pilgrimage resort for all devout botanists. A series of dried leaves from this Chamærops may be seen in the Goethe museum at Weimar.

The terminal bud or "cabbage" is said to be eatable.

Sestertius of Vespasian with Date Palm

MANDARIN (1), CHINOTTO (2)

2

Oranges and Lemons

"Oranges and Lemons!
Quoth the bells of St. Clemens."

THE different species and varieties of the genus *Citrus* are known by the name of Agrumi. The following are the most important: Orange, Lemon, Citron, Lime, Mandarin, Tangerine, Seville, Bergamot, Shaddock. The Seville, Mandarin, and Tangerine are closely allied to the Orange; whereas the Lemon and Citron are related, having the unwinged petiole, and other points in common. The Lime and the Bergamot may perhaps be hybrids between the Orange and Lemon (De Candolle).

An authority cited by Darwin ("Animals and Plants under Domestication") considers that there are four distinct species, viz., sweet Orange, bitter Orange, Lemon, and Citron. But Bentham believes that these four reputed species are all varieties of the wild Citron (*Citrus Medica*). The Shaddock, however, he would admit to be a separate species.

To begin with the sweet Orange (*Citrus Aurantium*): the origin of the specific name is curious. The Arabic and Persian "narang" gave "arang," then "orang," then Orange. Thus, the word is not derived from the Latin *aurum* gold, French *or*. By dropping the "n" and changing the vowel, the original name was made to suit the golden colour of the fruit. In the same way the old English "nadder," German "Natter," became adder by the loss of the "n." The Spanish word for Orange still keeps the initial "n."

A Niçois peasant, unless he is speaking French to a stranger, says "Portugal" for Orange. How is it that the Golden Fruit is called a Portugal in Italy, in Liguria, and in some other countries of Europe? In England also it was formerly called "the China or Portugal Orange." The explanation is that whereas the Citron came direct from the East, the Orange was introduced into Europe by the long sea route later than the time of Vasco da Gama. Thus, instead of spreading westward into Europe like the Citron, it would be carried eastward from the Atlantic Coast, and would bear with it the name of the Lusitanian shores where it first landed.

There are large plantations of Orange trees at Poros in the Peloponnese, in the Island of Sardinia, in Majorca, and in Sicily. By the lake of Garda, the tree requires a good deal of protection in Winter. In Florida, though the latitude is that of Cairo, much damage has been done by frost; and in California, equally far south, the trees do not escape injury. The Orange cannot endure protracted drought. Thus, in Sicily, each tree must receive 1,000 litres of water every twenty days throughout the Summer.

On the Riviera, the Orange is almost confined to the littoral region. Being less hardy than the Olive, it will not grow so far inland. The Riviera Oranges now go mostly to Germany, where the cheaper sorts sell better. (The Orange is a thing they do not make in Germany!) The greater part of the Oranges imported into England come from Malta, Lisbon, Valencia, the Azores, and Jaffa. Florida produces, in a good year, about 5,000,000 boxes; but, naturally, the greater portion of these is consumed in America. Provence and Var Oranges are much eaten in France.

One of the first importations of Oranges into England occurred AD 1290,[1] in which year a Spanish ship came to Portsmouth, from the cargo of which the Queen of Edward I. bought one frail of Seville figs, one of raisins or grapes, one bale of dates, 230 pomegranates, 15 citrons, and 7 oranges (" poma de orenge").

In the seventeenth century, Devonshire claimed to produce Oranges equal to those of Spain. We can hardly believe this. But it is certain that the Orange, Lime, and Shaddock may now be seen growing with the Vine and Fig at Kingsbridge, with no other protection in Winter than a wall and a screen of canvas.

The Orange is not always the small round-topped tree that adorns the gardens of Nice and Cannes. At Milis in Sardinia there stands a tree whose trunk is thicker than a man can circle with his arms. Its crown (says a traveller) is as majestic as that of an oak. Close by, there is a tree which is said to bear annually more than 5,000 fruits. Lindley mentions another at St. Michael's in the Azores which has been known to produce in one year as many as 20,000 Oranges fit for packing, besides the damaged fruit, which may be calculated as one-third more; but Haputale in Ceylon boasts a Mandarin-tree which has produced the extraordinary crop of 24,000 fruits in one year!

The Riviera Orange-trees are ornamental. We send little presents of the flowers to ladies who are about to be married. And strangers fresh from England buy bunches of the fruits to decorate their rooms. When more leathery than usual, they may be utilised as cricket balls; but I could not honestly recommend them for this or any other purpose. A writer, who cannot be accused of prejudice, says that the mere thought of a Mentone Orange sets the teeth on edge! And those from the banks of the Paillon are not much sweeter. Yet stay, there is one use to which a Niçois Orange might be put. They might be good for boot blacking! Cut your Orange in two; rub the juicy part on a sooty pot or kettle, then apply it to the boot; polish with a soft brush, and it shines at once. In some of the great Orange-growing districts the worthless fruits are thus turned to account.

The Greeks and Romans of classical times knew nothing of the Orange. Neither those golden apples of the Hesperides, nor yet the magic fruits which tempted fleet-footed Atalanta to linger in her race, belonged to the Aurantiaceæ. Apples they must have been, or Quinces, or perhaps Pomegranates, gilded by the glow of the poet's imagination.

I will not enlarge upon the botanical peculiarities of the Orange, but I will just call attention to the extraordinary fact that more than one embryo is often produced in a single seed (polyembryony). This occurs

SWEET ORANGE (3), BITTER ORANGE (4), LEMON (5)

also in Mistletoe and in Conifers. Notice also the blade of the leaf articulated to the stalk, and this again to the stem, as in Berberis, a sign that the leaf is truly compound: the immersed glands in the exocarp (rind), which are analogous to those in the leaf of Hypericum: also inside the rind the loose white stellate tissue, which resembles in structure the pith of a rush. The primordial leaves of the Orange are opposite, while those of the mature plant are alternate. This happens also in Beech, Scarlet Runner, and other plants.

From Professor Penzig I have the curious and interesting fact that seedling Orange-trees sometimes occur with trifoliate leaves.

Why does the number eleven so frequently occur in the carpels of the Orange? In such flowers as Cuphea we find eleven stamens, because the twelfth, which we see in Lythrum, is here suppressed to make room for the style. But the number eleven is not common in the essential organs of a flower.

In some parts of Europe gardeners believe that the best remedy for a diseased Orange-tree is to dig it up and replant it with the roots in the air and the branches underground. Max Miller in his "Auld Lang Syne," page 185, gives an instance of this treatment which was by no means successful. Those topsy-turvy trees in the "Orangerie" at Dessau must have presented a curious appearance. There is a legend that the famous Orange trees at Dresden were brought there as logs, rootless and branchless, and were thrust into the earth the wrong end upwards. De Vere asserts that the common maple is not destroyed if thus reversed.

The Orange-tree, both the sweet and the bitter species, is peculiarly liable to the attacks of the leaf-cutting ants. In the province of Canton it is usual to place in the trees colonies of harmless ants, which drive off the leaf-cutters and thus prevent the destruction of the foliage. The Lemon and the Mandarin are not attacked (Professor Geddes).

The little oblate Mandarin (*Citrus nobilis*) is extensively grown at Blidah, in Algeria. There are people who eat this Orange, peel and all.

At Savona is cultivated an Orange-tree popularly known as *Chinotto*. These little Oranges, only $^1/_2$ inches in diameter, are the kind used by confectioners in the manufacture of candied fruits. The Chinotto may possibly be a variety of the Mandarin.

The Myrtle-leaved Orange (*Citrus myrtifolia*) also bears very small fruits.

The *Tangerine* is well known for its peculiar scent, insipid juice, and flaccid rind.

The Oranges with red juice, which we call *Blood Oranges,* are said to come originally from Malta. The red-fleshed Orange fails to come true from seed.

The latest Bible commentaries give the astonishing piece of information that the Blood Orange is produced by grafting a branch of Orange on the stem of a pomegranate!

The Seville or Bitter Orange *(Citrus Bigaradia,* or *C. communis* or *C. vulgaris;* French Bigaradier), is stronger and hardier than the other species, and for this reason it is used as a stock to graft the better varieties. The quality of the produce does not seem to be affected by the nature of the stock. Thus if an Orange be grafted on the Lemon, the fruits are free from acidity. A tree which is not grafted will be from ten to thirteen years old before fruiting. Extraordinary results are produced by the intercrossing of the different varieties and species.

The Bitter Orange-tree may be known by the broader wing of the petiole. Although the fruits are uneatable, the flowers, as a compensation, are larger and more highly perfumed than those of the sweet Orange. From them is derived the volatile oil called Neroli (that is, *nero olio* or black oil), also the well-known Eau de Fleurs d'Oranger. For this purpose the tree is grown, as these essences are of better quality than those yielded by the flowers of the sweet Orange. "Petit grain" is a perfume extracted from the clippings of the tree, and from those young fruits which fall soon after the flowering. The fruit gives "Oil of Orange"; so that from the same plant three different perfumes are derived (Kerner). An enormous quantity of these essences and perfumes is manufactured at Grasse.

The long curly strips of aromatic rind, which we see hanging everywhere to dry, are destined to make marmalade, and to flavour puddings and drinks. It forms the main ingredient in curaçoa. My wife gives this receipt for marmalade: To three sweet Oranges add one bitter Orange and one Lemon. Take out the pips. Some prefer to dispense with the sweet Oranges altogether, and to put one Lemon to every three Sevilles. The bitter Oranges, from which the peel has been removed, are naturally to be had at a nominal price. I knew a person (a North Briton) who, purchasing these in large quantities, regaled himself. He considered this cooling diet a pleasant change from the oatmeal.

It is not generally known that the word "zest," in the sense of "relish," comes from "zest," a little slice of Orange peel. The French make a different use of the word. They apply it to something worthless, thus: *Je n'en donnerais pas un zeste*, I would not give a farthing for it.

The Lemon (*Citrus Limonum*) is more sensitive to cold than the Orange. A temperature of -3 Centigrade injures the tree. It is cultivated chiefly at Mentone, and on the Eastern part of the Riviera. But it prospers also at Villefranche, and at Nice in the Magnan valley. The Lemon bears flowers and fruit the whole year round. When grown from seed the tree is armed. The peel is said to be used for making Eau de Cologne. Hehn remarks that the German and French words "Citrone" and "Citron" are misnomers, and ought to be replaced by "Limone" and "Limon."

SHADDOCK (RIGHT), CITRON (LEFT)

The Citron (*Citrus Medica*) French Cédratier, bears large oblong fruits with a rough surface; yields a perfume; and "candied peel" is prepared from the thick, fleshy rind. Like the Lemon, it flowers at every season of the year. Being very delicate, it requires protection from frost, even on the Riviera. The trees are kept low, that they may be the more easily sheltered, and that the heavy fruits may not be shaken off by the wind.

This Median Citron with its "poma cedrina" was known in Europe at an earlier period than any other of the Agrumi. "Citrus," indeed, is but a corruption of "kedros." This name was given to the plant because the aromatic perfume of the fruit recalled that of the fragrant wood which the ancients called Kedros or cedar. The Citron is supposed to be the Apple-tree (Tappuach) of the Old Testament.

The "Cédrat des Juifs" is grown in the vale of Luri in Corsica, and is still used by the Jews for decorating their altars at the feast of tabernacles. Pliny relates how, in an *émeute*, the people, enraged with their high priest, pelted him with citrons from his own altar.

The berry of the Lime (*Citrus Limetta*) is generally globular. The juice is the tartest of the genus. It forms a well-known ingredient of Glasgow punch.

The Bergamot (*Citrus Bergamota*) is, perhaps, only a variety of the preceding (Hooker). It produces small pear-shaped fruits. The thin golden-yellow rind is filled with a sweet essence, much used by perfumers.

Citrus decumana, Shaddock, Adam's Apple, Pampelmousse, bears huge sulphur-yellow fruits.

A wonderful series of the species and varieties of the Orange group exists, or existed lately, in the grounds of the Villa Bermond, St. Philippe, Nice. These were collected by the naturalist A. Risso, who is known both as an ichthyologist and as an authority on the Agrumi.

Allied to the Aurantiaceae is the humble family of which Rue (*Ruta*) is the type. The following Rutal plants are common in the Riviera gardens; *Choisya*, a white-flowered shrub, with glossy trifoliate leaves; *Correa*, with covering of stellate scales; *Dictamnus fraxinella*, a native of France; this plant abounds in volatile oil to such a degree that the atmosphere surrounding it becomes inflammable in hot weather. The south African *Diosmas*, or Buchu plants, are also allied. They have a powerful (often offensive) odour. *Rue* itself hovers between a pleasant and unpleasant smell, like a weak character between good and evil. But the Spanish *Ruta montana*, the black sheep of the Orange family, takes "pecca fortiter" as a maxim. It will raise a blister on the hand through three pairs of gloves! If plants of this sort were common, botanizing would be a dangerous pursuit.

The Legend of the Lemon

When our first parents were driven out of Paradise, they determined to take with them the seeds of certain fruit-trees. For the primeval pair were still somewhat arboreal and frugivorous not to say pithecoid in their habits, and had not yet learned to subsist upon roots and grain. Adam thought the apple most worthy to be carried to the outer world. But Eve, disgusted with that fruit which had been the cause of such distress, hid in her bosom a couple of Orange-pips. One of these she dropped just outside the garden. The wretched seedling, missing the balmy air of Eden, degenerated sadly. The fruit was acid, and the rind had lost its rich colour and turned pale. Some say that a tear-drop fell upon this pip, and thus the fruit hangs elongate and sour. This was the origin of the Lemon.

The second pip she planted on the Riviera. This seedling, finding a more or less congenial climate, and a home as beautiful as that whence it was brought, succeeded better than the other. Its fruits were true to their origin, resembling (at least in outward appearance) those golden spheres of Paradise.

LEAF OF CITRUS MYRTIFOLIA, NATURAL SIZE

Notes:

1.   The famous Orange-tree at Rome, said to have been planted by St. Dominic, about AD 1200, at the monastery of St. Sabina, was still in a thriving state when I visited it in 1875. From the seeds contained in a fruit then given me by the monk in charge of the garden I raised two or three trees, which produced a fruit of a pale yellow colour, with a very smooth skin. In size they are decidedly larger than an ordinary Orange, and the flavour resembles that of the pommeloe.—T. H.

FLOWERS OF OLIVE

3
The Olive

"There the grey olive, year by year,
Yields its unfailing fruitage; there the vine
Ripens, unpruned, its clusters into wine;
There figs, ungraffed, their russet harvest grow,
And fields, unploughed, their wealth on man bestow."

HORACE, tr. DE VERE

AN Englishman who was spending a short time on the Riviera said to me, "Those Colzas are strange-looking trees." " What trees?" I asked, feeling somewhat puzzled. "The Colzas," said he, "that yield the Colza oil; there is hardly any other tree to be seen. How is it that you have been so long out here and never noticed them?" "You mean the Olive!" I exclaimed. "Nothing of the sort," he replied; "I am informed that those blue-green trees are Colzas." Probably he had been hoaxed, but it was useless to argue the point, so he returned to England under the impression that the coast from Marseilles to Genoa is covered with Colzas!

Similar scraps of botanical information are passed from one person to another until they are firmly established. Some gardener, driven to bay by a stranger thirsting for information, invents a name and re-christens the plant on the spot; or if he is wanting in courage and imagination he simply calls the flower or the shrub by the name of some plant which it resembles. A lady said to me one day, "Don't you like the perfume of that shrub? It's a Daphne." It happened to be a Pittosporum. Probably this lady's gardener found the word "Daphne" simpler and easier to remember, and it seemed to suit his mistress equally well. If you can count up to eight it is not difficult to make a guess at a Daphne by looking at the anthers.

The Olive (*Olea Europæa*), which clothes the hills and gives its peculiar character to the scenery of the Riviera, is allied to the Ash (*Fraxinus*), Privet (*Ligustrum*), Lilac (*Syringa*), and Phillyrea; less closely to the Jasmine. In each of these you will find the leaves opposite, and the stamens two in number. The Olive has been grafted on Phillyrea, and even on Ash; in the case of the Jasmine these grafts do not succeed. This family is sacred in the south of Europe, and sacred also in the north, for the Ash was the Scandinavian Igdrasil or Tree of Life, and the Olive, gift of Athene, was venerated in Greece.

I am inclined to think that the Oak, though exalted by the Druids, and still praised by the Anglo-Keltic race, must yield in point of utility to the Olive, and in beauty to the Ash. The Oak, like its modern patrons, does not thrive equally well in all localities. On the granite of Dartmoor the King of Trees is stunted to a size that would be convenient for leapfrog, and I have read of Oak trees no bigger than the dwarf Box of our borders.

A botanical treatise on my shelf alludes to the Olive as a "useful tree, but devoid of beauty." Against this Philistine statement I protest in the name of all those who have learned to love this tree, which, as Harriet King, sweet singer of Italian liberty, has said, "flowers and fruits in a perpetual peace." I will attempt no glowing description, nor will I enlarge upon the associations of the tree; those who are most familiar

OLIVE TREES, CAP MARTIN

with the Olive will be most diffident about describing it; he who is spell-bound by beauty is seldom lavish of his praise. Professor Flückiger has written on this point with much insight and good sense. We must wander often and rest long, he truly says, in these ancient Olive groves, in order to become acquainted with the charms that are peculiar to the tree. The venerable trunks which have bestowed food and fuel upon generation after generation should be viewed in the diffused sunlight, with glimpses here and there of the deep blue Midland Sea.

The form of the Olive is quite altered by cultivation, and it is difficult to know what the growth of the tree would be if it were less heavily cut back. It should be borne in mind that the Olive is a fruit tree, unmercifully pruned and trimmed; it is unfair to expect from it the free growth of a forest tree. Probably no other tree could stand so much cutting and mutilation without being completely disfigured. The severe pruning of the Olive is a tradition of the oldest times. Columella, writing early in the first century, cites an ancient saying to this effect: "If you dig round the Olives, you ask for fruit; if you put in manure, you beg for fruit; if you cut back the branches, you must have fruit." (Olivetum qui arat, rogat fructum; qui stercorat exorat; qui cædit cogit.) We should admire the Olive more if it were mingled with other trees, so as to form a less monotonous covering for the hill sides. About Mentone and on the Italian side of the frontier little pruning is done beyond taking out the dead wood.

The largest Olive trees that I have seen anywhere are at St. Pons, just below the church. They form a magnificent avenue running at right angles to the course of the river bed. There is no public thoroughfare, but the peasants are obliging, as one almost always finds them to be when reasonably treated. It is curious that the man who cultivates this farm is himself of gigantic stature. Is there anything in the air of St. Pons which favours the growth of both men and trees? I strongly recommend a visit to this Olive grove. If you approach the place by way of the Paillon, you should return to Nice by the little path that winds up to Rimiez; thence you can descend either by Cimiez or by Brancolar. Just above Cap Martin there are some remarkably fine trees.

A famous old Olive tree stood at Beaulieu, near the road; it measured twelve metres in circumference at the base, and about four metres at the point of bifurcation. This tree is now destroyed; it is said that a tramp lighted a fire inside it, and thus burnt it down.

Here and there an Olive tree occurs with small white fruits; these are of no use for making oil. There is a tree of this sort on the Cimiez hill, not many yards from the road, and I know of one or two others near Nice.

It is probable that the native country of the Olive is in the south-eastern part of the Mediterranean area. If this be the case, the Oleaster or wild Olive which occurs here must be an escape from cultivation. The Oleaster, like the Orange, Plum, Pomegranate, and many other fruit trees in the wild state, is armed. The leaves are much smaller than those of the Olive. An intelligent peasant told me that the seed of the Olive will not germinate unless it has passed through the body of a bird. "You may plant a bushel of them," he said, "but not a single one will grow." I asked him if there is any bird in this country large enough to swallow an Olive fruit, and he assured me there were more than one such. He gave me the patois name, of which unfortunately I did not make a note.

The Mosaic law forbad the gathering of the Olives in such a way as to leave nothing for the poor to glean: "Thou shalt not go over the boughs again" (Deut. xxiv. 20). This principle, if applied to modern commercial transactions, would be considered most unbusinesslike, and quite incompatible with ten per cent!

So great is the vitality of the Olive that it may be propagated by planting the knots from the trunk: these are dormant buds. It is said that a twig stuck carelessly in the ground will strike root. Olive trees are constantly seen growing in groups of three or four. I believe that these result, in almost every case, from the decay of a single large trunk; to replace this, a few of the innumerable shoots that spring up round the base of the stock have been allowed to remain, and have been grafted. Thus a group is formed. In fact, once an Olive is planted, there is no reason why it should ever disappear from the spot; to destroy it you must dig out every morsel of the stock.[2]

The Olive flowers in May, and the fruits are fully formed in the Autumn; but they remain, or should remain, on the tree during the Winter. The regular harvest is in March or April, but in some years a large part of the fruit falls in November and December. These windfalls are not wasted, for they will make oil, though inferior in quality to that made in the Spring. The saying is, "When the wine is in the vat, the oil is in the Olive." I have been told that the Olive trees in the Nice district produce a heavier crop each third year. Of course the date of the Olive harvest depends in great measure upon the elevation, that is to say, upon the climate. On the coast it may take place as early as November to January; but at a height of 1,000 to 1,500 feet it may be as late as June.

The commonest, if not the worst, enemy of the Olive is a fly called the Cairon (*Dacus Oleæ*). This insect lays its eggs in the fruit, and the larva eats the pulp. Fruits thus attacked fall off early, and the oil made from them is said to have a bad taste. The Cairon lays its eggs chiefly on the south side of the tree, or else those laid on the south side hatch better; for the fruits on the north side are less damaged by the larvæ, and do not fall off to the same extent.

It is said that a district planted with Olives will support twenty families for one which could otherwise find subsistence. Since the value of the crop has diminished from other substances being used as a substitute for Olive oil, I believe that the population of these districts has much decreased. So unprofitable has the Olive become, that the cultivation of the tree is being abandoned on several parts of the Riviera. Thus on the Pessicard hill, near Nice, a considerable space has been cleared for vines. And the aspect of the coast about Mentone, San Remo, and especially Ospedaletti is being rapidly changed by the cutting down of the Olives in order to plant roses. Perfume is good, and ornament; but we would not wish the Riviera to be entirely devoted to the production of these luxuries. We can never be reconciled to the disappearance of the Olive. Shall a valuable food-plant be destroyed to provide roses, and purely ornamental plants? There is beauty in the eglantine that clambers on the cottage porch; but to grow flowers by the acre is to invite famine and to insult Providence. O sacred laws of supply and demand! O vile commercialism! You would sow these sunny slopes with stink-weed if Dives breathed a wish for it!

Dr. E. Sauvaigo, author of a useful Riviera gardener's book, thus eloquently pleads for the Olive: "Ne désespérons jamais de cet arbre précieux: sa disparition constituerait pour notre zone une véritable calamité."

FRUITS OF THE OLIVE

The following verse is from a poem written at Cimiez on this subject by a poet whose name I cannot remember:—

"As gladly, gluttonous for gain,
Man digs the flowers and fells the trees,
So would he foul the sapphired main
Or tear the heavenly tapestries!"

But however the commercial value of the crop may vary, the oil is to these natives no luxury, but a necessity of life. The regular dinner of a labourer is a lump of bread, covered with slices of tomato, and smeared with Olive oil. Butter is not to be had in the villages which lie even a short distance from the coast. "Corn, wine, and oil": the blessing holds good here as in the East, for on these hills, up to an elevation of some 2,400 feet, the Olives alternate with narrow strips of wheat and rows of vines. The three crops grow together on the same hillside:

"The mystic floating grey
Of Olive trees, with interruptions green
From Maize and Vine."

Some persons are able to eat, and even to digest (dura ilia!) the Olive fruits. The Romans would seem to have packed their dinner, so to speak, between two layers of Olives:

"Inchoat atque eadem finit Oliva dapes."

Notes:

2   This applies especially to the country between Cannes and Marseilles. I have been told that a fearful frost occurred in 1819, killing down to the ground all Olive trees west of the Esterel. But as life remained in the stock, the peasants allowed several small trees to come up in place of each old one, as described above. East of the Esterel the trees were not destroyed by the frost.—T. H.

CERATONIA SILIQUA, THE CAROB

4

The Carob

"Husks that the swine did eat."—Luke xv. 16.

THE *Carob* or Algaroba, or Locust bean (*Ceratonia Siliqua*) is almost confined to a narrow littoral zone "where with its large glossy deep green pinnate leaves and tropical aspect it constitutes one of the most beautiful features in the coast line."

This tree, like the orange, is much less hardy than the olive. I have never seen it growing at any distance inland. Beyond the Riviera we do not meet with it in northern or central Italy. In fact the climate of Nice, Cannes, Mentone, and Hyères is that of southern Italy and Sicily.

Professor Martins, of Montpellier, regards the Carob, Dwarf Palm (*Chamærops*), Oleander (*Nerium*), and other tender plants of the Riviera as the surviving relics of a tertiary vegetation preserved by the exceptional mildness of this district. A single severe Winter, or even a single night of extreme cold, like that of January 13, 1820, when the thermometer fell to almost ten below zero Centigrade, would suffice to destroy the Carob and many other species.

Other botanists explain the presence of a southern evergreen flora on the Riviera by supposing that these plants are better able to press northwards on dry and warm calcareous formations than on clay soil, which is damper and colder. But these same evergreen trees and shrubs flourish also on those parts of the coast, at Cannes, for instance, where the soil is not calcareous. The evergreen shrubs in the Azores, Madeira, and the Canary Islands grow on various soils indifferently; even on basaltic and trachytic rocks.

The large chocolate brown saccharine pods are sold for feeding cattle. Boys have been known to eat them—what will a boy not swallow?—and in the last war against Turkey the unfortunate Russian soldiers were compelled to live upon them. In ancient times these Carob pods seem to have been, as they are still, the last resource of the poor and destitute. The "husks that the swine did eat" (Luke xv. 16) were Carobs; and John Baptist's "locusts" may have been none other than these same fruits. Hence the German name "Johannisbrod."

W. F. Kirby, the well-known entomological writer, gives me the following note on this point:—"Of course John may have eaten Carob pods, but there is no doubt that locusts themselves are intended in the narrative. The Jews were allowed to eat them, and they are still largely eaten by the Arabs, I suspect that the flavour of different species of grasshoppers varies, and it would also be modified by the food of the insects, for different travellers give a different account of their quality as food."

Mice and rats are fond of Carob beans. On the road from Nice to Monaco you pass numbers of trees provided with zinc collars to prevent vermin from ascending. Small animals cannot climb over the slippery surface of the metal. The farmer who first adopted this method of outwitting the hungry rodent was doubtless not aware that Dame Nature had anticipated his patent. The honey in flowers has to be carefully guarded against ants and other wingless insects which do not carry pollen-dust from one flower to another. These are unbidden guests at the banquet which the flowers provide.

One of the commonest ways of excluding these unwelcome visitors is to place in their way, as they ascend the stem, an unclimbable barrier. For instance, a smooth collar is formed round the stern by the connate bases of the leaves of Honeysuckle (*Lonicera*); Yellowwort (*Chlora*) protects itself in the same way. No ant, says Kerner, can scale this plant; when placed on the slippery, glaucous leaves he invariably falls off, tumbling down the "couloir" at the connate bases. Other plants form a slippery barrier by the projecting base of a single leaf. *Melianthus*, a Cape plant common in gardens here, uses its enormous stipules for the same purpose. The sugary, vinous honey in the corolla of Melianthus is worth protecting, for it is so abundant that a quantity may be collected by merely shaking the flowers. As I have mentioned this plant, I will add that I dislike its rank smell, that it is said to be ornithophilous (fertilized by birds), and that the buds are resupinate, that is, they come out upside down and have to turn through two right angles to bring the flower into position. This occurs in *Orchis, Cytisus Laburnum*, and other plants.

The word "Caruba" is Arabic; and the smooth hard lentil-shaped seed is said to be the origin of the carat weight used by jewellers, and borrowed from the East. It is thought that these seeds were chosen as a unit of weight because their specific gravity varies so little. Some authorities maintain that the word "Carat" is derived not from "Ceratonia," but from "Retti," the small shining red and black seeds of *Abrus Precatorius*, an African climbing plant of the Leguminous order. Each of these seeds weighs exactly one grain. They are made into chaplets, hence the name "Precatorius."

Not only is the glazed surface of the Carob seed proof against the gastric juices of animals, but it is found that they germinate more freely when they have passed through the body of an animal.

The Carob may perhaps furnish a clue to Virgil's

"Aureus et foliis et lento vimine ramus."

I have often been struck by the gorgeous colouring of this tree. When a branch for any reason fades, it shows by turns a russet brown, a metallic golden yellow, and a silver white. A carob tree will sometimes look like a huge bouquet, and a poet seeing this effect would not be likely to forget it. There is an objection to this theory, namely that Virgil, like Livy, was a native of Cisalpine Gaul. Now the Carob does not grow near Mantua, so that Virgil would not be familiar with the tree. Possibly the Mistletoe is the golden twig that gives access to the lower regions.

The Carob occasionally produces twice pinnate leaves. I have not found many instances of this great curiosity. Within a few yards of the church at Gairaut, near Nice, stands a tree which bears the subdivided leaves. The view from this spot will amply reward those who are not interested in twice pinnate Carobs. There is another specimen in the gardens of the Grand Hotel at Grasse.

The young pods, and also the flowers, of the Carob are considered to be poisonous. It is strange that as the pod ripens, the poison should lose its force. There is a tendency in many plants of this order (the Leguminosæ) to develop a poisonous principle in the pod. The universal English cottage garden plant *Cytisus Laburnum*, wild on the mountains here, is an example. Another instance is a shrub called *Anagyris*. I found it growing a few years ago in a dismantled garden at St. Philippe, also at Villefranche. Ardoino says that it is subspontaneous at the Nice Château. The filaments are distinct, the standard very short, and the leaf trifoliate.

Another leguminous tree with poisonous pod is the so-called Honey Locust (*Gleditschia*). This tree is armed with great three-branched spines. Botanists will notice that several buds grow one above another in the same axil, as in Paulownia and some other cases.

The pods of the Gleditschia are a foot long or more, and curved or undulating. They look at a little distance like rags hanging on a tree. The Honey Locust (what is the origin of this name?) is not uncommon in Nice; there are half-a-dozen by the roadside at St. Pons, and one sees it in gardens now and then.

The flowers of the Carob have no corolla, and the stamens are distinct: they appear on the old wood, sometimes even on thick branches. The tree is diœcious, or according to some authorities polygamous. A good Carob tree is said to be worth forty francs a year.

Melianthus major

PISTACIA LENTISCUS, THE MASTIC

5

The Pistacias

THE *Mastic* or Lentisc (*Pistacia Lentiscus* or *Lentiscum*) is the chief constituent of the underwood in this region. It is a diœcious, apetalous, evergreen shrub, with paripinnate leaves and winged petiole. There is no British wild plant of the Terebinth order to which the Mastic belongs, but several species are common here on the hills, while several others are cultivated in the gardens; and all are of considerable interest.

I have called the Mastic a shrub, but the fact is that if permitted to develop, it may become a tree. In the Villa Giribaldi, at Bordighera, there is a magnificent Mastic, probably one of the largest in existence. This proves that the plant can become arborescent on the Riviera. I think that it would frequently do so, were it not cut down for firewood. A tree which produces nothing eatable must be turned to account in some way. Either food or fuel is the alternative. But in the Greek Archipelago the Mastic is cultivated for an aromatic resin which it yields. This is used in the East to strengthen the gums and to perfume the breath: in England we make a varnish of it. Dentists also use it to stop carious teeth. The habit of chewing Mastic gum must have been universal, for the word "masticate" is connected with the name of the tree (Greek Lexicon). A beverage is prepared from this gum. In the late war between Greece and Turkey it was said of an unsuccessful Greek officer, "He is of no use but to sit in a café and drink Mastic!" The ancient habit of gum chewing has been revived in America, where the substance used is resin from the spruce forests of Maine. As the supply of this resin is not equal to the demand, an imitation is manufactured which consists of 75 per cent sugar and 25 per cent paraffin.

The wood is considered better than any other for toothpicks. Martial says:

> *"Lentiscum melius; sed si tibi frondea cuspis*
> *Defuerit, dentes penna levare potest."*

(There's nothing like fresh Mastic wood for toothpicks; but failing this a quill may serve your turn.)

In Chios, an island famed for Mastic resin, many of these trees were killed by frost in 1850, whereas the tree at Bordighera was uninjured.

Small red crescent-shaped galls infest the leaves: I have not seen these on any other plant. They are not unsightly, whatever harm they may do to their host. One of the best gardeners in these parts says that the Mastic is not sufficiently utilized in gardens: I quite agree with him.

The Mastic does not reach the same altitude as the Terebinth, and prefers drier and hotter situations. Mr. C. Bicknell says that it blossoms, as a rule, several weeks later than the Terebinth.

The Terebinth (*Pistacia Terebinthus*) is almost as common on the hills here as the Mastic. The two shrubs often grow together. This plant is dioecious and apetalous, like the last, but deciduous: the leaves are imparipinnate, with much broader leaflets. The fruits are ornamental; being first variegated, then red. The Terebinth has curious horn-shaped galls caused by the puncture of Aphis Pistaciæ. Mr. C. Bicknell informs me that on the Italian Riviera the shrub is called Scornabecco (goat's horn) on account of these excrescences. They are used in tanning. These galls are not very unlike the large pods of some leguminous plants, and I have known them to be mistaken by beginners for fruits. Unlike the galls on the Mastic, they are decidedly ugly; eventually they turn black, and are then still more hideous. *P. Terebinthus* prefers a calcareous soil. It is said not to ripen its fruits at Antibes. Grows with the Aleppo Pine up to close on 2,000 feet.

The Terebinth, as its name implies, yields turpentine, French "térébenthine," but the turpentine of commerce is now obtained mainly from certain pine trees (*P. palustris* and *P. tæda*) which grow in the forests of North Carolina and Virginia. In Chios and Cyprus the turpentine is collected during the month of July. Incisions are made in the stem, and stones are placed to catch the sap. It is clear, and about as thick as honey. The turpentine odour still clings to the closely allied mango, in spite of the careful cultivation which has brought this Indian fruit to such perfection.

We read in the Bible commentaries that the Terebinth is abundant in the south and east of Palestine, in localities too warm or too dry for the Oak, whose place it supplies, and whose Winter appearance it resembles. Though reduced (by the bill-hook and chopper?) to a shrub on the Riviera, the Terebinth must grow to the size of a tree in Palestine, for Judas is said to have hanged himself on a Terebinth. There is no specimen anywhere near Nice on which a man could hang himself with any hope of keeping his toes off the ground. Those persons who are unfortunate at Monte Carlo find out a great many different ways of putting an end to their lives, but they never attempt to make use of the Terebinth for this purpose.

A naturalist, writing of the Pistacias, cites Theocritus to the effect that, undeterred by the resinous sap, goats are able to eat the foliage; and he confirms the fact by his own observation.

As the Cypress overshadows the Moslem's tomb, so the Terebinth is planted by the grave of the Armenian.

The very rare *Pistacia Saportæ* has been found at Eza, on the Mount Boron, and elsewhere. It is supposed to be a hybrid between the

SCHINUS MOLLE, THE SO-CALLED PEPPER TREE

Terebinth and the Mastic, for it has the habit of the former and the evergreen leaves of the latter.

The translators of the Bible appear to have had great trouble with the Hebrew word for Terebinth; in fact it has completely baffled them. As a general rule it is rendered "Oak," but sometimes "Elm." The worst mistranslation of the word is that in Genesis xiii. 18: "Then Abram removed his tent, and came and dwelt in the *plain* of Mamre." The passage should read thus: "He came and pitched his tent under the *Terebinth tree* at Mamre." Near the spot where the Jordan enters the Lake of Galilee there is a famous Terebinth, on which the natives hang rags and votive offerings.

A third Pistacia (*P. Vera*) occurs now and then in gardens here. It is a diœcious tree. This is a drawback from the market gardener's point of view, because, in order to obtain fruit, he is obliged to grow a useless staminate tree which takes up room; so he remedies the defect in a very ingenious manner: he grafts a staminate twig in the middle of the pistillate tree, thus producing a pseudo-monœcious plant. The fruit is used in confectionery. Among the presents sent by Jacob to Joseph (Genesis xliii. 11) were Pistacia Nuts.

Of the same order as the Mastic and the Terebinth is the Sumach or Wig Tree (*Rhus Cotinus*; French "Arbre à Perruque"), a shrub with alternate exstipulate suborbicular leaves, which turn to a bright red in Autumn: one of the commonest shrubs in every copse and hanger. The Sumach is easily recognised, for when Winter approaches it stands out as a dash of fiery colour, strongly contrasted with the dark shades of the evergreen Mastic and the fading tints of the deciduous trees. The Sumach gives the signal for Summer to depart. At other times of the year the Wig Tree may be known by its extraordinary inflorescence. The sterile pedicels are altered into reddish plumose hairs: these form the "wig," a thing which cannot fail to attract the attention of any one who walks a very short distance beyond the suburbs of the town. When I first met this shrub out here, I recognised it at once from the drawings of the "wig" which I had seen in botanical text books at home.

The wood of the Sumach gives a rich yellow dye. It is known in commerce under the absurd name of "Young Fustic." You may keep it fifty years, it will still be "young"; in fact it is one of the few things that never grow old. Tons of it are imported with the currants from Greece. The rocky Ithaca, home of Ulysses, furnishes a large quantity. Fustic is an Arabic word.

I have not seen the Poison Sumach (*Rhus toxicodendron*) on the Riviera. This North American tree is so poisonous that erysipelas has been caused by merely touching the leaves. Some people are more susceptible than others to this poison.

In almost every garden, and in the open places of the town, is cultivated *Rhus trifoliata*, a graceful tree of the same natural order, in habit not unlike some of the Acacias; in fact it is easily mistaken for an Acacia. The evergreen leaves are palmate, with three long linear leaflets. The flowers are yellowish green, and insignificant.

Even commoner is the so-called Pepper Tree (*Schinus Molle*, the "Molle" of the Chilians), with its drooping pinnate foliage and bunches of coral fruits. It does not always thrive well in Nice. Fragments of the leaf, floated on water, move about by jerks, owing to the discharge of a volatile oil from the tissues. You must break off a leaflet near the base, and place it gently on the water with the convex side downward: it then glides along like a small green gondola. I have seen this navigation succeed perfectly; but it often fails for some reason. I think it is necessary that the weather should be hot. You must depress the stern a little in order that the propeller may act.[3]

The fruits of Schinus are said, by Hooker, to be "sugary and edible"; they are certainly so ornamental that it would be a pity to eat them if any other provisions are to be had.

Notes:

[3]   Sir Thomas Hanbury is an adept at this little experiment.

FIG. 16. PISTACIA TEREBINTHUS, THE TEREBINTH

CELTIS AUSTRALIS

6
Mulberry: Celtis: Fig

THE following genera form a great family, or rather alliance: Mulberry and Fig, Nettle and Pellitory, Elm and Celtis, Hemp and Hop. Just as the Rose family, or rather alliance, may be split up into Rose, Apple, Plum, Bramble (*Rubus*), Strawberry, &c.; so the Mulberry, Nettle, Elm, and Hemp may be considered as separate types, though they all agree in having no petals, and in several other characters. I have joined the Elm and Celtis for convenience. We are particularly well placed on the Riviera for studying this family, because several interesting genera and species are to hand which we cannot examine in England; the Paper Mulberry for instance, and the Celtis.

To begin with the Mulberry (*Morus*): the tree is stripped to feed the silkworm *(Bombyx Mori)* here as elsewhere. The white Mulberry (*M. alba*) is preferred for this purpose, whereas the fruit of *Morus nigra* is superior. The wood of the red Mulberry (*M. rubra*) resists water as well as the best oak, and is therefore used for ship carpentry. Next after the

Morus alba, as a food for silkworms, comes the many-stemmed Mulberry (*M. multicaulis*). In fact, it is preferred by many silk farmers, because it has great vitality, opens its buds early in Spring, and produces a great quantity of large succulent leaves. Silkworms are so fond of the pungent odour of the Mugwort (*Artemisia vulgaris*) that it is mixed with the heather in which the larvæ are to spin their cocoons in order to attract them. The French name of the plant is "Herbe St. Jean." This composite is not found on the coast, but it descends as low as Grasse. In some districts branches of pine are placed for the full-fed larvæ to spin up in. This is found to answer admirably, for the insects take to it willingly, and the cocoons are easily removed later on. The fruits of the Mulberry are not much valued here, at least one sees them rotting on the ground. Botanists will permit me, for the sake of simplicity, to call the Mulberry and the Fig "Fruits"; Hooker takes the same licence. It would be both tedious and pedantic to insist on every occasion upon strict botanical accuracy, to deny that the Daisy is a flower, and to call the Rose a monstrosity. An Irishman might possibly forgive you (for my countrymen are not vindictive) if you told him that his beloved potato is not a root; but who would brave the fury of a Scotchman if it were hinted that his national emblem is no Thistle, not a real *Carduus,* but only a vulgar Onopord?

Very close to *Morus* comes the Paper Mulberry or Chinese Mulberry (*Broussonetia papyrifera*). If you are supposed to know anything about botany, people will be sure to bring you leaves of this plant and ask you to tell them the name. What a comfort and satisfaction it is to some people to find out the *name* of this or that flower or tree! There are persons who delight to walk along a road and ascertain the name of the owner of each house or villa which they pass; but they do not claim to be ethnologists. Yet it is quite a common delusion that a person who knows the names of a great number of plants must be an accomplished botanist. Let me quote on this subject a couple of hexameters, the first which the Muse dictated to my son. Whether perfect or not, they are creditable, I consider, for a *coup d'essai.*

> "*Nomina qui rogitat Naturam cœpit amare:*
> *Causas qui quærit Naturae est verus amator.*"

It is difficult, as a rule, to name a plant from a leaf; but that of the Paper Mulberry admits of no mistake. The elegant outline and clean-cut curves make it quite unique. I recommend it as an excellent drawing copy. Notice that this tree bears leaves of very various shapes. As in the Mulberry, the younger leaves are more deeply cut than the older ones. The text-books call attention to the peculiar way in which the leaves on the lateral branches are brought to face the light.

LEAF OF BROUSSONETIA

The Paper Mulberry is common; you will see it in most gardens, and in open places. There is a row of them at Vence Cagnes, by the high road, trimmed in a peculiar manner. All the specimens which I have examined on the Riviera, with one single exception, are staminate. At the Nice Château I discovered a pistillate plant. The fruits became about the size of a small Hazel nut, and fell off without ripening. I returned the next year to the same spot, in order to ascertain whether this tree had been more successful in fruiting, but I found that it had been destroyed in widening the path. This kind of vandalism is so common out here that unless a given specimen is in your own garden, you can never count upon seeing it a second time. I believe that if a Niçois were admitted into the Garden of Eden, he would cut down the Tree of Life and sell the wood at so much per hundred kilos!

By far the finest Broussonetia in Nice stands in front of the École Normale in the Route de Gènes. Dendrologists should not miss seeing this handsome tree.

The Fig (*Ficus Carica*) is said to have been introduced into France by the Phoceans who founded Marseilles and Nice. I read in a very old German book of travels, written before Nice became known as a health resort, that the Fig tree was at that time specially cultivated between Antibes and Vence Cagnes, and that this district was full of Fig trees, so much so that it was called after them. But as one drives through that part of the country, one sees no greater number of Fig trees than there are elsewhere. Perhaps when this early book was written, the tree was still scarce in other parts of the Riviera, and was gradually spreading from certain centres of which this was one.

In the Vallecrosia Valley, between Ventimiglia and Bordighera, Figs were once so plentiful as to form an important source of revenue. Thus the village of Soldano had its "Book of Figs" in which an account was kept of the Figs sold or lent from the public store. The refuse fruit remaining was given to the poor. This district still possesses Fig trees of great size, and the small sweet black fruits are sold at the rate of twenty or thirty for a penny.—(Scott, "Rock Villages of the Riviera.")

The text-books teach us that Ficus has the staminate and pistillate flowers on the same plant, the former being at the entrance of the fruit, the latter, much more numerous, lining the cavity. But it appears from a paper by Dr. G. King in the Journal of the Linnean Society for June, 1887, that the tree is really diœcious: in other words (if I understand him) the staminate flowers in the cultivated Fig are barren. Thus the "common eatable Fig" is pistillate, whereas the Caprifig, which is, as Linnæus supposed, the staminate plant of the same species, has both staminate flowers and also the so-called "gall flowers." The different plants have the same leaf, but the receptacle of the Caprifig is globular, not elongate. The Caprifig grows wild on the Riviera, though Ardoino does not mention it. Another species is also said to occur here, viz., *F. sylvestris*. This is probably none other than the uncultivated form of *F. Carica*. In the St. André Gorge, also below Gourdon, and in other rocky places a wild Fig is common, and it grows in precipitous spots where a bird only could have placed the seed. I have not noticed the shape of the fruits on these wild Fig trees. Pliny was aware that minute insects pass from the Caprifig to the eatable fig, and he seems to have had some idea that these insect visits are connected with fertilization: so near was he to the great discoveries of Sprengel and Darwin.

I have heard that meat goes bad at once if kept in close proximity to a Fig tree. *Carica Papaya*, the Papaw, commonly grown in Southern India, has a similar effect on meat; but I think that the meat must be brought into actual contact with the plant. I have never tested this statement about the Fig tree, but Professor Penzig assures me that tough meat becomes tender when wrapped in fig leaves, or when cooked with a few of them. The Papaw is allied to the Passion flower, not to the Fig.

The Riviera Figs, when half dried, are considered to be purgative to a dangerous degree. Strangers should beware of them. When completely dried, they are wholesome.

At the roots of the Fig tree you will often find growing either a clump of Iris or the huge bulbs of the Giant Squill (*Urginea*). These remain above ground: they are sometimes as large as the head of a young child. I have often wondered whether the Iris grows spontaneously below the Fig. Certainly the Squill is planted there, for several peasants have not only assured me that this is the case, but have given me the reason for it. The Squill, they say, is useful to the Fig. I should not be surprised to learn that this utility, if such there be, is in some way connected with fertilization, or with the intricate question of Caprification. If the Squill is in any way useful to the insects that frequent the Fig, it would indirectly be of service to the tree.

It is a mistake to reject these popular ideas without sufficient evidence. When the farmers objected to the Barberry (*Berberis*) bush on the ground that it is injurious to corn, botanists ridiculed the idea. M. C. Cooke, in "Microscopic Fungi," 1872, wrote that "no fungi can be much more distinct than that found on wheat and that which infests the leaves of the Barberry." "What has a Barberry bush to do with the wheat harvest? Popular superstitions!" Yet the farmers were right, though they could neither prove nor explain their theory. For the Barberry Cluster Cup (*Æcidium Berberidis*) turns out to be identical with the microscopic fungus, the Corn Mildew (*Puccinia Graminis*) which does so much damage to the crops. De Bary and other cryptogamists have shown that these two parasites, however different in appearance, are but alternating generations of one and the same species.

An interesting question arises: if two plants suffer from the same parasite, as Wheat and Barberry, or are in some way useful to each other, as may well be the case with Fig and Squill, must we not suppose that they had their origin in the same district? And may not this consideration help to throw light on the history of some of our cultivated plants?

Professor Mayor asserts that the seeds of the Vine and of the cultivated Fig have lost the power of germinating. In the case of the Vine this statement is incorrect, for grape-pips will grow freely under favourable circumstances. In fact, if the refuse from the wine-press is thrown on the land as manure, the seedling vines are so numerous as to be a nuisance.

I am now about to relate a remarkable fact connected with the Great Squill, the friend of the Fig tree, and I beg to state that this is not what James Payn would call a "taradiddle": *mira sed acta loquor*—it is open to any one to repeat the experiment. I wished to see the flower of this gigantic bulb, so I planted one in a large plot, and took great care of it. Each year it grew bigger, and threw up its broad handsome leaves, but no flowers appeared. You might as well buy a raven to see if he lives a hundred years as keep the Great Squill to find out what the flower is like. I was about to spend the Summer in Switzerland, and was not returning to the same house in Nice; so I packed up my things, and stored my furniture. The Great Squill, I thought, could not hold out much longer without flowering, so I packed it up too, intending to replant it on my return. I trimmed off the roots close to the bottom, and cut away the leaves close to the top, put it in a brown paper bag which exactly fitted, wrapped the bag in a newspaper, tied it up with string, and threw it into the bottom of a trunk with other odds and ends. There it remained about nine months. When I took the bulb out again, I found that it had outwitted me after all, for it had actually flowered in the bag! The scapes were about a yard long, and were covered with a multitude of small flowers: these were quite dry, so that I was unable to tell whether they had been coloured or completely etiolated. The scapes were wrapped round and round the bulb, which had shrunk. What wonderful vitality this Squill displays! I planted the bulb again, but another *déménagement* caused me to lose sight of it, so that I have never seen the flower. A peasant told me of a piece of ground quite covered with this Squill, but I have seen only odd clumps of it.

The Fig tree is often whitewashed, trunk, branches, and twigs, as a precaution against disease. When in this condition, it presents an extraordinary appearance.

In the land areas around the Mediterranean, scale insects are numbered among the most destructive pests that the Orange and Fig growers have to contend with. Of these *Coccus rusci*, the parasite of the Fig, is just now attracting much attention in Italy. The diameter of a well-developed female is five millimetres, the colour is greyish-white, and they have the appearance of small cones upon the trunk and boughs of the tree. They cover themselves with a substance like wax, which effectually protects them from insecticides. (*Science Gossip*, February 1898.)

The Climbing Fig (*Ficus repens*) grows here luxuriantly even on a north wall. As in the case of Ivy, the leaves of the hanging shoots are unlike those on the climbing branches. The fruits become quite large, but I do not know whether they ripen.[4]

The Elm (*Ulmus*) is being gradually replaced as a shade tree (on the St. André road, for instance), by the Plane; a change which I believe is for the worse. The papery winged fruits of the Elm blow harmlessly about the roads, whereas the irritating spicules from the Plane tree fruits, if they do not actually cause lung disease, are very likely to aggravate it. The Elm was a favourite village tree in France. Under its shade people met to discuss politics or to make bargains. "Attendez-moi sous l'Orme!" meant "You may wait till the Greek Calends."

The *Celtis* (*C. australis*) sometimes called "Nettle Tree," German "Zürgel," furnishes the wood for those wonderful whips which the

TWISTED WHIP-HANDLE OF CELTIS WOOD

carters use. They make a report like a pistol shot. The handle is split and twisted like the strands of a rope. This wood is tougher and more elastic than an osier. The leaf is oblique, like that of an Elm, but narrower in outline, and thicker in texture. The flower has the broad spreading styles so characteristic of anemophilous (wind fertilized) plants.

Attached to the Celtis, the hamadryad of the tree, is a golden-brown butterfly, *Libythea Celtis.* I have taken it once only: it was perched on the road close to the Carabacel railway crossing. In appearance and in flight this Libythea is not unlike a Comma (*Vanessa C. album*). The larva is gregarious.

The Celtis tree is either wild or well-established on the Riviera: it is common enough at Nice, and is still more abundant farther west. At Antibes, just outside the fortifications, there is a considerable grove of these trees; none of them, however, is as fine as the specimen which stands at the octroi of St. Barthélemy, near Nice.

The largest Celtis which I have seen is on the Place Neuve in the town of Grasse. Three persons, stretching their arms, can hardly make them meet round the trunk. Higher up in the same town there are some fine specimens, but none so large as this one.

The Celtis is one of the claimants for the classic name of *Lotus.* The other competitor is the Jujube (*Ziziphus*), a fruit tree of the Buckthorn order which is common here. The botanical *Lotus* is a small leguminous plant. What flavour, or what magical efficacy these lotus fruits of the Celtis may have I do not know; but the *gamins* seem to appreciate them, if one may judge by the time they spend under the tree. These berries are not much larger than a pea. Some branches of this tree are often seen in leaf while others are in bud. At first sight the backward branches appear blighted, but they come into leaf later, and seem as healthy as the others. I have repeatedly observed this phenomenon in the Celtis, but am quite unable to explain it.

The native name for Hemp, "Canaba," is the same as the Greek, and as the scientific name of the plant, *Cannabis.*

Maclura, the so called Osage Orange, is grown in several of the gardens on the Cimiez hill, and I suppose elsewhere on the Riviera. It is a good-sized tree. The fruits do not seem to ripen, or to have their peculiar fragrance. They fall off before they are as large as a Mandarin orange.[5] We found them useful for rounders; but they hurt if they reach their aim, for they are very solid.

Notes:

4   *Ficus repens* much prefers a north wall; the leaves turn yellow or black if much exposed to the sun. *Ficus minima* is a pretty species from Japan.—T. H.

5   Maclura at La Mortola produces fruit quite uneatable, but larger than a St. Michael orange.—T. H.

LIBYTHEA CELTIS

OSTRYA CARPINIFOLIA

7

Oak: Chestnut: Ostrya

"Le chêne, de qui la tête au ciel est voisine,
Et dont les pieds touchent à l'empire des morts."

OF the Riviera Oaks we can hardly say that they reach up to the sky;
nor do their roots go down quite as far as Hades. Nevertheless the Ilex
Oak is often a fine tree: the Cork Oak also grows to a good size where
it has a sufficient depth of soil.

Four species are common here, three of them evergreen. The
deciduous tree is very variable. Professor Allman considers it to be a

variety of our northern oak; but the Earl of Ducie, an excellent dendrologist, refers to it *Q. pubescens* Willd. I have found near Nice trees of this species with the leaf pinnatipartite, that is, cut almost to the midrib.

The leaves sometimes remain on this tree through the greater part of the Winter, and fading to a rich brown, "form a pleasant contrast to the dark green of the Ilex Oak and the glaucous foliage of the Olive; while in the Spring the young shoots, clothed with a reddish brown pubescence, become an additional element of beauty in the woods."

The Ilex Oak or Holm Oak (*Q. Ilex*) is remarkable for having two different sorts of leaves. When dwarfed by bad ground, or cropped and kept low, it bears hard prickly foliage. In fact it is difficult to realise that this scrubby bush belongs to the same species as the tree which spread its cool shade over the clear fountain of Bandusia.

The leaves are frequently discoloured by the larvæ of *Lithocolletis messaniella*, a moth. No foliage stands the sea air better, or forms a better screen. Though cut back by the salt spray, the Ilex Oak will hold its own; witness those battered trees which border the path on the Peninsula of St. Jean. The acorns take two years to ripen.

Professor Boulger, from whose interesting and beautifully illustrated book I have taken several facts about the Ilex Oak, says that the tree is difficult to transplant, because in favourable ground a long taproot is formed, quite devoid of lateral branches. *Quercus Ilex* is wild as far north as Nantes.

The Cork Oak (*Q. Suber*) is common at Hyères, near Grasse, and in the Esterel, but is rare at Nice and Mentone. This tree ripens its acorns in the first season. The bark is removed from the tree at intervals of from six to ten years, after it has attained about thirty years of age. Cork previously collected is of inferior quality. It is said that the operation of removing the bark favours the healthy growth of the tree. This may be so, but the appearance of the trunk is certainly spoiled. The tree is evergreen: it prefers a granite soil.

The Kermes Oak[6] (*Q. Coccifera*) does not occur at Mentone, nor have I seen it near Nice, but the underwood about Hyères is mainly composed of this prickly evergreen shrub. It is said to grow at Antibes, and Mr. Bicknell reminds me that it is plentiful in a valley close to Vence

Cagnes. In the East the Kermes Oak becomes arborescent, like the Terebinth and some other Riviera shrubs. On this plant lives a species of cochineal, which yields a crimson dye.

In the moist climate of the British Isles the Oak finds the Beech a keen competitor; while on the arid Ligurian hill-sides it meets with rivals which are proof against both heat and drought. In both regions it is able to adapt itself and to prevail.

It is interesting to trace on the map those names which are derived from trees; we may thus often picture to ourselves the earliest appearance of the landscape, and realise the changes that have taken place since ancient times. Thus, from *Quercetum*, an Oak grove like that of oracular Dodona, or like those of Apulia, bowed by the north wind as Valgius by his sorrow, we have the French "chênaie" and the town of Quesnoy. *Quercetum* is of course the word *Quercus*, with the suffix *etum*. Le Rouret, a village near Le Bar, still remarkable for its Oak trees, is derived from *Roboretum*. Rouvre is in fact the French form of *Robur*. *Alnus*, the Alder gives *Alnetum*, an Alder grove, and Aulnay, a village probably not very far from some spongy ground. From *Castanea*, the eatable Chestnut, we have *Castanetum* and the village of Chatenay. Overlooking the Var just beyond Aspremont, is the hamlet of Castagniers. If you find the word Saussaie on the map of France, be sure that you have lighted on an osier bed, for "Saussaie" is but the Latin *salictum* for *salicetum*, a plantation of Willows (*Salix*). Similarly *Pinetum* is a Pine forest, from *Pinus*. *Olivetum*, *Dumetum*, and *Rubetum*, are other instances.

In England, also, the forest trees have left their trace upon the map. From the Oak are derived Oakley, Acton, &c. The Gaelic "Dair," an Oak, gives Derry, Kil-dare, and many another Irish place-name. Buckingham is the hamlet of the Beech (M.H.G. "Buch") forest, where the loutish Saxon churl fattened his master's swine. Thus we may often read in the names of our towns and villages the record of a forest growth which has long since vanished.

The poets relate that acorns formed the main sustenance of man before the day of cereals;

"Quercus ante datæ Cereris quam semina vitae."

A Spanish Oak (*Q. grammuntia*) has eatable fruits. On these the French soldiers were fed during the Peninsular war. These same Malaga acorns were the kind sent by Sancho Panza's wife to the Duchess, with the regret that they were not as large as turkey-eggs. The tunny-fish, as they pass along the coast of Spain in their annual migrations, consume quantities of acorns which have fallen into the water. Some varieties of the Ilex Oak also produce sweet acorns; these cannot be distinguished by their outward appearance from the bitter ones. The acorns of *Q. Ægilops* are eaten in Syria. Have we here a clue to the fact that the Oak is everywhere a sacred tree?[7] For what was more sacred to primitive humanity, what is more sacred now, if we but knew it, than that which stands between mankind and famine?

The Legend of Celeus tells how corn replaced the Oak as a food-plant and mainstay of life. The goddess Ceres, bereft of her daughter, sets out on her sad pilgrimage, searching the wide world for traces of Persephone. Passing through the land of Attica, she is hospitably entertained by Celeus. His home was Eleusis, where in later days they celebrated the Eleusinian mysteries. He has but simple fare to offer—acorns and blackberries; for wheat and barley are as yet unknown. His infant son, Triptolemus, is ill. The goddess gives a sleeping draught, revealing the virtue of the poppy. Her heart is touched, for Celeus' little daughter has called her mother, childless as she is. What favour can she give in return for such kind hospitality? The boy shall be made immortal; he shall never sail in Charon's barque nor cross the hated waters of the Styx. So Ceres lays the infant on the hearth, and begins to heap the burning embers over him. The mother rushes to save her child, snatches him from the fire, and thus in her blind affection robs him of the gift of deathlessness. On parting, the goddess said: "Immortal your infant may not be, but he shall teach mankind to raise from the all-sustaining earth a better food than the acorn and the berries of the bramble."

The British Oak is said to throw out its branches at an angle of 90 degrees. I have found the angle of ramification of the deciduous Riviera Oak to vary between 40 degrees and 60 degrees. Perhaps this mode of growth is more suitable to a mountainous district, for it is evident that a tree whose boughs are horizontal must thrust these against the ground if it happens to slope steeply.

Cork Oaks, Mandelieu

The Chestnut (*Castanea vesca*) serves a double (may we not say a treble?) purpose. It is a valuable food-plant; it gives a perfect shade; and, lastly, it adorns the landscapes of the mountain region. As you advance inland, the Olive is gradually replaced by the Chestnut: pass up higher still through the pleasant Chestnut groves of Bollena, Berthemont, Valdeblore, and St. Martin Vesubia, and you reach the Alpine region, where the Chestnut gives way to the pine, larch, and birch. In the Nice district this tree descends as near the coast as the Contes valley, within easy reach of the town; and earlier in this chapter I have mentioned the village of Castagniers in the Var valley as deriving its name from the Chestnut.

Very beautiful is the tree when tinged with the golden yellow of the ripening staminate catkins. In the hollows and recesses of the boughs the myoxus hides by day, and towards evening you see the large round soft eyes peering down at you timidly from above. *Satyrus Hermione* hovers near the tree, perching often on the furrowed trunk. First the wings are folded together vertically; then within a few seconds, if all is quiet, the front wings drop back within the others, and the insect is practically invisible. When I collected, as a boy, in the Vesubia valley, I used to call Hermione the Chestnut tree butterfly, for I did not know its name. It was naturally not to be found in Coleman's "British Butterflies," and volumes such as Lang and Hofmann did not then exist. *Circe* has almost as good a claim to be called after the Chestnut tree.

The Germans call Hermione the "door-keeper of the woods," for it guards the entrance of every glade: Waldportier, setzt sich gern an Baumstämme. If you stand still among the Chestnut trees, the "Woodporter" will sometimes settle on your head or shoulders.

In the mountain villages north of Nice the poorer folk subsisted until quite lately on the fruits of the *Castanea vesca*. Elsewhere the tree is equally important. They say that if a Corsican obtains possession of two or three Chestnut trees and a goat, he will never do another stroke of work. What, plough and sow and reap and toil, when you can lie under a Chestnut tree, and pick up the fruits as they fall!

In some parts of Switzerland, at Weggis for instance, the Chestnuts are being cut down because the price of the fruit has sunk so low that it is not thought worth gathering. Thus both the Chestnut and the Olive are threatened with extermination by the great law of "supply and demand," the one and only law that is sacred in this twentieth century.

To the same family, Cupuliferæ, with the Oak and Chestnut belong the Beech, Hornbeam (*Carpinus*), Hazel (*Corylus*), and the Ostrya. The Beech, as I have stated in another chapter, is not common in the coast region of the Riviera. The Hornbeam also is confined to the mountains. But the Hazel thrives in all places not too dry.

Less familiar to English botanists than any of these is the *Ostrya* or Hop Hornbeam. This tree might be taken for a large hazel, as far as the foliage is concerned. But it may be known at once by the conspicuous greenish-white infructescence, which resembles that of the hop. Hence the popular name. If the Ostrya happens to be in fruit, it is not possible to mistake it for any other plant.

You will find a number of these trees in the St. André gorge, near the entrance, and they grow in the shady parts of almost every valley that runs up into the hills. The avenue of the Villa Garin at Cimiez is shaded by the Ostrya, and there are a great many on the Nice Château hill, eastern side. In the more modern gardens the tree, being indigenous, is not much valued.

Notes:

6.
    The name Kermes is derived from the Arabic for worm, and is the parent of the French cramoisi and the English crimson.—T. H.

7
    As witness the name Gospel Oak given to places in England.—T. H.

SATYRUS HERMIONE

PINE CONES

8

Pine Trees

THE Aleppo Pine (*Pinus Halepensis*) is the commonest conifer in this part of the Riviera. Professor Allman calls it eminently the Pine of the Provence hills. It seldom grows, in this district, to the height of the Pinaster, and indeed, in some places, retains almost a frutescent (shrubby) habit.[8] Covering by itself alone, to the exclusion of other trees, wide tracts of country, or else accompanied by the Pinaster (*Pinus maritima*), the Cork Oak (*Q. Suber*), the Ilex Oak (*Q. Ilex*), the Arbutus or the Bay (*Laurus nobilis*), it is the form of arborescent vegetation which contributes most to the wooding of the hills and to the character of the landscape.

The peasants damage and disfigure this tree by cutting off the branches for litter; but they are not the only enemies of the Aleppo Pine.

The Procession Caterpillar makes its great silky nest in the twigs, and if not destroyed in time will often eat the tree quite bare. The legend runs that this insect used to devour the crops on the Cimiez hill. The afflicted farmers sought the help of a very pious monk from the monastery. Miss Ormerod had not yet taken the insect pests in hand. The jolly friar attacked the caterpillars with bell, book, and candle; excommunicated, cursed, and anathematized them; and finally drove them across the Paillon to the Mt. Gros. He also condemned them to change their diet, and to feed henceforth, not on the produce of the farm, but on the useless leaves of the Pine tree. From their contact with the monk they acquired the habit, which they still retain, of walking in procession.

But the Procession Caterpillar has a more dangerous enemy than the fat old monk. The larva of Calosoma, a coleopterous insect, forces its way into the silken nest and destroys the inmates. So voracious is this grub that it kills many more of the caterpillars than it can possibly eat. It is wisely protected by those who are interested in the preservation of the Pine Forests. Calosoma, as its name implies, is a beautiful and conspicuous insect. It is plentiful on the Continent, but very rare in England. The elytra are bright green, the thorax violet, and the head violet-black (J. G. Wood).

Just beyond the octroi, on the Route de Gènes, these procession larvæ may be seen about the date of the vernal equinox: I have observed them as early as the second week in February. They form long lines upon the road, the head of one insect close to the tail of another. I believe that the not strictly scientific experiment has been tried of placing the procession caterpillars in a circle; but it is not on record for what length of time they continued to crawl round and round. Possibly the spell was broken by the wheel of some passing carriage. Perchance, driven by fate, they are still describing their circle on the hill-side.

Exactly so the swarm of travellers behave: from London to Paris they go; then down to Nice or Cannes, by the "train de luxe" ; the more disreputable ones turn up at Monaco. Next they appear at Florence or at Rome, each following his neighbour, he knows not and he cares not why. Back then to the Italian Lakes, or Switzerland, or Aix, and on to London, where the round begins again. From hotel to station, from station to hotel, the great procession moves year in year out.

PINUS PINEA, THE STONE PINE

Grant Allen says that if a caterpillar be removed from the centre of the line, a signal is passed to the front and to the rear, and the procession halts. If the deserter does not return to his post within a reasonable time, the line re-forms and advances again. But if the leader be taken away, no member of the band seems able to supply his place. The rank becomes disorganized, and ceases to advance. It would be interesting to ascertain whether this captain (or captainess?) differs in sex from the rank and file. A caterpillar, when full-fed, though in one sense epicene, is already male or female.

The scientific name of this insect is *Cnethocampa Pityocampa*. The brownish hairy larvæ bury themselves in the earth when they have found a suitable spot. They pupate under ground, and lie dormant through the Summer. From those which my son kept, the imagines emerged in the middle of September. The moth is grey.

It is better to avoid touching these caterpillars with the naked hand; the hairs may produce a rash which is very irritating, and sometimes even dangerous. Writers on Entomology warn us against this caterpillar, and against another, *Porthesia Chrysorrhæa*. This latter turns to a moth with white satin wings. We have found it in the Esterels. The procession larvæ on the Mt. Gros creep along in Indian file, but there are other species which march eight abreast.

The "fir tree" of the Old Testament is thought to be either the *Pinus Halepensis*, or the *P. maritima*. Perhaps the "ash" wood, used for making idols, in Isaiah xliv. 14, is no other than the Aleppo.

The *Pinaster*, or Maritime Pine, or Cluster Pine *(Pinus maritima)*, abundant on some parts of our south coast, is also very common on the Riviera: the French call it "Pin des Landes." As these two trees are often found growing together, I will mention a few points of distinction between them. The Pinaster is more erect and regular, and its branches are less contorted than those of the Aleppo: also its shoots are thicker and stronger, and it grows more rapidly. It forms, in fact, a large and handsome tree when the branches are not lopped off for firewood. The Aleppo has a more rounded top, a smaller cone, and a less rigid leaf.

Le Maout regards the cone of the Pinaster as having a phyllotaxy of 5/13. I have examined many specimens from the Riviera and from the south of England, and I find that this arrangement involves a torsion of the axis. The 8/21 phyllotaxy is open to a similar objection, the torsion being reversed. The formula 13/34 holds for all the Pinaster cones which have come under my notice. They are wonderfully regular in structure, and exhibit no variation. For this reason they are easy to work out. Le Maout's diagram of the Pinaster cone is accurate; but this author draws his conclusion from one cycle only. If any botanist will take the trouble to follow out the phyllotaxy on this drawing through the full length of the cone he will find that the series of 1, 35, 69, 103, &c. forms a vertical rank (orthostich), whereas the series of 1, 14, 27, 40, 53, &c., and that of 1, 22, 43, 64, &c., fall away to the right and to the left. Exactly the same result will be obtained by covering an unopened cone with a coat of white paint and numbering the scales in ink.

The third conifer that flourishes by the coast is the magnificent Stone Pine or Umbrella Pine (*Pinus Pinea*); in French "Pin Parasol." This tree is more frequent and characteristic in central and southern Italy, "where, with its dark green spreading umbrella-like crown, it is inseparably associated with our conception of Italian landscape."

It is strange that so handsome a tree should not be more frequently planted. Probably it does not grow rapidly enough for these breathless days:

> *"Iam quæ seminibus jactis se sustulit arbos*
> *Tarda venit, seris factura nepotibus umbram."*

The Eucalyptus runs up faster, and is more in favour. A society has been founded in Nice for the planting of trees; they should place the Stone Pine at the head of their list.

The seeds, called "pignons," are used in confectionery. It is curious that the two Pines with edible fruits should grow, one, the *Pinus Cembra*, on the highest crests of the Maritime Alps, the other, *Pinus Pinea*, where the mountains meet the sea. *P. Cembra*, the Arolla Pine, German "Zirbel," is a Russian and arctic tree. Its seeds are the food of squirrels and other rodents, for we constantly find the hard shells nibbled through. I saw some birds which a man shot near the head-waters of the Vesubia: they were something like starlings, and their

VIEW FROM CAP MORTOLA, WITH ALEPPO PINES

crops were so full of the uncracked seeds of *Pinus Cembra* that these fell out in numbers when the bird was held up by the feet.

The Stone Pine is more abundant on the Riviera di Levante, as at Sestri, and farther south at Viareggio near Pisa; but the greatest plantations are at Ravenna, "Queen of the marshes," where these trees extend for miles. The "pinetum" at Ravenna yields an enormous quantity of the edible seeds. The embryo of these seeds with its cotyledons bears some resemblance to a human hand. The natives use them as a charm.

If the Riviera di Ponente has few Stone Pines, we make up for the deficiency by possessing the finest specimen of the tree. The famous Pin de Bertaud, which grows on the high-road between Cogolin and St. Tropez, is the largest in Europe, at least so the guide-books say.

What a strange region is this, where the tropic and the arctic floras meet; where the Pine, son of the snowy north, stands side by side with the Palm, daughter of the burning south! Here is realised the dream of Heine's Fir Tree:

"Ein Fichtenbaum steht einsam
Im Norden auf kahler Höh';
Ihn schläfert, mit weisser Decke
Umhüllen ihn Eis und Schnee.

Er träumt von einer Palme
Die fern im Morgenland
Einsam und schweigend trauert
Auf brennender Felsenwand."

Notes:

[8] Given space and good earth, *P. Halepensis* will grow as tall as *P. Pinea* or the Pinaster; witness specimens in the Mortola grounds. In Persia the tree attains magnificent dimensions.—T. H

ERICA MULTIFLORA

9

Arbutus and Erica

"Aliquid amplius invenias in sylvis quam in libris."
—ST. BERNARD

THE idler in Horace's first ode reclines "viridi membra sub Arbuto stratus": but our modern loafers prefer the luxurious seats on the Jetée-Promenade, or the cushioned lounges of the Casino. If one must kill time, the Horatian method is more to my taste. And I think that the bard of the Sabine hills, who makes few mistakes when Nature is concerned, had valid reasons for recommending the shade of the Strawberry tree for a midday siesta.

It seems to me that certain plants, of which the Arbutus is one, have a perception of the picturesque. Mark well the spot where this tree loves to grow, and you will find it has a special charm. Name the most lovely scenery in the British Isles: is it not where the evergreen foliage and the waxen bells of the Arbutus are reflected in the crystal waters of Killarney? And when you find among the Olive hills some charming nook, and you exclaim, "Angulus ille ridet!" be sure that the nymph of the Arbutus haunts that unfrequented spot. She is too wild and too high-spirited to be tamely imprisoned by the railings of every suburban villa like a Lilac or a Laburnum or a Hawthorn. It is difficult to transplant an Arbutus: gardeners rarely attempt it on the Riviera.

The butterfly, which lives upon the Arbutus, is worthy of the tree. *Charaxes Jasius* is one of the largest and handsomest of the European Rhopalocera. The English name is "Bashi Bazouk"; the French "Pacha à quatre Queues" is somewhat more appropriate, for it has four tails, two to each of the hind wings, and there is in the gorgeous colouring of the insect something Eastern which might explain the word "Pacha." The underside is even more striking than the upper. This splendid butterfly is much prized by lepidopterists: it is really a north African species, but is taken both on the Riviera and in Andalusia. It is so rare in Nice that you cannot count on catching even a single specimen in the course of the season. Nevertheless, there are years in which it is much more abundant. The aged naturalist Bruyat told me that he had seen Jasius quite plentiful on the Nice Château hill. The Esterel is a good locality, and an entomologist writes from Hyères that the insect is common there also.

An intelligent nursery gardener in this town saw a Jasius laying eggs upon a rose bush. He watched the little caterpillars when they were hatched, and found that they were able to subsist for a few days upon this food, but soon perished unless transferred to the leaves of an Arbutus. This butterfly resembles the Camberwell Beauty (*V. Antiopa*) and some other species in being fond of fruit: it is often seen perched on the figs which are spread out on reed frames to dry. It is also said to be attracted by decaying animal matter, like the Purple Emperor (*A. Iris*).

The fruit of the Arbutus is neglected by the natives here, as in South Italy: it is allowed to rot on the ground. If eaten in any quantity, it is said

DATE PALMS, HYÈRES

to cause numbness of the head, and even paralysis. I do not remember ever to have eaten more than a hatful at one time.

The Arbutus is liable to a "false quantity"; many people call it Arbútus. There is no excuse for this. As Professor Marsh has shown, the English language tends to throw the accent to the left; so that even if the Latin word had the penult long, it would naturally become a dactyl in English, just as the Greek word "theátre," pronounced a few years ago with the accent on the "a," has now become "théatre." In "Erica" the case is the reverse; we treat it as an English word, and place the accent on the first syllable, whereas the "i" was originally long. The false quantity on the word "Erica" has the genius of the English language in its favour.

Nearest in size to the Arbutus, in this same Natural Order, comes the Tree Heath (*Erica arborea*). It is abundant on the hills round Hyères, but less common at Nice. The brier root pipes, incorrectly spelled "briar root," are made of this wood, not of rose, as the name might lead one to suppose. "Brier" is a corruption of the French "Bruyère," Heath. We read that "the thick woody roots are dug up and prepared for the Paris manufacturers by the peasants of the mountain valleys, who find it a remunerative occupation, though their industry bids fair ere long to extirpate this beautiful and interesting plant." The scented flowers are pink; the stamens are included. I have found it in flower in the Esterel in March. The hairy branches may serve to identify the Tree Heath, even when it is out of flower. The name Mediterranean Heath, as applied to this plant, is a misnomer. Moggridge says that *Erica Mediterranea* Linn. is never found on the shores of the Mediterranean.

Erica multiflora abounds near Toulon and Hyères: Moggridge gives excellent figures of this beautiful species and of the last. He speaks of the Multiflora as making the woods on either side of the railway gay as the traveller passes eastward from Toulon in October or the early part of November. This Heath does not occur at Cannes or at Mentone, but it is plentiful in two or three spots within easy reach of Nice; for instance, at the Cap St. Hospice, and on the hills by the Magnan. The flowers are pink, with stamens exserted.

Erica Scoparia is not common: it flowers later than the Tree Heath, with which it may be found growing. The flowers are greenish.

Ling (*Calluna*) purples, as with us, the scrubby dried-up places where less enduring plants could not exist, and loves the steep banks of wooded ravines that face the sun.

The Alpine Rose (*Rhododendron*), the Bilberry (*Vaccinium Myrtillus*), Pyrola, and the other Alpine plants allied to the Heath, are as abundant in the mountains a few miles north of Nice as they are in Switzerland.

The Cape is the home of the Heaths. In America there is not a single species of Erica, but Ling (*Calluna*) is met with in Newfoundland and near Boston. England has five heaths; Ireland six or seven; in Spain and Portugal the species are still more numerous. The Riviera reckons four; with the Alpine *E. Carnea*, five. It has been conjectured that the Heaths spread from the Azores, or from some land in that direction now submerged; this is the traditional "Lost Atlantis."

FLOWERS OF MYRTLE

10
Myrtle and Eucalyptus

"Know'st thou the land where the lemon trees bloom,
Where the gold orange blows in the deep thicket's gloom,
Where a wind ever soft from the blue heaven blows,
And the groves are of laurel, and myrtle, and rose?"

GOETHE

TO the Myrtle family belong a number of aromatic plants, such as the Clove (*Caryophyllus*), and the Allspice (*Eugenia*). The following are also allied: Eucalyptus, Melaleuca, Metrosideros, Guava (*Psidium*), and Brazil nut (*Bertholletia*); all cultivated here with the exception of the last mentioned. The Guava is so closely allied that it may be grafted on the Myrtle.

Five or six dozen species of Eucalyptus are grown on the Riviera; at any rate over sixty appear in the list of the Villa Thuret gardens at Antibes. The tree is rich in an essential oil, and the aromatic odour is said to dispel miasma: for this reason it has been extensively planted in the Campagna of Rome, in Algeria, and elsewhere. Whether the Eucalyptus be febrifuge or not, and whether a decoction of its leaves does or does not cure Influenza, we may be glad to see it spread, for it must both purify the air and protect the ground from being dried up by the sun.

Not only do the various species differ much in ramification and in foliage, but the same tree changes its appearance at different stages of its growth. This may perhaps explain why opinions are so much divided about the beauty of the Eucalyptus. The Australian despises the "Gum Tree," as he calls it, because it does not spread sufficiently, and throw a shadow dense enough to form a shelter for his sheep. His low opinion of the Eucalyptus is based on utilitarian grounds; but, in any case, the British colonist would hardly appreciate a tree so different in habit from any which we see in the west of Europe.

How prone we are to measure things, not by any ideal arrived at by the reasoning powers, but by some standard fixed when thought was dormant and our dreams were facts! Our typical lion is still the same which lay, feet upwards, on the nursery floor; not quite so sticky, nor so deep a red, nor does the tail remove at will. Yet the beast is little modified, only somewhat enlarged. So the ideal tree must have a gnarled and knotted trunk; the massive boughs must spread out horizontally at just that height above the bracken which avoids the branching antlers of the stag. Umbrageous it must be, and patulous; the dense, leafy dome, refuge of squirrels and of many a bird, must admit no ray of light. In fact, our ideal tree is not unlike an Oak.

No wonder then that the Eucalyptus finds little favour in our eyes, since it departs from all our preconceived ideas. The trunk is not gnarled and knotted, but straight and smooth and pillar-like; the branches stretch forth far above the ground, so that there is no shadow at the base; and through the scattered blue-green foliage the light and air pass freely.

The *Eucalyptus globulus* will not stand cutting; we must not judge the tree by those specimens at the Nice station which have had their tops lopped off. Froude, who had the advantage of seeing the tree in its native country, has formed a high opinion of its beauty. The universal Eucalyptus, he says, "which I had expected to find grey and monotonous, is a proteus in shape and colour; now branching broadly, now feathered like a Birch, or glowing like an Arbutus, with an endless variety of hue, green, orange, and brown." Even those writers who are least disposed to admire the Eucalyptus admit that the genus contains trees of striking, and often picturesque aspect.

Though the corolla is wanting, the tasseled flowers have a beauty of their own; and the four-cornered fruits, with the frosty bloom which covers them when young, are not less ornamental. A point not often noticed is the delicate tinting of the trunk when the long strips of bark have fallen away. You may try in vain to count the various shades of grey and green and pink and brown that decorate the bole.

Beneath the trees the ground is strewn with the little pointed caps which have fallen from the opening buds. Bentley explains these as formed by the connate calyx-limbs; Eichler appears to refer them to the corolla. I have repeatedly found fruits with the calyx-laminæ quite distinct from the operculum, and this makes Eichler's explanation much more probable. The Globulus and some other species are said to ripen their fruits on the Riviera under favourable circumstances. Seedlings are sometimes found below the trees.

The rapid growth of the *Eucalyptus globulus* is remarkable; the tree gains about eight feet a year in this district, and even in the Isle of Wight a specimen has been found to increase at the rate of an inch per day during the Summer. Some species are said to attain a height of nearly 300 feet, being surpassed only by the *Sequoia gigantea*, of California. Among the loftiest species is *E. Amygdalina*, next in point of stature comes *E. globulus*.

In the central provinces of Chili and in the Island of Juan Fernandez the *Eucalyptus globulus* is more frequented by humming-birds than any other tree. A remarkable fact, if we reflect that the Trochilidæ are unknown in Australia, which is the home of the Eucalyptus, and that for this reason the flowers cannot be specially adapted to these birds. So great is the attraction of the Globulus for different species of Trochilus and Eustephanus that in Santiago during the months of July and August these trees are surrounded by a host of humming-birds.

The wood of *E. globulus* is very hard; a thing scarcely to be expected in a tree of such rapid growth. I have seen a labourer employed to split some of this wood give up the task; he said there is a twist in the grain which prevents the wedge from acting. The ash contains much potash, sometimes as much as 21 per cent.

The leaves are of two different shapes; the younger ones being oblong, sessile, and coated with wax: these have the stomata on the under side only, as is usual. The later leaves are stalked, scimitar-shaped, leathery, and hang with their edge to the sky, so as to present the least possible surface to the sun: these have the stomata on both sides, as in the case of the leaf-like organs called "phyllodes." In fact these long curved leaves have been mistaken for phyllodes.

How strange it is that through man's agency these trees should be brought hither from that changeless island, or rather, continent, beyond the equator! How many ages have rolled by since that distant Jurassic period, when pouch-bearing mammals fed in England beneath the shade of Araucarias and Cycads? Yet these long cycles count not for the land of the Eucalyptus. New plants, new animals, new forms of life have risen in Europe, and have passed away: yet in Australia the marsupials still linger. No otherwise it fares with many a human mind; new facts, new forms of thought, have dawned upon the world; in these they have no part; Progress has passed them by; primeval superstitions haunt their minds, strange palæozoic thoughts and theories long since decayed and fossilised elsewhere, and well nigh lost to memory.

Many species of *Melaleuca* are grown here. A specimen, with more stem than foliage, used to stand by itself in the south-west corner of the Jardin Public, Nice; another in the Lycée gardens is said to be the largest in Europe. A Melaleuca was entrusted to a native gardener. Now the local name for this tree is "Papyrus," that is, "Sedge" ; but a sedge is a water plant; so this gardener doused and soaked the tree until he killed it. Of the slender evergreen twigs "les fleuristes du littoral font une grande consommation pour la confection des bouquets."

The flowers appear in the beginning of June. They would be quite insignificant were it not for the branched thread-like petal-opposed stamens, which form an exquisite fringe of filigree. Those plants which have no corolla, or an inconspicuous one, adopt various plans for supplying the defect. The Anemone spreads its painted sepals out as flags; the same purpose is served by the gaudy bracts of the

Bougainvillea, abundant at Monaco; whereas the Bottle Brush and the Eucalyptus, like our own Thalictrum, produce a beautiful tassel of tinted stamens.

Metrosideros, a small Australian tree of the same family, is also cultivated. The leaves are opposite, entire, coriaceous, rather white below. The inflorescence resembles a holy water sprinkler. The English name is *Bottle Brush*.

Allied to the Myrtle, though not so closely as the trees just mentioned, is the Pomegranate (*Punica Granatum*); mysterious plant, symbol of fertility and plenty. The Hebrew name of the Pomegranate is "Rimmon," which proves that the tree was sacred to the bright Eastern god who "died and rose again," the Syrian Adonis. This was the mystic "apple" adjudged by the Shepherd of Mt. Ida to the great goddess whose power no mortal can withstand. This same "Forbidden Fruit" of Eden brought sorrow to our race, as the legend runs; and the six seeds sufficed to bind Persephone to six months of wintry woe. The Pomegranate, like every other cosmogonic tree, including the Christian Cross, was both sacred and accursed; the leaf was chewed to purge the soul from sin. It was thus both a tree of life and a tree of death.

Those blue, purple, and scarlet "Pomegranates," alternating with golden bells in Exodus xxviii. 33 are considered to be a distortion of the Egyptian lotus-flower (Flinders Petrie).

The generic name "Punica" testifies that we have received this plant, like so many others, either from Phœnicia, or from Carthage, a Phœnician colony. The ancient Moorish capital of Spain recalls the specific name "Granatum"; and the fruit figures in the arms of the city. From the Greek name for the flower Browning has taken the title of his poem "Balaustion." The blossoms are scarlet or white. The oriflamme is commoner than the pale flag of truce. The trees which I have examined bear a large number of staminate flowers which fall off, and only a few pistillate ones. Thus the Pomegranate produces much less fruit than any one would expect from the show of blossom. It is said that nightingales prefer the Pomegranate to all other trees. Canon Ellacombe, author of "In a Gloucestershire Garden," calls attention to the fact that Shakespeare noticed the affection of the Nightingale for the Pomegranate:—

Eucalyptus Globulus

"Nightly she sings in yon Pomegranate tree."

I wonder, he says, where Shakespeare got his idea. Pliny does not mention it in his wonderful account of the Nightingale. The Pomegranate, when wild, is armed.

TERRACE WITH CYPRESS TREES

11

Trees, Indigenous and Exotic

"Que d'aubre de pertout! lou beu terraire!"

IN previous chapters I have grouped together trees and shrubs which are related to each other; but this article will include species of different Natural Orders.

The Cypress (*Cupressus sempervirens*) may be feathered to the base, or it may grow as a tall smooth pole, surmounted by a tuft of intensely dark green foliage. The tapering spires afford a striking contrast to the rolling grey-green masses of the Olive. These trees are sometimes seen growing singly on the hill-side, but they are usually planted to shelter a well, or to form a shady retreat at the corner of some terrace. The ancient mansions on the Riviera are frequently approached by an avenue of Cypress. All through Italy these lofty trees constitute a feature in the landscape. Travellers will remember the remarkable specimens in Verona.

From earliest times the wood has been valued for its durability. Experiments lately tried in India prove that Cypress and Teak are superior to all other timber in resistance to decay and to the attacks of the termite. In Egypt and in Greece the bodies of the dead were encased in Cypress wood. Of the same material were the doors of the great temple of Diana at Ephesus, and the portals of St. Peter's in Rome, now replaced by brass. As a "box" to contain small articles is derived etymologically from "Buxus," the wood of which it is made, so I believe that both "coffer" and the classical "cophinus" are connected with "Cypress"; in fact Horace in one passage uses the word "Cupressus" as synonymous with "box." The root consonants K.P.R. occur in both these words; and, what is very remarkable, they are found again in the Hebrew "Gopher," the wood of which the Ark was built; for G.F.R. is equivalent to K.P.R. or C.P.R., as every philologist is aware. "Copper" also contains the same three radical consonants. The reason is obvious: the metal takes its name from the Island of Cyprus, where it was found, and the Island itself is called after the Cypress trees which abounded there. We have thus from the same root "Cypress," the tree; "Cyprus," the Island, called after the tree; "Gopher," the Semitic name for the same tree; "Coffer," the box or Ark made from its wood; "Copper," the metal found in the island; and lastly the "Cyprian" goddess, "diva potens Cypri."

The Gopher on which I have thus speculated is one of the unsolved mysteries of antiquity. I have stated in another chapter that one-half of the Bible plants are unknown to us; it would be more accurate to say that we are completely ignorant of two-thirds. About one hundred plants are mentioned in the Old and New Testaments. We know the order, genus, and species of about twenty: the order and genus of about

EZA

ten: the order alone of one or two. So that of all the trees, shrubs, and herbs alluded to, we are able to identify about one in three.

The Cypress is one of those plants termed "cosmogonic": it is a Tree of Life, and at the same time a Tree of Death. This is why the drowning world was saved in a coffer made of the imperishable Gopher wood. I believe the Ark or chest which bore Danae and her babe across the sea from Argos to the Cyclades was of this same sacred wood. But, on the other hand, the "funereal Cypress" is dedicated to Pluto, and planted by the tombs of the departed. The discovery was made in very early times that life and death are complementary, that the greatest blessing may be the greatest bane, and *vice versa.*

The superstitious dread of the Cypress still lingers among the peasantry near Nice. I wished to plant a few of these trees at one end of my garden to give shade; but the gardener, an honest and goodhearted old man, begged me not to meddle with them. "You will suffer," he said, "if you plant a Cypress." Thinking that he was afraid on his own account, I asked him to dig them up and bring them: I would plant them myself. I might as well have begged him to bring a tiger, and let it loose in the garden!

According to Professor Penzig the true type of Cypress is that with branches spreading horizontally.

The *Ailantus* is one of the commonest roadside trees in this district. It spreads in all directions by suckers, and I believe that the seeds also ripen. The Chinese name is "Tree of Heaven." The Ailantus belongs to a tropical order which has but one representative in the Mediterranean region; namely, the little *Cneorum,* sometimes called Mediterranean Quassia, a shrub which grows on the hills to the east of Nice. The Ailantus is easily known by its long deciduous pinnate leaves: there are as many as fourteen pairs of leaflets on one of these. The leaflets show a tendency to be pinnatifid. The tree is seen at its best when the clusters of winged fruits turn red.

Cneorum Tricoccon

The chaplain at Carabacel asked me the name of a tree which kept the sun from his window. I told him that it was the "Tree of Heaven," most appropriate to shade the dwelling of a "Man of God"; if a "Bird of Paradise" would only build its nest in the branches, the arrangement would be complete! Nevertheless, he had the top cut off it.

A species of silkworm, *Attacus* (*Bombyx*) *Cynthia*, feeds on the leaves of the Ailantus. The moth is very large and handsome, a magnificent insect, which will reward the lepidopterist who takes the trouble to rear it. M. Vérany, in the "Statistique des Alpes-Maritimes," recommends the planting of the Ailantus on a large scale, in order to feed this useful insect. Kirby says that it may be reared in England easily enough, but the silk is too difficult to wind.

Melia Azedarach and *Grevillea* are two more of the exotic trees which seem to be supplanting the European ones on the Riviera. We will take the *Melia* first: an Asiatic tree with twice pinnate deciduous leaves of a lustrous dark green, and fragrant lilac or purple flowers. The popular name is "Bead Tree" or "Pride of India." The Neem tree of the Anglo-Indian is closely allied.

The beads make a pretty necklace: you have only to scrape the fruits, they are ready carved, and are even provided with a hole for the thread. In those countries where the kernels are strung together to form rosaries, the Melia has obtained the name of "Arbor sancta." The tree has the reputation of being obnoxious to insects, and for this reason it is often planted near stables to drive away flies. Both the leaves and the fruits are considered to be poisonous. Birds which swallow these fruits sometimes fall to the ground insensible; but they soon recover from the effects of the poison, and are able to fly away, unless a small boy has twisted their necks. The young negroes lie in wait under the trees for this purpose. There are specimens in most of the gardens, in the Nice Château grounds, at the Quatre Chemins on the upper Cornice Road, and the village of Contes has a group of these trees on its "Place." Just at the door of the Villa (Hotel) Arson there is a Melia which I used to admire when I lived close by. A white rose had climbed over it, and when the two plants were in flower together the combination of colour was strikingly beautiful. Melia is allied to the Mahogany (*Swietena*). The coloured filaments are connate in a tube.

Grevillea robusta has evergreen foliage which (speaking unbotanically) reminds one of certain fern fronds. The orange-yellow flowers are handsome. The fruit, a follicle, resembles a little black peapod with long curved style. The stamens are adnate to the sepals. Grevillea, with Hakea and some other garden shrubs, belongs to the Proteaceæ, an order of Australian and Cape plants not represented in Europe. In the flowers of some Proteaceous plants the nectar is so abundant as to become an article of diet for the Australian aborigines. Grevillea is common in gardens; there are one or two specimens on the Quai Massena, Nice. In an English nurseryman's list I find the height of the Grevillea given as two feet!

Among the trees which appear to be less cultivated of late years on the Riviera are the Ash, Ornus, Maple, Negundo, and Linden. I have alluded elsewhere to the neglect of Elm and Ostrya.

The Ash (*Fraxinus excelsior*) is rare in the Nice valley, but the tree, or a variety of it, is abundant near Cannes in the valley of the Siagne. The fort at the end of Cap St. Jean, between Villefranche and Beaulieu, is called "Fraxinet." This looks as if the Ash had once grown there, but none are now seen on the promontory. This term "Fraxinet" seems to have been applied to several of the Moorish strongholds. There is, for instance, the great central fastness of Freinet (formerly written Fraxinet) in the Montagnes des Maures. Here, again, there are no traces of Ash trees, so that the etymology must appear doubtful. That the Ash can flourish on the Riviera is proved by the magnificent old tree in the centre of the town of Vence. More than half the boughs of this giant have been cut away, but the part which still remains is an ornament to the place.

The Flowering Ash (*Fraxinus Ornus*), producing the manna of Commerce in Calabria, is plentiful on this part of the coast. It is a modest little tree, which one easily passes by without notice until it attracts attention by its elegant feathery white inflorescence. The four strap-shaped petals seem at first sight to be distinct one from the other. If this were really the case, the tree would form an exception to the rule of its order, which is sympetalous; for the petals of Privet, Jasmine, Lilac, and Olive are connate. But the corolla of the Ornus is truly sympetalous, for the petals are joined at the base.

The Negundo Maple (*Acer Negundo*) is met with here and there by the roadside and in gardens. It is easily known by the light green pinnate leaf, and by the shape of the samara.

The Linden (*Tilia*) does not prosper as well here as in the North; but it is said to ripen its seeds, which is rarely the case in England. Large quantities of the flowers are picked each year and stored to make a "tisane."

But these deciduous trees are not much planted here. More characteristic of the Riviera are the pleasant Palm groves of the Torre di Cimella, Cimiez, or the tropical jungle of Tree-ferns in the grounds of the Villa St. Jean, Cannes.

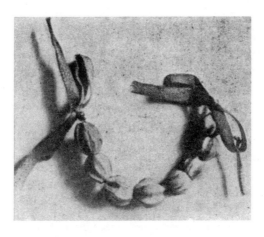

BEADS OF MELIA AZEDARACH

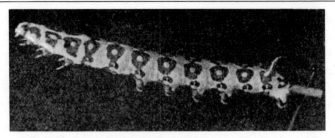

12
Euphorbias

THE Castor Oil Plant (*Ricinus communis*) is easily known by its large palmate-lobed leaves, and by the rank smell which these give out when bruised. It is of very rapid growth; a specimen at La Mortola grew to a height of over five yards in four years, with a woody stem thick in proportion. The Castor Oil Plant flourishes particularly well at Monaco, and near the Var I have seen it develop into a small tree. But it is unable to bear much cold, and is one of the first shrubs to be blackened by a frost. Even as far south as Athens it does not always succeed.

The fruit is highly elastic, like that of most Euphorbias; when it is sufficiently dry the carpels explode with great force. I have been startled by some fruits which I had placed on a shelf shooting their seeds right across the room. It is easy to understand the violence with which some tropical Euphorbias, such as the Sand-box (*Hura*) must explode, when a small fruit like that of *Ricinus* has so much strength.

Lubbock, "Flowers, Fruits, and Leaves," p. 53, strangely enough omits *Ricinus* from his list of plants which fling their seeds to a distance. These are Land Cress (*Cardamine*), Dog Violet, Geranium, Vetch (*Vicia*), Broom (*Sarothamnus*), Balsam (*Impatiens*), Woodsorrel (*Oxalis*), Squirting Gourd (*Ecbalium*), and two or three others, including the

Sand-box just mentioned. If the Violet can project its seed ten feet, and the Squirting Gourd twenty, it is probable that the Castor Oil fruit is able to throw fifty feet or more on level ground, if I may judge from the violence with which they are flung across a room.

The seeds of Ricinus bear a striking resemblance to a beetle, of which the caruncle or protuberance at the narrower end forms the head. It is not known whether the aim of the plant is to have its seeds eaten by birds, or on the contrary to prevent birds from eating them. It seems to me that a bird which ate one of these imitation insects would be likely to avoid them ever afterwards, as the small boy did in "Masterman Ready."

A species of silkworm lives on this plant. It is not found possible to prevent the eggs from hatching in the Winter; and this has caused the culture of the insect to be abandoned.

There is a legend that branches of Ricinus were strewn before Christ on his entry into Jerusalem; hence the specific name "Palma Christi" of some botanists.

Of the true Euphorbias with milky juice, that which strikes strangers most is the giant *E. dendroides* sometimes called the Emerald Bush Spurge, so abundant in all rocky places round Nice. Mr. C. Bicknell has given me the following note about the distribution of this characteristic plant. "I don't think" (he says) "that *E. dendroides* likes such a very modern formation as the tertiary sandstones and marls of the Bordighera district. It flourishes on the older rocks. There is a little of it in the Roja valley near Ventimiglia on the conglomerate, but only a little: thence eastward it does not reappear till Alassio."

The Bush Spurge cannot stand much frost: in fact the Carob alone is more delicate, as will appear from the following list, drawn up by Professor Martins, of indigenous Riviera plants in order of resistance to cold:—

1. Vitis vinifera.	*6. Olea Europea.*
2. Quercus Ilex.	*7. Punica granatum.*
3. Pistacia lentiscus.	*8. Laurus nobilis.*
4. Smilax aspera.	*9. Myrtus communis.*
5. Ficus Carica.	*10. Chamærops humilis.*

11. *Nerium oleander.*   13. *Ceratonia siliqua.*
12. *Euphorbia dendroides.*

On many species the handsome caterpillar of the Euphorbia Hawk Moth (*Deilephila Euphorbiæ*) is frequently seen feeding; and the larva of the rare and very valuable Nice Hawk Moth (*Deilephila Nicæa*) is also to be found upon these same plants. The two moths are hardly to be distinguished, even by an experienced eye, but the larvae are very different. That of the Nice Sphinx has along the back a row of large black markings, each of which is the exact representation of a pair of spectacles. These markings are so conspicuous that it is impossible even for a beginner to mistake the insect. If you have the good fortune to find the larva of this rare Sphinx, you may still be a long way from obtaining the imago, for they are very difficult to bring out. A lepidopterist at Cannes told me that out of forty larvæ he obtained but two or three moths.

Euphorbia spinosa forms bright green cushions on the rocky ground. The last year's twigs dry up and turn to spines. On this species the gregarious caterpillars of *Bombyx alpicola* are common; they feed up in April and May, and the chocolate brown moth emerges after a very short delay in the pupa stage. The white eggs are laid so as to form an elegant collar round the stem of the food plant. These larvae pupate freely, pinning their cocoon in any shady corner; but when the moths emerge, they will destroy themselves in a very few minutes if permitted to fly about in the cage. The male is smaller and much lighter in colour.

I have seen the Caper Spurge (*E. lathyris*) but once on the Riviera. The name seems to imply that the fruits of this plant are edible, and I knew a person who cultivated and ate them; but I can find in my botanical books no mention of the fact that they are eatable.

I take the following from Bicknell's "Flora of Bordighera," p 252. *E. lathyris* is used in Italy by vine growers, who smear the poisonous juice on the grape bunches to keep them from being eaten. [A similar use is made of the *Ecbalium*: see Chapter 16.] The same botanist adds that at Bordighera this spurge is supposed to preserve from injurious insects the roots of all other plants within a radius of four yards! They may occasionally be seen planted among tomatoes, potatoes, and even roses. *E. lathyris* is not truly indigenous.

Coast View, Looking towards Mentone

There is a small Euphorbia very easily recognised, and worth searching for; I mean *E. Chamæsyce*. It lies as close to the ground as the Knot Grass (*Polygonum Aviculare*) or the Herniaria, and spreads after the manner of a chickweed (*Cerastium*) in two-branched cymes. In order that one leaf on each alternate node may not be forced against the ground, the axis twists through a right angle. We see the same thing in other prostrate plants with opposite and crossed (decussate) leaves, for instance, in the common British Ground Ivy (*Glechoma*). This pretty little Euphorbia grew in the gravel walks of my garden when I lived on the Cimiez hill; I have not seen it since.

The Box (*Buxus*) covers large tracts in the mountains north of Nice, mixed with Vincetoxicum, Savory (*Satureia*), Calamint, and various other Labiates. It is remarkable that this covering of stunted Box is seen on the south side of the range, whereas the northern slope is clothed with conifers. This gives the mountains a quite different aspect when viewed from opposite sides. Either the mountain Pines and Larches are unable to endure the full force of the sun on the south side; or growing more slowly on the drier ground, they have gradually succumbed to the wood-cutter, and made way for the hardy Box bushes, which appear able to put up with any extremes of damp or drought, of heat or cold.

In the Pyrenees the barren condition of the southern slopes contrasts even more strongly with the fertile northern *versant*.

Young folks in Florence use Box twigs for the harmless game of *verdet*. It was played thus in the consulship of Plancus. A forfeit is agreed upon which must be paid by him or her who is first caught unprovided with some fresh green leaves. The match may last for weeks, and many are the devices for separating the other person from his precious sprig of Box.

Buxus is less closely allied to the true Euphorbias than is the Castor Oil Tree, yet it has the same three-lobed and elastic fruit. The ancients noticed the acrid properties of the Euphorbias, and for this reason distrusted all plants with tricoccous fruit.

The Riviera has twenty-five species of Euphorbia.

13
The Great Reed

"Syrinx Klage tönt aus jenem Schilfe."
Die Götter Griechenlands

OF the half-dozen giant grasses which adorn the gardens and the wild spots of the Riviera the commonest is the Great Reed (*Arundo Donax*). This arborescent grass is a sure sign of damp ground. Along the margins of the watercourses, says Professor Allman, its leafy stems grow to a height of twelve feet or more in picturesque groups of tropical aspect; while everywhere around their base, and vigorously pushing themselves through the soil, are the strong light green conical shoots which are to become the young stems of the new year.

Job asks (chapter viii. 11) if the rush can grow up without swampy ground, or the flag flourish without water. We do not know what plants are intended by "rush" and "flag" in this text. "Rush" appears to be some sort of sedge (*Cyperus*): the same word is translated "meadow" in Genesis, where those fat kine of Pharaoh's were feeding. As to "flag" we cannot be certain that the Iris is meant, even if the plant be indigenous in Egypt, for some species of Iris will grow on the very driest ground, as for instance the beautiful Dwarf Iris (*I. Italica*), on the sunny rocks of Gairaut near Nice. The rank growth by the river's brink, where the infant Moses floated in his little ark, is called

DISTAFF MADE OF ARUNDO STEM

"flags" in Exodus ii. 3; and the self-same word is translated "weeds" in the book of Jonah, chapter ii. 5, where "the depth closed the prophet round about, and the weeds were wrapped about his head."

The fact is that one-half of the Bible names of plants are quite unknown to us, and the English translations are mere guesses. This point is well illustrated by the water plants just mentioned, and by the Reed from which we started. All these various species, genera, and orders are inextricably confused.

The *Arundo* is probably the "Reed shaken by the wind" of Matthew xi. 7, for it abounds by the Jordan banks, where it forms impenetrable thickets, and the great Teacher painted for us in his parables the pictures which Nature had impressed upon his mind from childhood's early days.

Perhaps the Prophet was thinking of the nodding plume of the Arundo when he wrote of "bowing the head like a bulrush" (Isaiah lviii. 5). This plume, "panache," or, to use the botanical term, "Panicle," does not always crown the helmet of the Giant Reed. The plant often passes years without flowering; in fact Hooker says that it rarely flowers. But if my memory serves me, there are always a few of these Reeds flowering here and there in Autumn.[9] In 1885 the great brown feathery inflorescence appeared everywhere. The peasants say that when the great Reed waves its plumes aloft the Winter will be sharp. I have not made up my mind about this saying, whether it holds good or not.

ARUNDO DONAX, THE GREAT REED

The stems are hollow, and more or less closed at each node (joint); their surface, hardened with a siliceous (flinty) glaze, will turn the sharpest blade. It would be difficult to enumerate the different uses to which these Reeds are put. Each rustic "cabaret" has its reed-built summer-house or sun shelter, grown over, to improve the shade, with a *Gourd*, an *Ipomea*, or a *Boussingaultia* (French "Pomme de terre d'Afrique"). The Great Reed serves for fences, fishing rods, and for a hundred other purposes. On Reed frames the figs dry temptingly in the sun; and Reed railings hold the long lines of orange-peel which decorate the house-top or the open loft of the perfumer.

A distaff is very ingeniously constructed by making a number of parallel and vertical slits in a piece of Arundo stem and inserting small cross-bars to form the bulging curve on which the tow is placed. Hence the French name for this Reed, "Roseau à quenouille." These distaffs are used in every cottage on the Riviera, and I believe throughout the whole Mediterranean region.

Humboldt says somewhere (I quote from memory) that the three great stages of civilization are marked by the use men make of the Arundo. First, in the wild hunting stage it forms the shaft of an arrow or a lance. Next, in the pastoral state the shepherd, seated in the shade, plays on his flute of Reed while the cattle graze around. Then comes the third or agricultural stage, when the Reed is used for supporting the vine; and this use still remains.

Humboldt might have mentioned a fourth and final stage of society in which the Arundo plays its part, namely, that in which men no longer chase the game through leafy glade, or watch the flocks on grassy plain, or tend the vines on sunny slope; when all this work is done by slaves, or freemen in worse plight than slaves, while others take their ease. Might not this ease and luxury be represented by the pipe, the bowl of thick Reed, and the stem a thinner one? If the flute may stand as a symbol of the shepherd life, might not Sir Walter Raleigh's weed represent that of the idler? In any case the native home-made pipe is of Reed, like the arrow, the flute, and the vine prop.

By the way, those Reed arrows of Humboldt's appear to me to be very doubtful. Many Reeds look straight enough as they grow, but if you examine them with a view to arrow making, no fletcher would pass one in a hundred as perfectly straight. Moreover they split when they strike anything moderately hard. I think that Reed arrows would not score heavily in a modern archery match. Those sharp or "bitter" arrows in the Iliad were no ordinary Arundo stems.

In the south of Europe the Arundo is called a "Cane." This, of course, is the ancient name; but we have two strong reasons for not adopting it. First, the English word "Reed" is to hand, and is attached to the genus Arundo, for the smaller Reed, *Arundo Phragmites* is a British plant. Secondly, the word "Cane" is already claimed by three plants of different families, which have nothing in common but a slender stem. These are the Sugar Cane (*Saccharum*), an arborescent grass; the Rattan Cane, a climbing palm; and the botanical Cane or *Canna*, a broad-leaved endogen with handsome flowers. This plant is common enough here; I have seen it growing half-wild in a ditch. It has but one fertile stamen; and the smooth round black seeds are about the size of a pea.

The Great Reed was probably brought from the East through Cyprus, Crete, and Greece. The name, at any rate, is Semitic. From the Hebrew "Kaneh," a Reed, is derived a large family of Latin and more modern words. These will naturally be found to express something straight and hollow: for instance the straight measuring rod or "canon," the hollow "cannon"—compare the word "rohr," that is, Reed, for the Dutchman's rifle. "Canal" and "channel" are from the same source: so also "can," German "Kanne." If we suppose a primitive root, Kan = water; then as Canna is a water plant, so the Greek Khēn, a goose, would mean "water-bird." I am aware that this is not the received etymology, and I know that Professor Max Müller will not allow any connection between Aryan and Semitic roots; but I believe that both Aryans and Semites inherited from the peoples whom they overran many names of places and of things.

Where the ground is marshy, and favourable to the growth of these conspicuous grasses, the landscape will have a peculiar character. If these Reed stems were, as it appears, of great value for war or hunting gear, the spot where they could be obtained would be still more remarked and better remembered. The nearest town or village would take its name from such a landmark. Thus many a town is called after the Arundo.

VALLON OBSCUR, NICE

Cannæ, an obscure village in the far south-east of Italy, "*ignobilis Apuliæ vicus*," where Hannibal inflicted on the Romans that fourth and almost fatal blow; *Canossa*, again, whither Bismarck vowed he would not go, but went; then *Cannes*, neighbour and rival of Nice; lastly, a small but very famous village, renowned for the marriage feast, to which a certain Heretic and Reformer was invited from his home in Nazareth close by.

The position of *Cana in Galilee* is not known with certainty: two spots lay claim to the honour. Here is a short mention of the more likely site by Major C. R. Conder, leader of the Palestine Exploring Expedition. "The plain to the north of Nazareth is for the most part arable land, but near at hand there is a pestilent swamp surrounded by Reeds: whence the name of 'Kaneh,' or 'Canes.' Camping on the borders of this unhealthy morass, we suffered from the inevitable fever, as well as from the most notable mosquitos in Palestine." Ossian says of the high-bosomed Strinadona, the stately huntress of Tormoth wild, that she is "fairer than the down of Cana." This is the cotton grass (*Eriophorum*). It seems, therefore, that the name "Cana" is applied in the north of Europe to another order of water-loving plants.

The Arundo endures an amount of ill-treatment which would destroy any plant with less vitality. After the stems have been cut off near the ground, fire is set to the stumps, so that nothing can remain alive but the creeping stocks (rhizomes) which lie half buried in the mud. The ashes are left to manure the earth for the growth of the following year. The juicy shoots are greedily eaten by goats, asses, and other animals.

These reeds not only beautify the landscape, but they afford a welcome shelter to many a small bird or quadruped, and to many a flowering plant. The *Aristolochia* is almost always to be found on the borders of a Reed-brake. Where the Aristolochia is very plentiful, and the ground is spongy, you will find the *Thaïs*, a butterfly little valued by collectors in spite of its exquisite markings, for the unlucky insect is easily found and easily caught. Thaïs abounds at Cannes, but is unknown in the Nice valley: it may, however, be found at no great distance from Nice.

The Arundo extends up the valley of the Vesubia, north of Nice some thirty miles. It halts exactly where the Olive does: neither plant passes the gorges of the Sirol.

The Great Reed grows moderately well in England, but is liable to be killed by a severe winter.

Notes:

[9]   Mr. C. Bicknell reports that in a thicket of *Arundo* at the mouth of the Nervia there is a mass of flowers every Autumn.

THAÏS POLYXENA

ZEA MAYS, INDIAN CORN

14
Indian Corn

*"Plumes of green bent o'er his forehead,
And his hair was soft and golden."*

MAIZE (*Zea Mays*) ranks among the seven cereals; wheat, barley, oats, rye, millet, rice, and maize—an iambic pentameter line which I have written without intending it. These are the seven pillars which support the temple of humanity, the seven-fold staff of life.

Polenta, or Indian Corn porridge, is the chief food of the Piedmontese: the natives here call them "Polenta eaters," just as they call the French "faiou," that is "scarlet runners," or eaters of haricot beans. The word "faiou" is a corruption of "Phaseolus," a scarlet runner. "Flageolet," a kind of haricot, is an absurd distortion of the same Latin word.

These Piedmontese do the hard manual labour in this part of the world: they work as navvies, porters, and so forth. They are, many of them, powerfully made men, and the Niçois are ludicrously afraid of them, for they consider them capable of any act of violence. These rough fellows from the head waters of the Po seem to have a stronger northern element than the milder inhabitants of the valleys that slope towards the Mediterranean; they are taller of stature, and more given to drinking and fighting: more like our own navvies in fact.

Polenta may be a very wholesome food when eaten in moderation, but the exclusive use of Maize porridge brings on the dreadful disease known as "Pellagra," which has devastated certain districts of north Italy.[10] It is said that a little meat cures the Pellagra in its early stages. Goethe, in his "Italienische Reise," foresaw the dangerous effects of this monotonous diet. Is it not possible that a northern meat-eating race, settling in the south, may find themselves unable to endure the change to a purely vegetarian diet? Possibly these north Italians would suffer equally on an unvaried diet of rice or potatoes.

Many, if not all, races of men are correlated with certain conditions of food and of temperature: an invading race therefore which has to submit to a change of food or climate may be at so great a disadvantage that the earlier population may reassert itself. Thus the Teutonic element has dwindled away in France. The same thing is happening in England: and in Ireland one or more prekeltic races seem to have reoccupied the west and south.

One sometimes sees the ears of the Indian Corn hanging up to dry under the eaves, but this most artistic and natural decoration is less frequent here than by the Lake of Geneva. The dried leaves are used to stuff mattresses; on these one could sleep, "tant bien que mal," were it not for pieces of the stem and knobs from the axis of the cob which are mixed with the leaves.

"If you find fern seed, you may hear the grass grow"; but if you enter a field of maize, without any "fern seed," you will hear a cracking sound at intervals. I suppose this to be the splitting of the sheaths.

To economise ground, and to save bean sticks, a scarlet-runner (*Phaseolus*) is sown at the foot of each Maize plant. Each stem bears, as a rule, more than one ear, but I do not remember ever seeing more than three. When the seeds are set, that is, after fertilization, the farmer frequently lops off the top of the plant with the staminate spikes, which grow at the end of the axis. Deprived of its terminal tuft, and burdened with a scarlet-runner, the Maize has an overloaded look. Long suffering it stands in the burning sun; mutilated and supporting a gaudy parasite, yet ripening its heavy load of grain. How well this represents the lot of many a mortal!

The corn-fields of the Riviera are made bright with all, or almost all, the wild flowers which adorn the crops at home: Poppy, Corn Campion (*Githago*), Corn Centaury (*C. Cyanus*), Venus' Comb (*Scandix Pecten*), Camelina, rare in England, and many more. But this district has a number of cornfield weeds which are peculiar to the south. The graceful *Gladiolus* is universal and abundant; the curious *Specularia* (a Campanula) is sprinkled through the crop, and forms banks of deep purple in the corners of each terrace. The inferior stalk-like ovary of this plant is furnished with bracts. The blossoms of the Specularia mark by their opening the hour of seven a.m. on the floral clock of Linnæus. In St. Barthélemy, Cimiez, and other spots not yet completely built over, if you will forsake for one short hour the Promenade Anglaise with its blinding glare, and venture so far afield in the early spring, you will see the flowers of the wild Anemone (*A. Coronaria*), and the equally wild Tulip forming a fine contrast with the tender green of the young grain. I have also found in some places the Pheasant's Eye (*Adonis*) growing plentifully in the corn.

The wreath of the Ligurian Ceres is a rich one, though her domain consists not of broad rolling acres, but of long narrow terraces built up with infinite labour and repaired with constant toil.

Before leaving the Indian Corn, I must mention an interesting peculiarity. Adventitious roots are thrown out above the base of the stem. There is a tendency in many Endogens to produce these roots, chiefly I think when the plant stands in a swampy place or is over-watered. It is easy to see how the Pandanus of the Mauritius has raised itself above the ground, and stands propped on its pillar-like roots. My son found an abnormal plant in which the pistillate spike grew at the end of the axis, surrounded by the staminate spikes: these bore perfect flowers through the greater part of their length. This looks as if Maize were not originally diclinous.

In some of the villages east of the Var the peasants are so dishonest

PROMONTORY OF ST. JEAN
(FROM AN OLIVE GROVE AT BEAULIEU)

that they steal the corn from their neighbours' fields. I noticed people sleeping out in the fields when the crops were ripe, and inquired the reason. I was told that they were protecting the corn.

Dr. Schweinfurth relates a curious custom of some African tribes. When strangers approach their territory, they hang up by the path a cob of Indian Corn, a feather, and an arrow. The meaning is: "If you touch either the produce of our fields, or our domestic animals, we declare war against you."

In his interesting work on Plant Mythology, De Gubernatis cites the following Calabrian legend. A mother had seven daughters; six of them span busily, but the seventh looked on. When her sisters went to church she ate up all the food that was in the house. On their return there was a scene. A travelling pedlar, hearing the noise, looked in and asked what was the matter. The mother, with ready wit, seizes the opportunity. No man who knows this girl will marry her; but here is a stranger! She tells him that her six daughters are loudly praising their sister because she eats so little, and does as much work as all the rest together. The pedlar marries her on the spot, to the great delight of all her relatives. He takes the idle glutton home, gives her a large supply of flax to spin, and goes forth to sell his wares. She never thinks of spinning, and regales herself with a huge pot of Maize porridge. But retribution is at hand: the husband is returning: there stands the dish of polenta, but the flax is not begun. "Ne sachant à quel saint se vouer," she calls in despair the fairies to her aid, and, scorning the vulgar flax, she spins the yellow porridge into cloth of gold. Perhaps there is a meaning in this south Italian nursery tale. The poet will not and cannot toil, at least he cannot work for gain; he looks on while the pageant of life passes by, and feels that he has no part in it. Men call him idler and dreamer, but he weaves golden thoughts wherewith to embroider the dull warp and weft of other looms.

I have never found that red ear which Longfellow describes, that "Maize ear red as blood is," which was so welcome an omen to the Indian maiden.

How tenderly true to Nature is the legend of Mondamin, friend of man—

"With his soft and shining tresses,
With his garments green and yellow,
With his long and glossy plumage!"

How exquisitely the poet tells of Mondamin—

"Sleeping in the rain and sunshine,
Till at length a small green feather
From the earth shot slowly upward,
Then another and another,
And before the summer ended
Stood the Maize in all its beauty,
With its shining robes about it,
And its long soft yellow tresses!"

Notes:

[10]   Mr. C. Bicknell believes that Pellagra is caused by eating Indian corn which is in bad condition.

TRUNK OF AN OLIVE TREE, ST. PONS, NICE

15
Giant Grasses

"La Nature, c'est toute vérité,
Et c'est aussi toute poésie."

DURRA, or Danna, or Guinea Corn, or Negro Corn (*Sorghum*), another Giant Grass, is grown everywhere round Nice. I am ashamed to confess that I at first mistook it for Maize, but one day approaching nearer I noticed that all the flowers are together at the top, whereas in Maize the staminate and pistillate flowers, though on the same plant (monœcious), are in separate spikes. If one takes the trouble to compare these two great Grasses, it is not possible to confuse them. But it requires a certain effort to examine and compare: it is much easier in botany, as in other subjects, to take things for granted. Here is a great broad-leaved grass six or eight feet high; it is not a Bamboo, nor yet an Arundo, *ergo* it is an Indian Corn. This kind of reasoning is common enough, even with persons who know their "Barbara Celarent."

The confusion which sometimes falls upon a botanist is chronic among the general public. Plants are confounded with one another which do not seem to have anything whatever in common. How much those people lose to whom all vegetation seems the same, who neither know nor care what natural order this or that flower belongs to! Their outlook must be that of an ant or a bee. The sense of colour exists, and to a certain extent the sense of form; they can distinguish a blue flower from a red one, or a bell-shaped from a star-like blossom. Like the bee, they may even prefer a blue flower to a vulgar yellow one. Nevertheless they miss all the interest and almost all the beauty of the changing year. Nature to them is but a vast monotony.

The botanist knows nothing of monotony: no climate and no season can be dull to him. Place him

"Pigris ubi nulla campis arbor æstiva recreatur aura,"

he will yet find some object of interest; an anemophilous cabbage at Kerguelen, or a rolling Nostoc, or at the worst he will be able to study the Lichen-gonidia question. If his lot be cast

"Sub curru nimium propinqui solis,"

he will recognise some of the strange forms of vegetation described in Kingsley's "Letters from the Tropics": for he delights to know

"Quid quæque ferat regio et quid quæque recuset."

In the botanist's calendar, as in that of October, 1793, each day in the year is sacred to some plant or dedicated to some flower. For the lover of Nature a walk in the woods, even in Winter, is a Feast of Tabernacles, and the Summer is one long Floralia.

And where can the invalid find so good a solace as in Botany? What occupation or pursuit is so well adapted to silence that "strepitus Acherontis avari," sad sound familiar to so many of those who visit the Riviera?

But the Durra has been kept waiting while I sing the praises of Botany. It is well called "Negro Corn," for it is the main support of the negro race. The Ligurians do not seem to eat the grain; they give it to pigeons and poultry. A Provençal poet speaks of the Roquemaure fowls fattened on Durra, "mi d'escoubo." The tough, wiry spikes of the inflorescence are used for making brushes, whisks, and brooms. For this purpose mainly it is grown. Ask at the grocer's for a "balai en paille," and you will generally find a number of the shiny brown grains still adhering to it. Here then is a rival of the Genista, the broom and besom plant of our own latitude. "Broom" in English means both the Genista and the bunch of its twigs which we use for sweeping. The Kymric "bala" has the same double meaning, and I believe that Lake Bala, in North Wales, is so called from the Genista growing round its shores. From "bala" is derived the French word "balai."

Our northern plant is not restricted to the humble service of feeding fowls or sweeping floors: it has decked the helmet of the Plantagenets, and sailed the seas at the mast-head of Van Tromp and De Ruyter.

Durra is classed near to *Andropogon,* a south European and subtropical genus, of which half-a-dozen species are figured by Moggridge in his "Flora of Mentone." In the valley of the Zambesi the Negro Corn rises to a height of fifteen feet.

The Bamboo (*Bambusa*), even in this climate, grows much thicker and stronger than the Arundo; but we can form no idea on the Riviera of the size and beauty of this arborescent grass. On the Malabar coast it is said to reach a height of one hundred feet, with a circumference of twenty-nine inches. The botanical name of this giant species is *Dendrocalamus.* Those who have visited the tropics know to how many uses the wood is put.

When well watered the stems run up very rapidly. A newspaper correspondent writes thus jocularly from Japan: "One morning we discern a tiny pointed green shoot in the grass: by evening it is well above the ground: in twenty-four hours it would make a respectable

CASTELLAR

walking stick; and if you should be so ill advised as to hang your hat on it at night, you could not reach it in the morning." That beats Jonah's Gourd!

The Bamboo hardly ever flowers on the Riviera.[12] It flowers rarely even in the countries where it is indigenous. The flower approaches nearer to the Lily type than do most grasses; it is hexandrous, like rice (Oryza), and has a whorl of three lodicules.

It is a remarkable fact that when at last the plant comes into flower, it does so at the same precise moment all over Europe, Africa, and India! In 1868 the flowers appeared on plants as far apart as Paris and Marseilles, and the Government Gardens of the Hamma in Algiers. Moreover, the Bamboo dies down after flowering, and generally perishes. But it is not certain that no life remains in the rhizomes. Some authorities suppose that a given species disappears on these occasions, and is renewed by seed. M. St. Hilaire passed through a Brazilian Bamboo forest in full flower. They were fifty feet high. But on his return a few months later the whole had vanished.

In some Eastern countries (says Freeman Mitford in the "Bamboo Garden"), the rarely recurrent flowering of the Bamboos is regarded as a sure presage of calamity. However this may be, it is certain that in times of famine the Bamboo, if it flowers, is a godsend to the natives. In Orissa, in 1812, the seeds, cooked and eaten like rice, gave their only food to many thousands. Day and night the people watched to gather the precious grain. Again, in 1864, some 50,000 people visited the Soopa jungles to collect the seed.

Between the nodes of certain species is found a beautifully opalescent substance called Tabashir, which is regarded as an infallible nostrum for every ailment. In chemical composition this is a hydrous silicate.

Job's Tears or Elephant Grass (*Coix lacryma*) is a tall grass which grows well here, though it is not common. This is one of the most graceful of a graceful family, and well worth growing by any one who can spare a little space from sunflowers and scarlet geraniums.

Coix derives its English and also its French name, "Larmes de la Madeleine," from the polished lavender-coloured beads which it produces. In botanical language, the pistillate spikelets are enveloped in an involucre which becomes stony when ripe.

The huge tufts of the Pampas Grass (*Gynerium*) give us some idea of a South American landscape. The species is diœcious, that is to say, the staminate and pistillate flowers are on separate plants. The pistillate plant may be known by the larger size and greater spread of the panicles.

The Smaller Reed (*Arundo Phragmites*) is common here, as in England. It is closely allied to the Pampas Grass; in fact Bentham would include these species under the same genus.

Notes:

[12] The Bamboo flowers occasionally at Mortola: the flowering causes it to die. At Kew a special part of the gardens has latterly been devoted to Bamboos and Arundos. It is astonishing to see at least fifty species growing in the open air. In China, Ceylon, and Java the young shoots of the Bamboos are commonly eaten.—T. H.

ECRALIUM ELATERIUM, THE SQUIRTING GOURD

16
Gourds and Pumpkins

"Fair gardens, shining streams, with ranks
Of golden melons on their banks."

TWO plants only of the Gourd family grow wild in Europe: one is the
well-known Bryony (*B. Dioica*), graceful ornament of the banks and
hedgerows here as in the north; the other is the curious Squirting
Gourd (*Ecbalium Elaterium*). You will find this latter plant in dry, hot,
dusty places, on ruins, rubbish heaps, &c. It is common all along the
coast. A harmless-looking plant enough, lying close to the sunburnt soil
with its rough grey-green leaves; for it has no tendrils, and cannot raise
itself up by laying hold of some support, as other plants of its order are
wont to do.

Now, every living herb has its secret; some special mystery of leaf or stem or fruit or seed. In many cases the riddle has been guessed by botanists, in others we are still at a loss. If you do not know the secret of the Squirting Gourd, beware how you examine it too closely, for this lowly and harmless-looking plant can smite you in the face if you intrude upon its privacy.

The little fruits, less than two inches in length, are filled with a watery juice: when they are ripe the least touch breaks them away from the stalk, and where the stalk was fixed a hole is left; through this the liquid is thrown out with great force, and along with it the seeds. This liquid is a violent purgative. It is sometimes found useful by the farmers, thus:—If people steal your grapes, cause the Squirting Gourd to play upon the bunches which are most likely to be pilfered. The thief will have cause to regret his dishonesty. But you must be careful not to offer any of these medicated grapes to your friends. Even when grown in England, this little Gourd has been known to throw its seeds to a distance of some twenty feet: out here it can probably do better still. The scientific names of this plant are singularly appropriate, for both have reference to throwing or driving. The flowers are yellow, but inconspicuous.

An immense variety of Gourds, Pumpkins, and Melons is cultivated on the Riviera. The Pilgrim's Gourd (*Lagenaria*) supplies the peasant with bottles and flasks. As the horn was the primitive drinking vessel of pastoral folk, so the gourd may well have been the earliest goblet of the agricultural races. In Gaelic "corn," a horn, means cup; on the other hand the Italian "chiccera," cup, is said to be derived from a word meaning gourd. Gourds were used as moulds and coated with clay to form water-bottles. In baking the clay the gourd of course was burnt away. Thus a jar was produced with a rounded base, unable to remain erect unless placed in a stand or hollow made to fit. Even when the gourd was no longer used as a mould by the potter, these inconvenient water-bottles were still manufactured in imitation of the earlier ones. By cutting a slice off one side (a tangential section of the fruit), and leaving the stalk end stopped, a scoop or ladle is formed; this is everywhere in use. Negroes can make a musical instrument out of a Calabash, I suppose some sort of banjo; but the natives here have not sufficient

GROUP OF GOURDS

ingenuity for this; they prefer to hire a barrel organ and take turns at the handle.

Decorated with various drawings and devices these Gourd flasks are sold in all the shops. At the Gourd Fête, held on the Cimiez hill under those grand old Ilex Oaks, about March 25th, you may see Gourds, "Cougourdon" the natives call them, of every size and shape and price. The flower of *Lagenaria* is white and perfumed.

As to the Melons and the Water Melons (French "Pastèque"), their varieties defy description: they may be rounded or elongate; yellow or green or white or almost black; striped, streaked, dotted or dashed with colour; ribbed, furrowed, or ornamented with elegant designs, with delicate tracery or strange hieroglyphs. These species come botanically under the genus *Cucumis*, together with the Cucumber.

The Pumpkins (*Cucurbita*) are not less wonderful in size and shape and colouring. *C. Melo Pepo*, the Turban Gourd, is commonly grown in the Nice Valley. It has a curious appearance, because part of the fruit above the calyx is of a different colour from that below.

A Gourd we often see is so exact an imitation of an Orange that you may easily hold it in your hand without suspecting what it really is. I have planted this beautiful Gourd at the foot of a Ligustrum in order to see the effect of the yellow fruits against the dark green leaves.

According to Mr. John Smith, A.L.S., "Bible Plants," these may have been the Wild Gourds which the unbotanical youth "came and shred into the pot of pottage" (2 Kings iv. 39).[13]

Another Gourd grown here has a fruit resembling a Hen-Egg; the size and colour are accurate enough, but the form is not always perfectly ovoid. Either the orange Gourd is a more successful mimic, or else it is easier for a vegetable to imitate another vegetable than to copy a product of the animal kingdom. Yet another common and very pretty Gourd is pear-shaped, about the size of an average pear, and delicately tinted with green and yellow.

A curious Gourd with the thin end curved is specially grown here for the manufacture of Pipes. These you may see in the window of any tobacconist's shop. They appear to colour like a meerschaum, but as I have never smoked one of them I may be mistaken. I suppose that this fruit, with its hard and durable shell, belongs to the genus *Lagenaria*. The ornamental Gourds just mentioned, on the contrary, have thin shells which cannot be preserved.

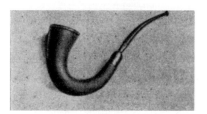

PIPE BOWL MADE FROM A GOURD

The great yellow corollas of the Gourd are stuffed with something eatable and made into a dish; but I have not seen *Gourd seeds* for sale here as a sweetmeat. In Naples they are to be had at the corner of every street; they are dipped in something that gives them a peculiar flavour. Forty years ago I used to spend spare centesimi on this luxury. What can be better adapted to a schoolboy's slender income than a handful of bonbons for the tenth part of a penny? I think that if these same salt-tasting Gourd seeds were offered now, however cheap, they would hardly be regarded as a treat. There are many other things besides Pumpkin seeds that one ceases to appreciate after the lapse of forty years.

To ascertain the time at night the Apache Indians employ a gourd on which the stars of the heavens are marked. As the constellations rise in the sky the Indian refers to his gourd and finds out the hour. By turning the gourd round he can tell the order in which the constellations may he expected to appear.

Here is a piece of information for amateur gardeners: the right moment for planting Gourd seeds is while the church bells are ringing on Easter eve; so say the peasants. I suppose a chapel bell would do just as well. Some chapels make noise enough on a Sunday morning to start any Gourd seed germinating. Still one could hardly expect the jangling of schismatical bells to have the same effect as the orthodox carillon.

"Poets and moralists," says A. R. Wallace, "judging from our English trees and fruits, have thought that small fruits always grew on lofty trees, so that their fall should be harmless to man, while the large ones (such as Pumpkins) trailed on the ground. Two of the largest and heaviest fruits known, however, the Brazil-nut fruit (*Bertholletia*) and the Durian of Borneo, king of fruits, grow on lofty forest trees, from which they fall as soon as they are ripe, and often wound or kill the native inhabitants. From this we may learn two things: first, not to draw general conclusions from a very partial view of nature; and secondly, that trees and fruits, no less than the varied productions of the animal kingdom, do not appear to be organized with exclusive reference to the use and convenience of man."

La Fontaine's villager came to the conclusion that a Pumpkin is much safer lying on the ground than hanging from an Oak tree. When an acorn strikes him on the nose, he remarks

"Que serait-ce donc
S'il fût tombé de l'arbre une masse plus lourde,
Et que ce gland eût été gourde?"

This philosopher, though the acuteness of his intellect prevented him from sleeping, did not quite exhaust the question. What would happen, he might have asked, if a Pumpkin weighing a hundred and fifty pounds, as they sometimes do, were to explode like the Squirting Gourd? Who would be brave enough to face such a vegetable bomb-shell? At a distance of half a mile we should not be in safety if a Pumpkin were to behave as does the little *Ecbalium*. There is no *a priori* reason against the thing. Nature, in her great manufactory, could accomplish it without the smallest difficulty, just as we can make either a parlour pistol or a Krupp gun that will shake the earth and sky.

ORNAMENTED GOURD FLASK

There is an exquisite little climber of this order which ought to be more often grown out here: I refer to the *Abobra*. The long stems rise from a thick perennial stock, as in Bryony: the leafage is particularly neat and trim, and the bright red fruits are ornamental. I doubt whether the Bryony descends as far as the coast, and if not we have here an excellent substitute.

M. Ch. Naudin, the late learned Director of the Government Gardens at Antibes, made a special study of this Natural Order. His work on the Exotics cultivated here is well known.

Notes:

[13]   Other botanists identify the Prophet's Gourd with *Cucumis prophetarum*, a curious hairy species.—T. H.

17
Plants of
Palestine—I
Caper and Anemone

"Ye are the Scriptures of the earth,
Sweet Flowers and frail:
A sermon speaks in every bud
That woos the summer gale."

TRAVELLERS have called attention to the similarity between the Flora of the Riviera and that of Palestine.

It is indeed remarkable how many plants mentioned in the Bible are common on this coast.

CAPPARIS SPINOSA, THE CAPER

Mount Carmel is clothed with a brushwood of Oak, Mastic (*Pistacia Lentiscus*), Arbutus, and Myrtle: the same shrubs occupy the waste spots on the hills round Nice. The Jordan valley is bright in Spring with Cistus, scarlet Anemone, white Garlic (*Allium*), Narcissus, and many other flowers which we have here in abundance. The common *N. Tazetta* is probably the "Rose of Sharon" (Cant. ii. 1). On the Riviera di Levante, as in Palestine, the Oleander (*Nerium*) lives in the stony torrent beds. The beautiful Styrax of Syria is found near Hyères. Laurustinus (*Viburnum Tinus*) grows wild here as there. The delicate white Broom (*Retama*), the "Juniper" of Scripture, blooms with us in Spring, as it does in Gilead. Later on, towards Summer, the walls and rocky places of the Riviera are festooned with the large pink and white blossoms of the Caper (*Capparis spinosa*).

I will take the last-mentioned as an instance of a Plant of Palestine. In the eloquent but materialistic passage in Ecclesiastes xii. 5, the word "desire" should probably be translated "Caper," thus: "The flower of the Caper shall wither," "Beauty shall fade away." The Caper is a fit emblem of death or decay; growing, as it does in the East, on ruins and on tombs, and having a flower both beautiful and short-lived. It is common on the Colosseum, and elsewhere in the neighbourhood of Rome. The flowers are indeed very fugacious, more so even than those of the Cistus, for they appear sometimes to be blighted off almost as soon as they open.

The untimely wilting (to use an archaism) of the Caper blossoms must strike even unobservant persons, for they are conspicuous both by their size and by the position in which they grow. The reason is not clear; it may be that when the stigma happens to be fertilized without delay, the corolla, no longer needed, withers. It is well known that the corolla of many flowers will persist much longer when fertilization is delayed. A great deal of honey is secreted in the nectary, and the flowers appear to be largely, if not entirely, dependent on insect visits. It would be interesting to observe what insects frequent the Caper. Müller, the great authority on these questions, gives no information.

The French version of the passage in Ecclesiastes is worth transcribing, for it is full of music, and not wanting in solemnity: "Quand on redoutera les lieux élevés, et qu'on tremblera en marchant, quand l'amandier fleurira, et que le chant de la cigale sera un ennui, et quand *l'appétit* faiblira, parce que l'homme s'en va dans la demeure qu'il ne quittera plus." Here the Hebrew word for Caper is translated "appetite," a meaning it often bears, because the flower buds are universally used as a condiment. This use of the buds accounts for the fact that the plant is so rarely seen in flower when it grows in accessible places.

Of all the plants which live in the Sahara, *Capparis spinosa* alone has a leaf with broadly dilated lamina. To obviate this serious disadvantage, the leaves are placed edgewise to the sun. This is accomplished partly by an alteration in the position of each petiole, partly by the torsion of the axis, the plant working always in the direction of least resistance. Although some varieties appear to be distichous, the Caper has a 2/5 phyllotaxy (Professor J. Massart, "Voyage au Sahara"). It would appear that the Summer heat and drought on the Riviera are not sufficient to drive the plant to these expedients, for I have not noticed the leaf-blades turned so as to have their edges vertical.

Ardoino calls the Caper subspontaneous, which implies that it is able to sow its seeds in this climate, but I have never yet found a ripe fruit. It has not been found possible, even at Kew, to cultivate the Caper under glass.

I have noticed a curious fact in connection with the Caper, namely that the common *Cabbage White* butterfly (*Pieris Brassicæ*) will sometimes lay her eggs upon it. Now the Crucifers or Cress Flowers are the proper food plants of these white butterflies (Pieridæ). But how ever does this insect know that the Caper is allied to the Crucifers? By what hidden faculty is this little creature made aware of a fact which the most accomplished botanist could never suspect? A fact which becomes clear only by the study of intermediate forms which do not exist in Europe. By what divination does she foresee that the little larvæ, if hatched upon this plant, will live? For the Caper blossom bears no resemblance to that of a Wallflower, a Stock (*Matthiola*), or a Cabbage. All these are more or less closed, and contain two short stamens and four longer ones, whereas the Caper flower lies wide open to the sun with its tassel of uncounted stamens. Must we not believe that even the smallest living things are animated and informed by that same Great Power in Whom we also live and move?

"Eminet in minimis Maximus ipse Deus."

Or as the Father of English Natural History, turning from prose to poetry, exclaims:—

"The God of Nature is their secret guide."

Surely there are in plants, as in human beings, hidden points of agreement which time alone reveals; yes, and deep differences which do not show upon the surface.

How little do we know of plants if we examine only the details of their structure! We need, as Ruskin says, to learn not only the anatomy

CAPPARIS SPINOSA

of plants, but also their biography; how and where they live and die, their tempers, benevolences, malignities, distresses, and virtues. We must study them from their youth to their age, from bud to fruit. Then perhaps we too, like the Cabbage butterfly, shall be able to detect hidden relationships and properties which we do not now suspect.

Professor Penzig remarks that Capparis and its allies have in all their parts a strong scented sulphurate oil common to Cruciferæ, Tropæolum, Reseda, and some other plants. The presence of this oil may perhaps attract the butterflies.

As I have mentioned the affinity of the Capers to the Crucifers, I will add that the mignonette (*Reseda*) is likewise allied to this family. Of this fact also the white butterflies are perfectly aware: for the Bath White (*Pieris Daplidice*) lays her eggs upon the different species of Reseda.

In the preface to "Modern Painters," Ruskin, speaking of the wild-flowers in Titian's "Bacchus and Ariadne," mistakes the Caper for a Rose. This strange error is corrected in the later edition.

A rare Capparis (*C. rupestris*) occurs on the Riviera, not a hundred miles from Nice. As I know of but one single plant, and it is possible that very few others exist in this region, I abstain from indicating the locality. This species has not the spinous stipules.

Solomon's Hyssop, which grows out of the wall, is thought to be a Caper; the other plants suggested are Marjoram (*Origanum*) and Savory (*Satureia*).

The next Plant of Palestine which I shall take is the Anemone, so abundant in the Holy Land that "they carpet every plain, and luxuriantly pervade the land in every soil and in all situations." The writer from whom I take these words ("Helps to the Study of the Bible") considers the Anemone to be a kind of Lily. Let us hope that his theology is sounder than his botany! Although the Anemone is a long way from a Lily, botanically speaking, yet it is probable that the scarlet anemone is the flower alluded to in Matthew vi. 28: those "*Lilies of the field* which toil not, neither do they spin": those little stars which light up the terraced hill-sides and outshine the glory of Solomon.

"Fair lilies of Jerusalem,
Ye wear the same array
As when imperial Judah's stem
Maintained its regal sway:
By sacred Jordan's desert tide
As bright ye blossom on
As when your simple charms outvied
The pride of Solomon."

In the land adjoining my garden in the outskirts of Nice the Anemone is cultivated for sale. People stop to admire; and well they may, for the ground is variegated with every shade of colour, painted like that Vale of Henna where Persephone sported with her maidens.

Half a dozen species of Anemone are figured in Moggridge's splendid volume on the Flora of Mentone. The purchase of this book is an extravagance which one does not regret. We owe to Mr. Bicknell, of Bordighera, a volume of equal beauty, and (unfortunately for small purses) of equal cost.

A Yellow Anemone (*A. Palmata*) is peculiar to Hyères; the sepals are numerous and narrow, the leaf lobed, not deeply cut, and several flowers are produced on one radical peduncle or scape. Of this great rarity I cannot write *vidi vivam spontaneam*. Besides all the varieties which are found near the coast, the Alpine Anemone, with its white or sulphur flower and dishevelled tuft of hairy fruitlets, is as common on these mountains as in Switzerland.

The bright colours of the Anemone are not due to the corolla, for the flower is not provided with petals. The allied Hellebores are almost in the same case. To the Globe Flower (*Trollius*), abundant in these mountains, nothing remains of the corolla but a few small yellow straps concealed among the stamens. Hellebore, which flowers here very early in Spring, has its little cornets; and the quaintest forms are assumed by the reduced petals of Nigella, a pretty blue flower of the same sub-order which is plentiful in the month of May. The popular name is Love-in-a-Mist; it is also called Devil-in-a-Bush "from the horned carpels which peep viciously out of a finely divided involucre." When the scientific name is so euphonious as Nigella, it is not easy to see any pretext for these popular periphrases.

The flowers of the Anemone are very tough: they stand a long railway journey without fading. It appears that the coloured (petaloid) sepals are more enduring than petals.

Mr. Hamilton, of Bordighera, has written, in French, an illustrated book on those plants which are common to the Riviera and to Palestine.

ANEMONES

18
Plants of
Palestine—II:
Storax, Retama,
and Acacia

Styrax officianalis, the
Storax

"There is a lesson in each flower,
A story in each stream and bower.
On every herb on which you tread
Are written words which, rightly read,
Will lead you from earth's fragrant sod
To hope and holiness and God."
ALLEN CUNNINGHAM

THE Storax or Styrax, a beautiful flowering shrub of Palestine, flourishes also on the western Riviera, at the base of Mt. Coudon, near La Farlède, north of Hyères. Moggridge gives an excellent picture of this plant. It is well worth while, he says, to make a journey to Hyères in the month of May on purpose to see the bushes of Styrax in full flower. When arrived at La Farlède, which is about an hour's drive distant from Hyères, inquire for the cart track which the inhabitants of the village know as the Pas de Galle, and follow this till, after about a quarter of an hour's walk, you reach a stream descending from Mt. Coudon, where the banks are clothed with this beautiful shrub.

The Styrax yields a resinous balsamic juice, used in perfumery and medicine. The incense burned in Romanist churches is derived from a tropical species of the same genus.[14] The plant, or the gum that exudes from it, is more than once mentioned in the Bible.

It is strange that the Styrax, so attractive with its white flowers and yellow stamens, should not be cultivated in the gardens of the Riviera.

But gardens, like churches and schools and ladies' costumes, are ruled by fashion, or as some prefer to call it "orthodoxy."

Styrax is not yet admitted to rank as a garden plant: its beauty, its rarity, its star-spangled twigs, its perfumed gum, all these do not avail. Even that most uninteresting of all rank straggling shrubs, the Deeringia, looks down upon the lovely Styrax; for is not the former an "ornement des massifs"? Was it not brought from the Antipodes? Residents in Nice or Cannes may not set eyes upon the Styrax; but those who stay at Mentone, and visit Sir Thomas Hanbury's wonderful garden, should not miss the fine specimen growing near the house.

The White Broom or Retama (*Retama monosperma* or Genista Retem)´is a small desert tree which abounds near the Jordan, and also farther south by Sinai. Major Conder, in his work on Palestine, mentions the Retem among the characteristic growths of Gilead. A bright, cheerful little tree it is, which a Zulu, a Bashi Bazouk, or even a lawyer, might stop to admire; in fact, it deserves to be ranked among those trees described in Genesis ii. 9, as "pleasant to the sight." The Retama is common in the gardens here, and should be commoner.

This is the tree mistranslated Juniper in 1 Kings xix., under which Elijah lay despairing and wishing for death in the desert beyond Beersheba. Through the snowy canopy of the Retem the angel descended to comfort the prophet and protect him from the vengeance of Jezebel. Under what tree would a weary prophet be more likely to be visited by angels and bright thoughts and hopes?

Humboldt describes a Retama as adorning the peak of Teneriffe at an elevation where no other plant can grow. Happy tree, fit shelter for a prophet. Its home is in the desert where no one says, "This land is mine, stand off!" where no one buys or sells or cheats. Or else it lives upon a distant peak, rooted in a crevice of the lava flow. Here competition is not, nor care; for no rival covets the barren spot, and there is naught to shut out the ocean breeze that fans its drooping sprays of small white flowers.

Like Victor Hugo's poet:

"Il aime un désert sauvage
Où rien ne borne ses pas;
Son cœur, pour fuir l'esclavage,
vit plus loin que le trépas."

I have seen at the Battle of Flowers a carriage completely covered with this Broom. The effect, I admit, was good; but what a gap there must have been in the garden which supplied this decoration! How many trees were disfigured to ornament one carriage for one hour!

Disregarding the title of this chapter, I will include some plants which do not belong to Palestine.

Allied to the Broom is the Acacia. Over fifty species are cultivated on the Riviera. I will describe a few of the most remarkable.[15]

The pride of the Cannes gardens is the *Acacia dealbata*, which thrives better there than on the calcareous soil of Nice. Nevertheless, it can and does grow in Nice. This is the "Silver Wattle" of the Australians. It will sometimes grow to the height of 150 feet in that country. An immense quantity of these Acacia flowers is distributed all over Europe. The gardeners obtain them as much as a fortnight before the natural time by cutting off the twigs and forcing the flower-buds to expand prematurely under steam.

Acacia pycnantha (Benth.) is the "Golden Wattle" of the Australian colonists, and is generally considered as their national flower. As such it forms the subject of one of Gerald Massey's tuneful lyrics. This shrub seldom attains 30 feet.

A. retinoides, commonly called *A. floribunda*, has narrow phyllodes not unlike willow leaves. It produces its yellow globular flower-heads the whole year round. No other Acacia flowers in Autumn on the Riviera.

Next after the three species above mentioned the commonest are the peculiar *A. cultriformis*, and *A. longifolia*. The latter is very hardy, but the odour is disliked by some persons.

At Grasse, Cannes, and elsewhere on the Riviera, the *Acacia Farnesiana is* extensively grown for the sake of a perfume extracted from its golden-yellow globular flower-heads. The French name is "Cassis." It is a spinous shrub or small tree, with delicate twice-pinnate leaf. This Acacia is abundant in the deep depression of the Jordan valley, where it

ACACIA DEALBATA

is rendered conspicuous by a parasite allied to the mistletoe. When this parasite is in flower the tree has the appearance of being on fire. Hence it claims the title of "Burning Bush."

Another species worthy of mention is the *Acacia horrida*; and a horrid shrub it is in the classical sense of the word, for it bristles with great white shining spines six inches long and more. These ivory stilettos are as sharp as any needle, and it is easy to understand that a man or an animal dashed against this shrub would be badly injured if not killed. The *Acacia horrida is* not a favourite in the Riviera gardens. I know of only one specimen in Nice.

The Acacias derive their name from these armed plants, for the syllable "ac" implies something sharp or keen. So the "Ac-anthus" is thought to have been some prickly plant (the botanical Acanthus is found in most gardens here). Compare also the Latin "ac-us" a needle, "ac-utus" sharp, "ac-ies" line of battle, "ac-etum" vinegar.

Many of the Australian Acacias are leafless. I do not mean to say that their twigs are bare like an Oak or an Ash in Winter. Nothing of the sort. They are plentifully provided all the year round with organs that look exactly like leaves, and serve the same purpose. These leaflike organs are really flattened leaf stalks (phyllodes). Some of the Acacias in the Riviera gardens afford admirable illustrations of this theory. You will find species which produce two sorts of leaves (I speak unbotanically), the plain, narrow, uncut variety—these are phyllodes; and also similar ones surmounted by the regular feathery twice pinnate leaf. This peculiarity is sketched on page 119 of Lubbock's interesting little volume on "Flowers, Fruits, and Leaves."

Our English trees, this writer remarks, may be said, as a general rule, to be glad of as much sun as they can get; but in tropical countries some plants at any rate find the sun too much for them. The phyllodes of these Acacias and the phyllode-like leaves of the Eucalyptus, also an Australian plant, avoid the force of the sun by preventing their edge to the sky.

A. dealbata, A. Farnesiana, A. lophanta, and some other species, have true leaves, not phyllodes.

It is curious that in some species, for instance *Acacia Salicina,* the seedling reverts to pinnate laves, whereas the older plant has only phyllodes. In like manner the young Eucalyptus does not show its long scimitar-shaped leaves.

Alphonse Karr, the littérateur and naturalist of the Riviera, in his "Voyage autour de mon Jardin," Letter vii., explains at length the mystic meaning of the Acacia in Masonry. How did he obtain this information? Though uninitiated, he knows a great deal more about the craft than many free and accepted Masons. I fear that M. Alphonse has been guilty of eavesdropping!

The Shittah Tree, of which the Tabernacle was constructed, is supposed to be an Acacia (*A. Seyal*), the only tree which grows to any size in the Arabian desert, and the same from which gum arabic is obtained. This tree is mentioned in Isaiah xli. 19.

Some commentators see in the Burning Bush of Moses a thorny Acacia (*A. Nilotica*), called Seneh in Hebrew. This tree gives its name to Sinai and to the Desert of Sin. Neither of these two interesting species appear to be cultivated on the Riviera.

Many Syrian plants such as the Oleander, Terebinth, Jujube, Arundo, Olive, Palm, Fig, &c., will be found in other chapters.

Notes:

14   It has lately been shown that incense is derived from *Styrax officinalis,* the species which is found on the Riviera and in Palestine. The gum is collected in the Levant. See "Science Papers," by Daniel Hanbury, F.R.S., pp. 8 and 129.—T. H.

15   In the Mortola gardens seventy species of Acacia are grown.—T. H.

NERIUM OLEANDER

19
Poisonous Plants

THERE are families of plants, as there are races of men, whose nature is marked by a certain harshness and malignity, and whose function it is to prevent this world from being too pleasant a place. Among the most dangerous orders is that to which the Oleander (*Nerium*) belongs. The plant itself is poisonous, both flower and leaf and bark and wood. To use the wood as a meat skewer may lead to fatal results. Closely related is the deadly Ordeal Tree (*Tanghinia venenifera*) of Madagascar, most poisonous of plants: a seed the size of an almond suffices to kill twenty people.

The Oleander, French Laurier-rose, grows wild in the torrent beds as you approach Genoa, and it abounds in a valley close to St. Raphael, which is called La Vallée des Lauriers-roses;[16] in Palestine also "it flourishes abundantly by the water-courses, and lines every valley." It is possible that Oleander is intended by the word translated *Willow* in the Old Testament. It may have been on this flowering shrub that the captive Hebrews hung their harps when they sat down and wept by the rivers of Babylon (Psalm cxxxvii.).

The Periwinkle (*Vinca*) is closely related to the Oleander, as the most unbotanical person might infer from the mere aspect of the flower. A poet praises it as

"L'aimable Pervenche aux pétales d'azur."

I do not assert that the "sky-blue Periwinkle" is dangerous: Anne Pratt does not include it in her book on poisonous plants: still one is inclined to mistrust any near relation to the Oleander. A poet with more knowledge and less sentiment would hardly use the epithet "amiable." In Italy and the south of France the Periwinkle is called the "Flower of Death," and to include it in a bouquet would be of evil omen.

Two beautiful climbing plants, Allamanda and *Mandevillea* (the "Sweet-scented Chili Jasmin," as gardeners absurdly call it), belong to this order. This latter plant, according to the gardeners' books, is "very vigorous and easily cultivated" in this district; it ought, therefore, to be much commoner than it is. The fruit is remarkable. It is joined at the base and apex, forming a loop over a foot long.[17]

Near to the Oleander and Periwinkles come the Asclepiads: so near that they have sometimes been included in the same order. Here again we find dangerous properties. Many of these plants have a milky juice like that in the Euphorbias, and in some Composites such as Lettuce. This is well seen in the Physianthus (or *Arauja*), a climber very common in the Nice gardens. *Gomphocarp* has the same white sap; a plant which I have sometimes found half wild on the road to Monaco. To this order belongs also the foul-smelling Carrion Plant (*Stapelia*): I have grown it in a sheltered corner. In the Mortola gardens a dozen Cape and one Sicilian species are grown in the open air.

All these, though common enough, are garden plants: but there is one, and only one, European wild plant belonging to the Asclepiads, namely, the little *Vincetoxicum*, which disputes every inch of waste ground on the hills with Box and Savory (*Satureia*). Vincetoxicum abounds on the Mt. Chauve, but you need not walk so far to find it, for it grows as near the coast as the entrance of the Vallon des Fleurs, that is, on the outskirts of the town.

Many of these Asclepiads, if not exactly poisonous, have something spiteful about them: they ill-treat the insects which carry their pollen grains for them. If you look into the flower, you see neither stamen nor stigma, these are concealed, but there are wedge-shaped slits: in these the foot of a butterfly or the tongue of a bee gets caught. If he has strength enough to pull his leg out again, well and good; his leg or his proboscis will merely be decorated with a couple of little tags, something like the horns which an Orchis places on the head of a bee. A butterfly may have as many as a dozen of these tags glued to his foot. But a weaker insect, an ant for instance, will not be able to set himself free again if his leg is entangled in one of these traps; he must remain a prisoner, or leave his limb behind. I have watched a house-fly vainly struggling to escape.

When the pod of a Vincetoxicum or a Gomphocarp splits down one side, it shows the seeds tipped with white silky hairs: those in the Oleander pod are chocolate brown. I have seen these silky hairs from the fruit of a Physianthus (the climbing plant mentioned above) used by milliners as an ornament for a lady's hat. The wearer would find it hard to explain the origin of the fluffy decoration: indeed, a botanist might be puzzled by such a curiosity. These silky hairs much resemble those in the fruit of a Willow, but the latter spring from the base of the seed.

The Oleander feeds the caterpillar of a lovely moth, one of those that fly very swiftly just about sunset, *Deilephila Nerii*. The colour is that of malachite, and the pattern on the wings is not easy to describe. The veteran naturalist Bruyat told me that he had often found these larvæ on the Oleander bushes in the town; I have not been so fortunate.

VINCETOXICUM OFFICINALE

Mr. Bicknell says that quantities of them may be collected in the Nervia valley. The *Oleander Hawk* larvæ must be poison-proof, like Mithridates, king of Pontus.

A striking butterfly of the genus *Danais* is attached to the Asclepiads. As these plants are fairly common in the gardens here, it might perhaps not be difficult to naturalize the insect on the Riviera. Collectors would have to give him a few years' start. I read somewhere that Danais was actually established in Naples, but perished in a severe Winter not long ago. It is curious that the Danaidæ whose larvæ feed on poisonous plants have bodies of so acrid and disagreeable a flavour that (according to Drummond) none of the creatures which prey upon butterflies will touch them. And they proclaim their bad taste (in two senses of the word) by gaudy patterns of the brightest colours. It is obvious that the more conspicuous their livery, the safer they will be. For an animal which has tasted one of these insects will wish in future to avoid the disgusting morsel, and will find it all the easier to do so.

The Oleander has a whorl of three leaves at many of its nodes or joints: a transverse section of the stem below the node, differentially stained, makes an interesting object for the microscope.

A strange error is abroad to the effect that the leaf of the Oleander is not net-veined.

Another dangerous plant is the *Coriaria*, a shrub with small entire opposite leaves. You will find it plentifully by almost any of the little footpaths which lead up from the valley to the hills. The leaves contain a narcotic poison which causes an animal to stagger and fall. Hence the native name "ubbriaco," that is, "intoxicated." What makes the Coriaria all the more dangerous is that animals seem to like it. I have not observed whether goats are able to eat this plant without bad effect. I have seen a goat eating Euphorbia, which most animals reject. Some thirty years ago I tried an experiment with a goat. It was at Eastbourne. She was tethered, and seemed hungry. I had been reading that Crucifers are wholesome, and I wished to know whether the goat would give the same verdict as the botany book. So I gathered a quantity of different plants, and arranged them in bundles according to their Natural Orders. I then placed them in front of the quadruped, and stood back to see what she would do. To my satisfaction she selected the bunch of

Crucifers. It was possibly an accident: I dare say she would just as soon have eaten some Coriaria.

The Coriaria is the only genus in the order, and no one knows to what this order is allied. This straggling shrub is "sans aveu": it is thoroughly disreputable—they ought to plant it by the Casino at Monte Carlo—there is no redeeming point that one can find. It is neither useful nor yet ornamental, as some rascals are; it has not the perfume of the Myrtle, nor the flower of the Cistus; it gives no food nor shade; a common-place vegetable miscreant.[18] The leaves are often used to adulterate Senna, which thus becomes a dangerous drug. The plant furnishes a varnish which is of little value (*peu estimé*), it also yields a substance called redoul or redon, which is used as a dye and in tanning, but it is not much grown (*peu cultivé*).

Coriaria is not far from being evergreen, for the leaves persist in sheltered spots through the greater part of the Winter. The red papillose stigmas resemble those of the *Phytolacca Decandra* (Ink Plant, or Poke Weed, or American Currant), so that some botanists have suspected a relationship between these plants. The Ink Plant is very unwholesome, if not absolutely poisonous: but it has this advantage over the Coriaria, that with its purple stems and black-red fruits it may claim to be more or less ornamental. In fact it is very suitable to cover a rubbish-heap or to fill up some waste corner.

Now the fruits of the Phytolacca are used, with very injurious effects, to colour sweets and wine; and for this reason it is forbidden to grow the shrub in Spain and Portugal. Finding one day a clump of Ink Plant close to a cottage, it occurred to me to ascertain whether the peasants here make any use of it; so I inquired. They answered quite freely that they sold the fruit to a confectioner in Nice! How many unaccountable headaches and colics would be explained if we only knew what we had swallowed! Were we but acquainted with some of the ingredients of our eatables and drinkables, we would often exclaim with Horace "Non descendet in ventrem meum"!

The Ink Plant is common enough in the Nice valley. Those gouty-looking trees along the Promenade des Anglais belong to the same order, though one would hardly suspect it. Some botanists even place them in the same genus. The wood is spongy. I do not accuse them of being poisonous; but I cannot tell what claim they have to line the "Bay of Angels" with their swollen stems and pollard heads.

Among other hurtful plants Henbane (*Hyoscyamus*) grows here, but I have never found either Nightshade (*Atropa*) or Hemlock (*Conium*).

Sophora, a leguminous tree, has poisonous properties, and ought not, therefore, to be grown for shade. In habit it bears some resemblance to a Robinia.

Notes:

16   Camporosso (that is Redfield) near Bordighera, is supposed to take its name from the abundance of this plant growing in the bed of the river Nervia, on which the town is situated. The Oleander is wild also in the Mortola valley.—T.H.

17   *Mandevillea suaveolens* is from Buenos Ayres, and named after Sir John Mandeville, who introduced it into England. As it does not flower till June, it is not well adapted for Riviera gardens.—T. H.

18   I wish to plead for it that it will cover the most sterile spots, which would otherwise lack vegetation altogether.—T. H.

SPHINX NERII, THE OLEANDER HAWK MOTH

CYTINUS HYPOCISTIS

20

Parasites and Wall Plants

THE most remarkable parasitic plant in this district is the *Cytinus*. It grows on the roots of the Cistus. The best place to search for it is the promontory of Antibes or that of St. Jean. It is fairly common in both of these localities. You may recognise the plant from the figure at the head of this chapter.

For all its bright colour, Cytinus is degraded in structure. Degradation is associated with parasitism, not only in plants and the lower animals, but also in man; and a certain brilliancy is often gained as usefulness is lost. Cytinus is classed by Hooker with Rafflesia, prince of parasites, a plant of the other hemisphere, whose flower is some three feet in diameter, and weighs as much as fifteen pounds.

There are many stages and degrees of parasitism. Some plants, like Eyebright (*Euphrasia*) and Rattle (*Rhinanthe*), have not quite lost the power of extracting their own carbon from the air. These can exist, though poorly, even if their roots should fail to fasten upon those of some other plant; for they are provided with leaves. Now, leaves are a sign of vegetable honesty. *Orobanche* (Broomrape) and Cytinus, with their leaves reduced to scales, rank lower than the semi-parasitic Eyebright and Rattle. Lowest of all is the absolutely leafless Rafflesia. This ponderous flower is a striking instance of that complete success which often attends complete dishonesty. One single leaf, or even one abortive scale, would ruin the Rafflesia; one solitary scruple would upset the politician or the financier.

Osyris, a small shrub, abundant all round Nice, is suspected of partial parasitism. The leaves are narrow, and the little yellow flowers have three petals, with the stamens petal-opposed. Compare the flower with that of Cneorum, and you will find that they are not unlike, though there is no relationship. On the staminate plant the flowers are more numerous than on the pistillate one, for this latter must economize the sap to form its fruits. The same thing is observed in many plants that are diœcious, for instance in the common white Campion (*Lychnis dioica*).

Osyris has a little relative, the Thesium, which lies under the same accusation, namely, that of robbing his neighbours. This flower has four petal-opposed stamens. It occurs on the South Downs of England, but is much commoner out here. These two plants are of interest as being the only European representatives of the Sandalwood family (Santalaceæ). The parasitism of this plant was first noticed by W. Mitten, Esq., F.L.S., of Hurstpierpoint, an excellent botanist, and an authority on the Mosses. This gentleman is father-in-law of Alfred Russel Wallace.

On the stony ground everywhere is another pretty little culprit, *Odontites lutea.* The yellow flowers all face one way; by this peculiarity you may know the plant in bud or flower or fruit. *Odontites* belongs to the Figwort (*Scrophularia*) family, an order much given to parasitic backsliding: as witness Rattle and Eyebright, mentioned above, and various Bartsias, all found in this district.

Orobanches (Broomrapes) abound. *Felipæa ramosa* occurs frequently

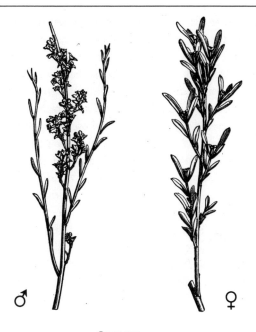

OSYRIS ALBA

near Nice. Ardoino gives it as parasitic on Hemp and on Tobacco; but I have generally seen it on Pitch Clover (*Psoralea*).

The tangled red meshes of Dodder (*Cuscuta*) are much commoner here than I have ever found them in the north.

The Mistletoe (*Viscum*), which they sell at Christmas for our especial benefit, does not grow on the coast. The natives regard it as something very curious. There is a good deal of it on the Pine trees in the Thorenc valley, behind Grasse. Goats eat Mistletoe greedily when it is offered them. At Caussols it occurs on Willow and on Hawthorn. By the way, I have never seen our British Hawthorn on the Riviera; it appears to be replaced by *Cratægus monogyna*. This plant may be known by the single style and the leaves more deeply cut, but it resembles the other very closely. The famous Glastonbury Thorn belongs to the one-styled species.

The Mistletoe on Pine has much narrower leaves than that on Hawthorn, in this district at least.

Now for the plants which live upon walls. The Caper (*Capparis*) should come first, but I have mentioned it elsewhere. The yellow-flowered *Nicotiana glauca* forms a graceful little tree when it chances to grow upon the ground. But I think that no one will dispute its place among wall plants, for it can grow in the driest chink of any wall or terrace. I have seen this shrub not only grow, but even flower and fruit on the stern of a Palm tree at some distance from the ground; behaving in fact after the manner of an epiphyte or air plant: for I suppose that it was not acting as a parasite. This Nicotiana grows freely from seed. If it appears on a terrace, or in the crevice of any decorative work, it is best to pull it up at once, as it will do mischief by forcing away the plaster. The long narrow flowers are ornamental, and the capsule, as might be expected, differs little from that of the Tobacco.

Two little linear-leaved plants of the Composite order, and belonging to the genus *Conyza* (or *Phagnalon*) may be found clinging to almost every old wall. The one, *C. saxatilis*, has trim little bronze thistle heads on long stalks; the other *C. sordida*, has smaller and more numerous flower tops.

Another common wall plant is *Theligonum*, with its inconspicuous greenish strap-shaped flowers. This watery herb will thrive in any shady corner, but the most likely place to find it is on some old masonry with north exposure. The allied pellitory (*Parietaria*) is gathered here to make a tisane; the stalks only are used, the leaves being carefully removed. Cotyledon abounds, and various species of Sedum.

Ceterach and Maiden Hair (*Adiantum*) complete the list of what may be called the regular Wall Plants. The former is a pinnate lobed fern, covered beneath with reddish brown scales. This plant is able to endure the sun; but the Maiden Hair requires both shade and moisture. It grows in wells and under railway bridges, even in the town. The vertical walls of the Vallon Obscur, Nice, are covered with the graceful fronds of the Maiden Hair wherever the public has not been able to reach it and carry it away.

But Nature's mural decorations are not confined to these. The Red Valerian (*Centranth*), the Campanula (*C. Macrorrhiza*), the *Antirrhinum*

(Snapdragon), and other showy flowers hang out their brilliant tapestry. And many a humble Composite and Crucifer that cannot find a *pied à terre* below is glad to lodge where lodging may be had, even if it be a long way from the ground.

Miss Nona Bellairs, in a little book of travels, gives the following delightfully unbotanical story of a wall-frequenting plant which revealed the existence of a ruin. I quote verbatim: "Beyond the Porta Pia, on the Campagna of Rome, a botanist went wandering in search of flowers. After a while he came on one peeping up from the grass that he had never met with before except growing on a wall. Some theory or other was started, so he gathered the flowers and sent them to the Linnean Society. They too were astonished, and sent them back to some of their learned members then in Rome. They went to the spot, found the flowers, and dug for their roots, when they found traces of an ancient wall. Then archaeology put in a word. It was conjectured that long years ago some great man had been buried in that locality and the precise spot forgotten. The little flower spoke again, and guided by her voice they dug down and discovered the ancient sarcophagus and the trace of a basilica, the tiny flower spreading all around where the walls lay."

I see no reason why there should not be some grain of truth in this little story. But what is this wall plant with deep roots and "tiny flowers"?

Frond of Ceterach officinarum

21
Climbers

THE wealth of climbing, creeping, and trailing plants is very characteristic of the Riviera. Nothing strikes us more if we compare these gardens with those of our own country. When we take a house at home we find some Ivy and a Virginian Vine (*Ampelopsis*) upon the wall, and perhaps a Rose covering the summer-house. You bring in from the hedgerow or the coppice Travellers' Joy (*Clematis*), Hop, Honeysuckle (*Lonicera*), Bryony, Bittersweet (*S. dulcamara*), and Tamus, if you can get it to grow. Those who care for annuals can sow the blood-red Trophywort (*Tropæolum*) and the tender Canariensis, food for snails. By the way, why should gardeners persist in calling the Tropæolum a "Nasturtium," that is, Watercress?

We will add Thoreau's Apios, Everlasting Pea (*Lathyrus*), Jasmin, Pyracantha, a Climber seldom seen out here, and the homely cottage garden Tea Tree (*Lycium*). That makes fourteen or fifteen: and you will not easily run the number up to twenty.

As I have had occasion to mention the Lycium, I will stop to inquire why it should be dubbed "Tea Tree." The shrub is a Solanum, with a flower very like that of the Bittersweet (*Dulcamara*). The light blue Ceanothus, a Rhamnus, is another Tea Tree; and I wonder how many more there are. The famous plant used as a substitute for tea in the New England States, when the trouble arose with England, is allied to the Heaths and Azealas. Paraguay tea is, I believe, a Holly. *Chimonanthus fragrans* makes such a good tea that there is talk of cultivating it on a large scale. The shrub is common in the Riviera gardens. I have seen specimens eight or ten feet high. The scented yellow flowers appear while the plant is bare of leaves. If we called the Camellia a Tea Tree, it would hardly be *tiré par les cheveux*, for the shrubs are allied; and we should not be very far wrong if we called the Wild Plum, or Sloe, a Tea Tree; for we have been buying Sloe leaves all our life under the name of Pekoe and Bohea.

How scanty the list of British climbing plants appears when we come to reckon up the species which can be grown here in the open air! First we have all, or almost all, the northern wild and cultivated plants. To these must be added three, which occur here "in the savage state," as a Frenchman would say. These are the Clematis *Flammula*, the Smilax, and the Madder. If we include the lovely Atragene, from the mountains, it will make a fourth. *Vinca*, the Periwinkle, can scarcely be called a climber.

The Flammula is a much smaller plant than its sister, the Vitalba. It straggles under the Olive trees, wherever the peasants have not cleared it away; and growing, as it does, in the open, where there is little to take hold of, it rises but a short distance from the ground. Yet it will run some yards if placed upon a railing. The white Jasmin-like flower is more ornamental than that of the Vitalba. Flammula is evergreen.

Smilax clambers over each hedge and thicket, and covers every rock and ruin with its prickly zigzag stems, holding by a thousand little hooks, and letting fall ruby clusters of berries, and festoons of sweetly scented flowers. Kingsley speculates how this plant can have crossed the Atlantic in some past geological epoch; for one or two species only are indigenous in Europe. The home of the Sarsaparillas is in the forests of the Amazon. Some of the tributaries of the mighty stream are said to be coloured by the sap of these plants. In the Miocene period Europe possessed as many as eight species of Smilax. Lyell ("Elements of Geology") figures a couple of these fossil leaves. They differ but little from those of the common Riviera plant. Smilax is diœcious and evergreen. This is one of Lindley's dictyogens, that is, Endogens with net-veined leaves. The tendrils are stipular. Darwin, in his Essay on "Climbing Plants," says that Smilax is remarkable for possessing both tendrils and recurved spines.

The Madder (*Rubia*) grows with Smilax everywhere, but does not climb so high. It is easily known from the ordinary hedge Galium by its bright black berries and its verticels of rigid dark green leaves. Madder, the root of this, or of a closely allied species, is a most important dye. It gives the much admired Turkey-red colour, also madder-brown and yellow. Large quantities are exported from Smyrna, Trieste, and Leghorn.

We have now disposed of the "savage" climbers, so we turn to the cultivated ones. Of these the number is so great that I can enumerate only a few of the commonest. Some half-dozen are described in other chapters, viz., Ipomœa, Bougainvillea, Boussingaultia, Mandevillea (or Echites), Allamanda, and the Climbing Fig (*Ficus repens*). I have spoken also of the Gourds; and of the Physianthus (or Arauja) with its milky juice and silken seeds. The Vine needs no description. *Tacsonia* with its tubular pendulous flowers, and the *Passion-flower* are as well known as they are beautiful. One of these latter plants in my garden spread twenty yards in two years, and might have extended still farther if it had been watered all through the Summer. It produced a multitude of flowers, but no fruit, although the blossoms appeared to be perfect.

Buddleia: *B. Madagascariensis* and *B. Lindleyana* may almost be reckoned among climbers. One species has violet flowers. The Climbing Groundsel or Drawing-room Ivy (*Senecio scandens*) has, besides its English alias, two Latin ones, *Delairea* and *Mikania*. It is an untidy plant, and, from a botanical point of view, quite unlike an Ivy. This

SMILAX ASPERA

Composite appears disposed to establish itself on the Riviera. I have found it growing, covered with its yellow flowers, among brambles in the Var and in the Magnan valley.

The Vine, the Gourd, the Passion-flower, the Pea, and other plants have tendrils; the Virginian Vine (*Ampelopsis*) holds by suckers, the Ivy by adventitious rootlets; Convolvulus and Honeysuckle are stem climbers, they twine round their support. The Rose and the Bramble (*Rubus*) are provided with recurved prickles, which make it impossible for the trailing branch to slip downwards; but, if you cut the sarment through below, you may easily pull it upwards and so disengage it, for the prickles will offer no resistance when the direction is reversed.

The hedge Galium is furnished with little hooks: Smilax has both tendrils and recurved prickles. But the Climbing Solanum (*S. jasminoides*) has neither hooks nor tendrils, nor any of the arrangements which I have enumerated. It holds by the petiole just like a Clematis. The leaf-stalk plays the part of a tendril, and when it has laid hold of some object it becomes much thicker and more rigid.

The Leguminosæ are represented by the magnificent *Wistaria* (French Glycine), and the *Kennedia*. The former does not fruit on the Riviera; it has the disadvantage of being deciduous. The Scarlet Runner (*Phaseolus*) is even more useful than ornamental, as it forms a staple article of diet in France. Some species of *Thunbergia* are "sensibles au froid," but *T. coccinea* is considered by the gardeners to be "très rustique." Trained over an archway these climbers have a particularly good effect, for the bunches of flowers hang down and form a decorative fringe.

Mühlenbeckia looks well on the trunk of an Aleppo Pine. There is no special beauty in the wiry stems and small dark green leaves; and the flowers are about as ornamental as that of its relative the Knot grass (*Polygonum aviculare*); yet the plant is not to be despised. It is curious, if not beautiful. Notice the edges of the young leaf revolute as in Rumex, and the white waxy fruits.

A still greater contrast to all ordinary vegetation is afforded by the *Ephedra*, a kind of climbing Conifer from north-west Africa. It forms a dense tangle of thin, jointed, leafless twigs. The pistillate plant bears small red fruits. I have seen a porch covered with *Ephedra*, and the plant

VINE AND ELM

struck me as being admirably adapted to this purpose. There is a good specimen in the Jardin Public, Nice. A species of *Ephedra* can be made to cover hot sandy places where no grass will grow. It may be pegged down and cropped close, and will even endure to be submerged by a high tide.

Climbing *Aristolochias* are not very common in the Nice gardens; nor is the strange *Philodendron*, an Aroid with pierced leaves. But the Mexican *Maurandia*, flowering all the year round, is a favourite; and so is the charming little *Medeola*, an Endogen.

The pale blue *Plumbago Capensis* strikes the eye at every turn. A scrap, a few inches long, detached from the stock, not only strikes root, but even flowers at once. *Cobœa* has large purple bells which are green when they first expand. A specimen which I purchased perished during the Summer, killed I suppose by the drought.

The thick-leaved *Hoya* flowered in one of the gardens I used to frequent, but I have not often seen it near Nice.

To make up the list of most notable climbers of the Riviera gardens, I will add the *Tecomas* and *Bignonias*. Within a few yards of the central Boulevard in Nice, there is a lofty Cypress completely grown over by one of these lianas. We are apt to take it for granted that Nature cannot be improved upon. Nothing can be more incongruous than a mass of bright red blossoms upon a sombre Conifer. Nevertheless, the combination pleased me, and I wondered that no one had thought of it before.

What is there in these scandent plants that fascinates us so? Can it be that, like the magic Beanstalk of our early years, the Climber seems to figure by its rapid growth and brilliant blooms the passage to some higher region, the pathway to some land of dreams? In the dense dark tangle of a tropic forest, as the traveller toils along, he sees no sign of life, no bird or flower. Round him on all sides are towering tree trunks crowned with a mass of foliage which shuts out the light of day. Depressed and gloomy he walks, as it were, in a deep dungeon where no ray of light or hope can come. But far above his head there is another region, full of life and light and beauty and delight. Though he cannot reach up to it, nor catch a glimpse of it, the climbing plants, those great lianas with rope-like stems, have raised themselves aloft and spread abroad their luxuriant foliage and their brilliant blooms. Here, in the warm, unshaded sunshine, flit and hover birds of most brilliant plumage and insects of the brightest hues.

Perhaps we admire the Climber because it leads the thoughts upwards to something above us and beyond.

Did space permit, I could wish to conclude this chapter with those exquisite verses on the Vine by Harriet E. Hamilton King in the "Disciples," but I will not mutilate this perfect little poem by making an extract from it.

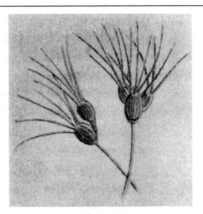

ÆGILOPS OVATA

22

The Vallon Des Fleurs

"Vallon! j'ai bien souvent laissé dans ta prairie,
Comme une eau murmurante, errer ma rêverie;
Je n'oublierai jamais ces fugitifs instants;
Ton souvenir sera, dans mon âme attendrie,
Comme un son triste et doux qu'on écoute longtemps!"

VICTOR HUGO

I TAKE this Valley as a type of those shady glens that lie between the Olive hills, not on account of any special beauty of scenery or abundance of wild flowers; but because it is so easily accessible from Nice. The tramway terminus at St. Maurice is within a short distance of the entrance.

It is doubtful whether the name "Vallon des Fleurs" had originally any reference to flowers, or was merely a corruption of some other word. "Vallon" in the patois of this district means not so much the depression between two hills as the actual stony bed of the stream or rivulet.

While I was walking one day in this Valley, a stranger, guide-book in hand, accosted me, and inquired if this was the famous "Flower Valley." I answered in the affirmative. "I see no flowers," he said and retraced his steps with a disappointed look. This traveller was evidently "doing" the Riviera, and considered that this particular sight was not "up to the mark." But how many flowers do you expect to find in a spot which is plundered for six months every year by an army of strangers who pour out daily from a hundred hotels with great baskets that must be filled? During the six Summer months the natives patronize the place and tear up every flower that has escaped the Winter visitors. The wonder is that anything remains, that Nature even partially repairs such constant loss. Yet there is quite enough, as we shall see, to interest any one who will be interested.

"I see no flowers!" that scurrying stranger said. I should think not! If you have to hurry back to Mrs. So and So's reception, or to dress for table d'hôte or to pack up your goods in time for the "rapide," you are not likely to see much that is worth seeing in one short scuffle through the Vallon des Fleurs, or any other valley for that matter.

Yet there are plenty of flowers within a yard of us; the bank is covered with *Draba.* You may easily pass the minute crucifer without noticing either the white flower or the flattened pod. Draba flowers, I suppose, thus early in the Spring because it has not strength to stand the Summer sun. Growing on the top of walls and on the roofs of cottages where the roots cannot descend to any depth, it would be dried up later in the year. So, frail and ephemeral as is this little cress, it does not wait for Autumn, or even for the solstice, but flowers and fruits, and fades away in the early days of Spring. This Draba is, of course, a common British plant.

Hard by is a little grass, also quite inconspicuous; nevertheless I do not exaggerate when I assert that it may well be the most important herb that grows. For *Ægilops* is thought by De Candolle to be the origin of our cultivated wheat. If this be so, we must believe that some prehistoric benefactor of humanity noticed the grain of this little grass to be large out of all proportion to the leaf and stem, and that he conceived the wonderful plan of developing this plant into a food supply for millions, and a bulwark against famine for all future generations.

Little did this skin-clad savage dream, as he watched and tended the Ægilops, choosing each year the finest grains to sow afresh, and guarding the precious plant against all danger of a cross from its uncultivated relatives—little could he imagine that he was following out a scientific process of natural selection, and trying the most interesting experiment which has ever suggested itself to the mind of man. Here was research unattended with suffering and torture, wholly beneficent, and yet quite unendowed. For this man, though we know not when and where he lived, laid the first foundations of agriculture, made civilization possible, and so increased a thousandfold both the good and the evil of this mortal life. In some parts of Italy this grass is gathered, and the grain is separated by setting fire to the ears; the seeds then fall out slightly roasted. Corn parched or scorched in this way is still a favourite article of food in some parts of the East. Confer Virgil, Æn. i. 179; Ruth ii. 14, &c.

So much for the Ægilops; but it has no flower, as we are accustomed to speak of flowers. So I will take from the border of the copse a real "flower," and a curious one, the *Plagius*. I dare say you might call it a "Bachelor's button," or something of that sort; but it has no popular name, as far as I am aware. If you wish to know what it is like, you have only to take a common Ox-eye daisy and pull off all the white petals (ray florets) as poor Margaret does in "Faust," leaving the orange disc; that is exactly like a Plagius. If you show Plagius to a friend he will say, "Ha, ha, I know how you made that flower. It's no use trying to play your tricks on me!" There are even botanists who declare the Plagius to be a mere monstrosity, a miserable deformity, a daisy deprived of its frill by some curious freak of nature. But if this orange button were a mere monstrosity, it would tend, when it varied, as all vegetables do, to revert to the type from which it has departed. Instead of this, it is stated that flowers of Plagius have been found provided with a ray quite different from that of the Leucanthemum. The plant is particularly abundant in the valley of the Vesubia, just beyond Levens.

After this yellow disc let us pick another button, only this time blue; a flower which will be equally new to English botanists. This also we can find near the entrance of the valley; it has no English name. Linnæus called it *Globularia*. There are several species, one of which, *G. Alypum,* flowers not only in the Spring, but also through the Winter months. The inflorescence is in a head, like that of a Composite or a Scabious, and the floral envelopes are in fives; the corolla is bilabiate or strap-shaped, and the stamens are four, the upper or posterior one being suppressed as in the Labiates; the ovary is superior, and the stigma more or less two-lobed. This curious plant has therefore the inflorescence of a Composite, but the calyx, corolla, and stamens of a Labiate.

Close at hand the Globe Thistle (*Echinops*) may be found abundantly; a plant so ornamental that one is surprised it does not attract the attention of artists with its soft blue spheres. This well rounded inflorescence is not strictly analogous to that of a Thistle or a Burdock (*Arctium*), for according to Henslow's beautiful wall diagrams, which hang before me, each floret composing the blue globe represents a separate capitulum. *Echinops* is common from the coast to a height of 3,500 or 4,000 feet above sea-level.

GLOBULARIA ALYPUM

Without its flowers, the Leafless Lily (*Aphyllanthes*) might easily be mistaken for a rush. It is in fact, says Moggridge, intermediate in structure and aspect between the lily and the rush families, and appears to belong properly neither to one nor the other. Hooker places this lily in a small family with a few nondescript genera near to Juncaceæ. *Aphyllanthes* is more plentiful on the Nouvelle Route de Gènes than in the Vallon des Fleurs.

Coris is the only plant of the Primrose order (that I know of) with bilateral corolla. The leaves are thickish, and in habit the plant is not unlike a Stonecrop (*Sedum*). As to the flowers, they are decidedly pretty; the colour is given in the floras as a "bluish pink." You may find Coris at the entrance of the Vallon des Fleurs; and wherever the ground is dry and stony you will see it growing along the top of the railway embankments.

Late in June we have found *Catananche cærulea* in the Vallon des Fleurs. The flower, as its name implies, is of a beautiful blue; the long narrow leaf does not show much among grass, so that when out of flower the plant is not easily found. Catananche is particularly worthy of mention, because Professor Oliver considers it "the handsomest of the ligulate Composites." The bracts of the involucre are so dry and scarious that they make a crackling noise when slightly pressed. The plant is much more abundant a few miles inland. I have tried unsuccessfully to grow it in a pot. Catananche is able to endure the severest winter on the south coast of England: it ought therefore to be commoner in English gardens than it is.

APHYLLANTHES MONSPELIENSIS, THE RUSH LILY

I need not call attention to the conspicuous flowers of a Cranesbill (*Erodium*) with which the grass is studded, nor to the Violets which literally cover the ground a little farther on. A valley which branches to the east is full of *Hepaticas*; when these are in flower you may often find the way to the spot where they grow by the blossoms scattered along the path. There are people who can find no use for flowers except to destroy them and tread them under foot. On Corpus Christi day the Cours at Grasse is strewn with a thick carpet of yellow Broom flowers. The peasant girls have been busy before daybreak laying the bright bushes bare, and bringing down the golden ornaments of the hill-side, to be crushed by the feet of the mumbling priests. The meadows by the Trent at Nottingham are thickly covered once a year with Crocuses. The first of these corms was planted, it is said, by a French prisoner or refugee. The "Queen of the Midlands" is proud of these beautiful flowers. The Nottingham "lambs" take great interest in them. On Crocus Sunday they assemble on the meadow; they leap and trample on Crocuses, they tread them down and tear them up. "Placuisse nocet!" Their beauty is their bane. By the evening not a flower is left, but the road to the town is strewn with the débris of Nature's beautiful handiwork, just as you may see the Promenade at Nice, Cannes, or Mentone, after the vulgar and rowdy "Battle of Flowers."

Against this wanton destruction the botanist protests in vain. But think you that there is no "Flowers' Revenge"? that Freiligrath's small fairies will not pierce you with their elfin darts?

"Wir verblühn, doch eh' wir sterben,
Mädchen, triff dich unsre Rache!"

Barlia longibracteata (*Aceras, Loroglossum*), the largest and handsomest orchid of this district if not of the whole Riviera, abounds in the Vallon. On the Italian side of the frontier "it is becoming very rare, as many of the places where it formerly grew have been turned into cultivated terraces." It loves a fresh and shady spot. Called after Barla, who made a special study of the Riviera orchids, and wrote a monograph ("Iconographie") with beautiful coloured plates. Among the other orchids common in this Valley the white *Cephalanthera ensifolia* is conspicuous. Wild Tulips would be more plentiful if they did not grow so near the path.

If you are fond of sweet perfumes, you can fill your pockets with Melissa, a Labiate with the habit of a Lamium. The odour of this plant is like that of the Scented Verbena (*Aloysia triphylla*). In the Hepatica Valley, just mentioned, the *Clematis vitalba* (not the Flammula) reaches a development which I have never seen in England. It reminds one of those tropical lianas, rising as it does to the summit of the highest trees, with a stem as thick as the wrist. The main Valley ends in a recess, which would be beautiful if it had not been completely denuded, in these last few years, of the Oak and Pine and Arbutus and Flowering Ash (*F. Ornus*) which used to shelter and adorn the spot. Sad to say, the Vallon des Fleurs is now desecrated by a pigeon-shooting establishment.

23

The Summer Drought

IN many of the countries bordering on the Mediterranean little or no rain falls during the Summer. In Nice this dry period lasts about four months, from the first week in June to near the end of September. But it may be of much longer duration. This applies only to the coast region, for the valleys of the Maritime Alps are watered all through the Summer by refreshing thunder-showers.

In Naples the rainless months are three: June, July, and August; in Malta, Greece, and Sicily, four or five; in Palestine, seven; and in Egypt as many as eight.

The vegetation of the Riviera has little to fear from severe cold in the Winter, but those plants only which are specially adapted can successfully resist the Summer drought. In the chapter on Lizards, I have mentioned some shrubs which actually lose their leaves during this long dry period, giving up the struggle as it were, and reviving when watered by the Autumn rains. And in the chapter on Succulent Plants I have shown how well fitted are these vegetable reservoirs to survive the thirsty ordeal.

The Mediterranean flora, and that of the Riviera in particular, has other methods. The succulent plants just mentioned start with a good supply of water; but the great mass of those which have no such provision are compelled to waste as little water as possible. To this end they become torpid during the drought, and protect themselves by a hairy covering, so as to reduce transpiration to a minimum. Even the succulent species must economize their water supply to the utmost, and it is interesting to observe that they have fewer stomata than any other class of plants, excepting of course those which are submerged.

Nowhere in the world, says Kerner, is the hairy covering on foliage as a protection against exhalation so abundant and so varied as in the floral region surrounding the Mediterranean. The trees have foliage with grey hairs, and the "Phrygian undergrowth" (as Theophrastus calls it) of shrubs and smaller plants, which clothe the sunny hills, is also grey or whitish. The aspect of the landscape is so much affected in this way that we are tempted to speak of the flora as "ever-grey" rather than "evergreen." There is an endless variety of this hairy coating on the leaves; it may resemble cotton, or wool, or silk, or felt.

This drought-resisting arrangement is well seen in the Composites, especially in the genera Andryala, Artemisia, Evax, Filago, Inula, Santolina, and Helichrysum. Every one of these occurs on the Riviera. Andryala has pale yellow flowers, and the down which covers the plant is also yellowish. I used to find it on the Route de St. Laurent, near Nice. Artemisia is represented here by as many as ten species. Nearly all of these are confined to the mountains, including *A. Absinthium*, which makes the well-known drink. But a rare species, *A. gallica*, not to be distinguished from the British *A. maritima*, grows near Cannes and on the islands. This plant has a pleasant smell. The minute rosette of Evax is common at Antibes, on the stony ground between the station and the town. *Filago spathulata*, the common Cudweed, called by Bentham, *Gnaphalium germanicum*, and by Gerard, *Herba impia*, forms a carpet on the unraked garden path. The great rank Inula is ubiquitous. Round its yellow flower-heads swarm the tailed blue butterflies *Lycena Telicanus*, and sometimes *L. Bœtica*. Santolina, another aromatic plant, is cultivated here, and subspontaneous. Helichrysum, the wild Everlasting, is plentiful everywhere.

Professor Penzig would add *Cineraria maritima*, and *Diotis candidissima*, a littoral plant rare on the Riviera.

Among the Leguminosæ there are many of these drought-proof (xerophilous) plants, which wear, like John Baptist, a hairy mantle. I will mention a few. *Anthyllis Barba Jovis*, a littoral shrub with silvery down: *Dorycnium hirsutum* and *D. rectum: Cytisus triflorus*, a rather uncommon shrub: I have not seen it growing, but a friend brought a piece of it back one day from the Magnan Valley: *Cytisus argenteus* (Argyrolobium), so named from its whitish silky hairs, inhabits the most arid spots.

There are also numerous hair-protected plants in the Labiate Order. For instance:—Species of Salvia, Teucrium, Marrubium, Stachys,

BEAULIEU AND THE CLIFFS OF PETITE AFRIQUE

Sideritis, Lavandula, Phlomis. All common here, with the exception of Phlomis, which is cultivated in gardens. I believe that I have found it subspontaneous on waste ground between Carabacel and Cimiez. The commonest *Cistus* and the *Helianthemum* (Rock Rose) which one meets oftenest are hairy. In the Daphne family, the specific name of the rare *Thymelea hirsuta* speaks for itself. *Lavatera maritima*, pearl of the rock-bound coast, is clad in a pale pearly green. *Cynoglossum Creticum* has "feuilles grisâtres pubescentes"; and the wild *Heliotrope* is likewise a "friar of orders grey." These examples must suffice. Most of the families represented on the Riviera can show plants similarly shielded from the sun.

In some cases the leaves are silky underneath. For instance, *Genista cinerea*. Can this be a protection against the heat radiated from the ground? It is significant that this shrub lives "sur les collines très-sèches," and is of very small stature, so that the leaves are raised but little from the burning soil.

Amelanchier, whose cheerful white blossoms light up every rocky gorge, has its buds thickly swathed; but as the leaves expand they discard the cottony covering. Perhaps, living in more humid spots, it is less liable to be dried up and parched. The tomentose wrapping may serve to guard the buds and the delicate young leaves against the attacks of caterpillars. I believe that leaf-hairs frequently serve this purpose. It is certain that we often see trees with glabrous leaves, *ex. gr.* willows, completely denuded by different larvæ.

Cistus tuberaria, a conspicuous plant, which we have found whenever we have visited the Esterel, presents a remarkable phenomenon. The leaves of the radical rosette are covered with grey hairs, while these on the flower-scape are green and glabrous. You might suppose that two different plants were joined. Kerner's explanation seems to be as follows. The leaves of the rosette are more permanent, and have to go through the Summer drought, whereas those on the upright stem will disappear as the fruit ripens.

Of the individual hairs which compose those sun-shields I have not room to write. But the epidermal appendages of the Riviera plants are well worth study. The branched hairs of the disagreeable and dangerous Plane tree (*Platanus*) are figured in Botanical books; as also are the globular glands which hold the perfume of the Lavender, perched each upon a little stalk, and sheltered under spreading hairs. The spangles of the sacred *Storax*, and the lancet-shaped sting of the beautiful *Wigandia*, may be taken as other instances and types.

I have explained two different methods of combating the drought. A third consists in hanging the leaf-blades edgewise to the sky, so as to present the smallest possible surface to the sun. The (later) leaves of *Eucalyptus* are an instance of this arrangement.

Again, it is possible that by rolling in the margins of the leaf a plant may gain an advantage in the scorching Summer days, for it will thus diminish the area exposed to the sun's rays, and also lessen evaporation by hiding some of the stomata. Familiar examples are the pretty pair of wall-weeds, *Phagnalon* (or *Conyza*), and the still prettier Everlasting (*Helichrysum*). *Rosmary, Erica*, and *Coris* may be added.

Yet another plan is adopted by *Nerium Oleander*, the stems of *Cactus*, and some other plants. Here the epidermal cells are thickened by secondary deposits.

It is obvious that in the warfare with Phœbus Apollo a herb or shrub may use more than one weapon. Thus we see that the Cactus has three devices at the least.

Among the most successful drought-resisting plants, wild or cultivated here, are *Nicotiana glauca* and *Diplotaxis tenuifolia*. And they are more or less mysterious, for in neither case is it evident by what means they retain their moisture. I have never seen the former plant inconvenienced by drought; and as for the ubiquitous ever-flowering yellow crucifer, it flourishes when most other weeds dry up and wither.

Lastly, a large class of plants substitute for the tender tissue of the leaf some tougher organ, which, being supplied with chlorophyll, serves the same purpose, and is better able to resist the sun. As I have described almost all the following plants in other chapters, I will now do no more than bring them together and enumerate them. I confine myself, of course, to those Leafless Plants which are common on the Riviera.

Ruscus (the Butcher's Broom) has flattened branches instead of leaves. The closely-allied *Asparagus* is also leafless. *Opuntia* and the Cactus tribe possess no leaves. *Kleinia* (a succulent Composite) seems to do quite well without them when they fall off. *Casuarina* has thin jointed branches, *Polygonum platycladon* has green ribbons, as a substitute. Many *Acacias* (Wattle trees) use their dilated leaf-stalks (phyllodes) as leaves, and look as well garnished as any other tree, leafless though they are. The truculent *Colletia*, and divers species of *Spartium*, are scantily supplied with foliage. *Lathyrus Aphaca* and *L. Ochrus*, common "weeds," depend upon their stipules, for the laminæ (leaf-blades) have run to tendrils. *L. Nissolia*, the Grass Vetch, is no better off. We gathered it at Caussols, above Grasse. You will find no leafage in the dark tangle of the *Ephedra*, a climbing Conifer from North Africa. We must add the charming blue rush-lily, *Aphyllanthes*, and *Buplevrum*, in the Umbellates. *B. fruticosum* is a favourite shrub in the Riviera gardens.

This list of Leafless Plants does not pretend to be complete: the Botanist will easily enlarge it. But it may serve to show how many plants find it to their advantage in this region to dispense with leaves.

PALIURUS ACULEATUS

24
Armed Plants

"AS we approach the district where some great war is raging, the traces of the struggle become more numerous and more striking. At one place the ground is furrowed by the heavy round shot, or torn up where a shell has burst. A little farther on we come upon an earthwork or a broken bridge, the wreck of a waggon or a tumbril. At last we see the flashing bayonets and glancing helmets of the combatants."

So, as we leave the well-watered shores of the Atlantic, and travel towards the east and south, we find at each step fresh evidences of a struggle, a fierce contest with heat and drought which vegetation is compelled to wage.

This struggle reaches its climax in that belt of rainless regions which girdle the earth at a short distance from the tropics. The Sahara is continued eastwards through Arabia, appearing again in India under the name of Thur, to the south of the Punjab. In the New World, Mexico forms part of this barren belt.

The plants of these desert lands are armed almost without exception; armed to the teeth, like the Bedouin who roams over the sandy waste. The leaves, unable to withstand the burning sun, grow tougher, and expose less surface to the light. In our moist climate the herbage eaten off by browsing animals is soon replaced by a more luxuriant growth; but the plants of the desert cannot hope to escape destruction by a rapid renewal of the parts destroyed. They defend themselves therefore by thorns and spines.

On the Riviera the number of spinous plants is so great that one is at a loss to enumerate or describe them. I have mentioned in other chapters the cruel *Acacia horrida,* with its enamelled daggers six inches long, the sharp weapons of the ruthless *Agave,* the trident brandished by the Honey Locust (*Gleditschia*), the threatening thorns of the *Cactus,* and other plants effectively if less conspicuously armed.

Our British Hawthorn (*Cratægus oxyacantha*) is represented in Liguria by a species (*C. monogyna*) which closely resembles it; the Thistle, like its patron the Scotchman, is ubiquitous; but the golden Gorse (*Ulex*) is absent from the Riviera.[19] However, there is a substitute a shrub as unapproachably prickly, and almost, if not quite, as beautiful. I mean the *Calycotome spinosa.*

In one respect this plant must yield to Gorse; it cannot boast of flowers the whole year round. *Calycotome* is used everywhere for fences; not in the living state, but dried, when it becomes if possible more disagreeable to meddle with.

Again, the foliage of our Holly (*Ilex aquifolium*) is not more defensive than that of the Holm oak (*Quercus Ilex*) when stunted to a shrub.

The harsh *Rubia peregrina,* confined in Britain to the south-western counties, is one of the commonest Stellates in the district. Madder (*R. tinctoria*) is so closely allied that it is sometimes considered to be a mere variety of the *peregrina.*

And as for the *Smilax*, we have no climbing plant that we can compare with it for hooks and prickles.[20]

The wild *Asparagus,* with its innumerable little spikes, is as abundant here as on the rocky shores of Greece, where it strove in vain to shelter the fair Perigyne from the fiery suit of the Sun-god Theseus. The descendants of the nymph held the plant sacred. The wild Asparagus may have its uses, but as a shelter from the sun it is certainly inferior to every other plant that grows. It is still to be found on Asparagus Island, at Kynance Cove, Cornwall. The wild Asparagus is said to have a better flavour than the cultivated: we never tried it. Our Christmas decorations usually consist of Asparagus, Smilax, Mastic, and Ivy, with an odd scrap of Holly and Mistletoe purchased in the market.

Dorycnium suffruticosum owes its spinous appearance to the rigid character of its short branches (Holmes).

The common *Juniper,* with narrow leaf and black berry, is found in the mountain district and to the west of Cannes. *J. Oxycedrus,* a taller tree with larger fruit, occurs at Nice, and to the east. The berries are red, and the leaf is broad with two white lines. A third species (*J. phœnicea*) may be found here and there on the steep rocks. The scale-like leaves are imbricate. Ardoino gives these localities: Mentone, Monaco, Eze, St. André, St. Martin-du-Var.

A French botanical writer states that the Juniper has the stomata more numerous on the upper than on the under surface of the leaf. We should expect a plant affected with so strange a peculiarity to reverse the leaves, in order that the stomata may not be exposed to the sunlight. It would be interesting to observe whether this is effected by the pendulous position of the twigs, or by the curving axis which one sometimes sees in Junipers. I had a small Juniper in my garden which bent over so much that the leaves near the apex must have presented their under surface to the sky. When I tied this plant to a stick, so that it was forced to remain erect, it died. The experiment would be worth repeating. And it would be important to ascertain what is the position of the stomata in those Junipers which have the axis perfectly erect, and the twigs not pendulous.

The *Oxycedrus* Juniper, with its sharp tipped leaves, is reasonably armed against attack. But what shall we say of those Dead Sea Apples (species of Solanum) which we see out here?

> *"Dead Sea fruits that tempt the eye*
> *But turn to ashes on the lips."*

Can anything be more wantonly and offensively aggressive? The Japanese gentleman has his two swords; the backwoodsman carries a revolver in every pocket, and a bowie knife to boot; the pirate wields his cutlass and fires off his blunderbuss; but all these desperadoes have a weak point somewhere. Not so the Dead Sea Apple: the very midribs of the leaves are set with spines an inch and more in length. These Solanums are not uncommon on waste ground. They are particularly abundant by the roadside at Beaulieu.

Xanthium spinosum is a plant not far behind these others in what an American would call "cussedness." Even the fruit resembles a little pincushion. I well remember how much trouble I had in picking one of these in order to examine it. Xanthium is classed near the Composites. It stands some two or three feet high. I have found it at Antibes, by the Paillon at St. Pons, and in the Magnan torrent bed, not far from the sea. Bentham says that Xanthium sometimes appears on ballast heaps on our south coast. I have repeatedly seen the fruits of this plant, together with others unknown to me, adhering to the wool of which mattresses are made. I conclude that this wool has been brought from some region farther south than the Riviera, where the flora is very different and the Xanthium much commoner.

Succulent plants, being peculiarly tempting to herbivorous animals, are specially well armed. The Succulent house at Kew, from the uncouth forms and truculent aspect of its inmates, has been called the "Chamber of Horrors."

Many plants which do not parade their armament are, nevertheless, uncommonly well protected, "très défensives," as they say in French. Try to thrust your hand into the heart of a Palm Tree, for instance, and you will find to your cost that the lower leaflets of each frond are so completely shrunk and hardened that they might almost serve as packing needles.

We must pass over a vast number of small plants and weeds which

Opuntia Ficus Indica

may take as their motto "Nemo me impune lacessit": *Eryngo*, the so-called Sea holly, very abundant everywhere; several species of *Centaury*, with bristling bracts; *Galactites*, adorning the dusty roadside with its fringed flower heads and variegated leaves.

Others again may write themselves "armigeri," as we used to do at Oxford, but their device is "Defence, not Defiance." Though determined to protect themselves, they are not truculent. Take, as instances, the stiff little *Asterisk* with its yellow stars, not the very ugliest variety of yellow; and the amethystine globes of the *Echinops*. To resist aggression, and yet not become so hardened as to lose all sense of beauty and of harmony, is an ideal rarely attained by vegetables or by men.

The Carlines make no attempt at ornament; self-preservation is their one and only law; "Noli me tangere," "Stand off!" the sum of their philosophy. Their straw-coloured flower-heads glisten in the sun, but no one admires them, no poet enshrines them in his verse, no artist draws their outline with pencil or with brush; for there is about these plants the same "disgusting dryness" which marked the speeches of William the Silent. From Karl the Great the Carlines derive their name. Since the time when they cured his plague-stricken army, they have been of no use or service to any one. At 3,000 feet, and perhaps lower down, the Stemless Carline thrives. Ensconced in a hollow of the stony ground, with all its branches and all its internodes suppressed, shrinking back into a short spiky mass, and so secured against all possible attacks, it devotes its whole energy to the production of one great solitary disc.

The dangerous *Opuntia tunicata* has barbed spines covered by a silvery sheath. Plants of this sort should be grown only in a botanic garden, and there beyond the reach of visitors.[20]

Last, and worst of all Armed Plants, come the Buckthorns (Rhamnaceæ), which claim the sad distinction of furnishing the crown of thorns. *Paliurus*, or Christ's Thorn, is a shrub with slender curving branches and alternate subsessile shining leaves. The stipules are altered into stout pines; and one of each pair points forward, while the other is curved back like a boat-hook. Ornamental when decked with its clusters of small yellow flowers, and remarkable when it bears its curious fruits (seed cases), which resemble a head with a broad-brimmed hat on. Hence the French name, "Porte chapeau." Paliurus is common in

OPUNTIA: A WELL-ARMED SPECIES

Palestine and abundant also in Italy, where it is planted for fences. It grows near Grasse, but is rare on the Riviera. This remarkable shrub is said to be hardy in the south of England. The Jujube Tree (*Zizyphus*) conceals beneath each leaf a very effective hook, which tears anything it catches.

One of the most extraordinary shrubs which you can find in the Riviera gardens, where so many strange plants grow, is the Colletia (*C. cruciata*), belonging to this same family. It has no leaf, no vulnerable spot. There is nothing that a famished beast could make a mouthful of, for the whole plant consists of great curved spines, placed one above the other. So closely do many of these resemble an anchor that you would not find it easy to say in what respect the model could be made more perfect. Count Egloffstein showed me a branch of Colletia which he had broken from a plant growing apparently wild, near his villa on the Cimiez hill. There can be no doubt that this was a garden escape.

Notes:

[19]   *Ulex nana*, the dwarf gorse, is plentiful about Marseilles.—T. H.

[20]   *Smilax aspera*, the Bacchic ivy of the ancients.—T. H.

[21]   A still more formidable plant is *O. microdasys*, the excessively small spines of which, after lodging in the skin, cannot be detected except by the aid of a magnifying glass, and are most difficult to extract.—T. H.

GROUP OF ALOES

25
Succulent Plants

THIS heading is intended to include those water-storing plants of various orders which the French gardeners include under the title of "plantes grasses." Many of these might be described as "thick-leaved," but this term would not apply to the Cactus and some others, which are leafless, the reservoir of water being in the cells of the stem. Succulent plants are peculiarly adapted to the climate of this district; for their power of resisting drought enables them to live through the Summer, which is always dry, and sometimes altogether rainless.

Let us start with those "American Aloes," in green tubs, which guarded Mr. Numpkin's house door; those prickly plants into which the wily Mr. Muzzle contrived, with great dexterity, to overturn both Mr. Tingle and Mr. Job Trotter, as they withdrew, discomfited, from the magistrate's house.

The *Agave* is thoroughly characteristic of the Riviera. Its bayonet-pointed leaves figure in the foreground of every photograph, and the great flower-stem, branching like a candelabrum, with rigid regularity, enters into the composition of every sketch and water colour. What would the artist do without the Agave? Yet this plant is no native of Europe. Though now so completely naturalised, it is a stranger and intruder like ourselves, for it was brought over, not long ago, from Central America. Professor Penzig very pertinently remarks that hardly any of the characteristic Riviera plants are indigenous. He instances the following, Orange and Lemon, Olive, Vine, Cypress, Opuntia, Date Palm, Fig; and he asks "what remains?" Not much indeed! But surely the Dwarf Palm (*Chamærops*), the Oleander, the Pistacias, and some others are both indigenous and characteristic.

The Agave is said to ripen its fruit as though it were truly a native; but I think that it is propagated chiefly by the suckers which it throws out so abundantly. These are very troublesome in a garden, for they may come up under some plant which you cannot disturb, and then it is difficult to get rid of them.

The terminal spikes, and those curved spines which border the leaf, inflict a painful wound, which becomes inflamed; for this reason the Agave is better suited for a barrier or for some dry waste corner than for the frequented part of any garden. This plant is equal to a man-trap; woe betide the thief who climbs over a wall and drops into an Agave upon the other side! The spines[22] are merciless, and the name is most appropriate; for did not the Theban Agave, in orgiastic frenzy, tear to pieces her own son, Pentheus, on the pine-clad slopes of Mount Cithæron? I may mention here that we have altered the quantity of this word, and changed it to a dactyl. The middle vowel is long, thus "Agāve."

AGAVE, WITH OLIVES AND YUCCAS

The Mexican national drink, "pulque," is obtained by cutting off the flowering bud. The saccharine juice then flows out so abundantly that one plant will yield from one to ten litres daily for six months. When fermented, this juice contains about as much alcohol as good cider. The frugal Scotchman would find the Agave a great resource, if it could be planted north of the Tweed; especially in those districts where the blue ribbon prevails. But "pulque" is a poor substitute for the genuine Scotch whiskey. It is to be hoped that this Bacchanalian vegetable will never be introduced into the Emerald Isle. An Agave to each mud cabin: that is, ten litres of liquor per day for every Irishman: and suppose he were to grow half-a-dozen Agaves!

From the leaves an excellent fibre may be obtained for cordage. *Agave rigida*, the so-called Sissal hemp, is largely cultivated for this purpose in the Bahamas. The industry is said to be a profitable one. The natives of the islands call the plant "Pita." There is also another use to which the Agave is put. The flower stalk, which rises green and tender, like a huge asparagus, becomes quite brown and dry when the flowering is over. In texture it then resembles cork, but it is lighter and softer, more like pith. Cut into hoards about a centimetre thick, this substance serves admirably for lining entomological boxes, because the slender pins used for very small insects penetrate it more easily than cork. I took an Agave stem to the saw mill to be cut up (it grew in the beautiful ground of the Torre di Cimella), and I found that boards measuring 15 inches by 3 or 4 cost about a halfpenny apiece.

The Agave is monocarpic: that is, after flowering once it perishes. Before flowering the great leaves curve inwards as if to protect the bud. There is a popular idea that the Agave flowers only at the age of a hundred years; but the real time is given as the fifth to the eighteenth year. It is stated that the plant may be compelled to flower by cutting off the leaves: the Agaves slashed by the sabres of the French troops in Algeria are said to have flowered prematurely.

The Agave is constantly called an Aloe: the mistake is universal. The *Aloe* is of a different habit, and does not perish after flowering. Having a superior ovary, it is classed with the Liliaceæ, whereas the Agave is placed near the *Amaryllis*. Of the two plants the Agave is very much commoner in Nice.

The *Opuntia*, sometimes called "Prickly Pear" or "Indian Fig," is (like the Agave) an American plant but completely established on this coast. It is very abundant on the rocks of Monaco. On this Cactus the cochineal insect is cultivated in Mexico and the Canaries. The fruit is edible, but here at any rate worth little. Dr. Bennet showed me in his garden at Mentone an abnormal plant on which the fruits grew one above another. The effect was very curious. At Naples I saw a field covered with the leaf-like lobes of this Cactus or a very similar species, but I was unable to ascertain for what purpose they were thus laid upon the ground.

The Candle Cactus (*Cereus*) grows well here: some of the species reach a height of fifteen to eighteen feet. When hard pressed by thirst, the Mexican mules lash out at the base of these great leafless pillars, and, wounding the Cactus with their iron-shod hoofs, they obtain some of the water which is stored in the stem. The spines are so threatening that no other animal, however thirsty, will defy them.

Mesembryanthemum is admirably adapted to this climate. Not far from a hundred species are grown. The commonest, a coarse plant, I think it is *M. edule*, spreads rapidly and hangs down everywhere on walls and terraces. The leaf is triangular in section. The fruit, as the specific name implies, is edible. The flower bears an outward resemblance to the inflorescence of a rayed Composite; hence the old name "Fig Marigold." They are said, like the rose, to range through all the colours with the exception of blue. You may sometimes see these creeping plants so covered with flowers that the green part is completely hidden. A section of the ovary shows a remarkable placentation, which arises, according to Eichler, from the more rapid growth of the outer wall. A similar peculiarity is seen in the Pomegranate. Eichler's book, which I have just quoted, is a marvellously complete treatise on the structure of the flower, but marred by heaviness and dulness. "*Mesembryanthemum*" means "flower of the midday" or south: the same root occurs in "ephemeral," &c.

Beside the three orders already mentioned, the Crassulas (Echeveria, &c.), furnish succulent plants. Juicy plants are found here even in families where our British species give no indication of thickened leaf or stem. Who would suspect a Kleinia (or Cacalia) of belonging to the

Compositæ? What a surprise it is when a flower like a Groundsel (*Senecio*) appears on this smooth green cylinder! Kleinia is furnished with a very few small leaves, like those of a Sorrel Dock (*Rumex Acetosella*). A slight chill brings these off, and the plant then looks still more like a sausage. It does not appear to suffer from the loss of its leaves.

The great majority of the plants in the Succulent House at Kew belong to the following seven orders: Liliaceæ, Amaryllidaceæ, Cactaceæ, Euphorbiaceæ, Crassulaceæ, Asclepiadeæ, and Compositæ. Almost all of these are represented on the Riviera in the open air.

Notes:

[22]   *A. applanata* has perhaps the most formidable spikes of any, and it is said to have been adopted by the French as a military defence in some parts of Africa.—T. H.

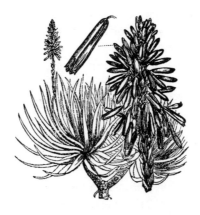

INFLORESCENCE OF ALOE

ST. JEANNET, VILLAGE AND CLIFF

26
Peculiar Plants

"Les herbes out chascune leur propriété, leur naturel et singularité."

THE *Aspidistra* may be popularly described as a tuft of leaves growing in an ornamental pot: for we do not see it quite so often in the open ground. The plant is peculiar because it appears to have no stem or flower or fruit; the leaves seem to come up out of the soil. It is also peculiar because it haunts every nook and corner of the town. You cannot escape the Aspidistra. It greets you in the noisy station, and welcomes you in the hall of the hotel. It presides over the table d'hôte, and awaits you on the verandah. As you make your purchase in a shop, it stands on the counter at your elbow; and when you enter the café, you see it reflected in the mirror with the bottles of vermouth and amer.

The Aspidistra overhears all the scandals that are whispered in every salon of the Riviera, and sees every coin that you venture on the red or on the black. This long-suffering plant patronises every bazaar and shows no sign of being bored; it is present at every prayer-meeting, and, for aught I know, at the functions of the ritualists. If you call upon a friend, the Aspidistra guards the staircase; and if the cruel Fates compel you to consult your doctor, the leafy sentinel looks callously upon you from the table of the waiting room:

"Heu, loca felici non adeunda viro!"

The reason is not far to seek why this Chinese plant should be so much employed and such a universal favourite, both at home and abroad. It can endure a great deal of hardship and neglect; being *très résistant, presque sans soins il se comporte toujours bien.* What a grand thing it is to be *très résistant!* A tough constitution enables the Aspidistra, as it does many men, to dispense with every other quality.

I said that this plant appears to have no stem, but if you look closer you will see the stock from which the leaves proceed. There is, roughly speaking, no flowering plant without a stem. Even the dandelion (*Taraxacum*) has a stem, though it is shortened to a disc.

As for the flowers, which are concealed at the base of the leaves, they are of a dull red, and large in proportion to the plant. They have been studied by an Italian botanist named Delpino, but I can find no account of them in English or German works.

A bell-shaped chamber is formed, a sort of Mamertine prison, in which I believe that small insects are confined, just as they are in the little dungeon of the Arum.

I found no prisoners in the flowers which I examined, but they were growing in the hall of a hotel where insects are scarce. The floral organs are in fours (tetramerous), like those of Paris, which is sometimes classed near to Aspidistra.

You will not easily find a more peculiar plant than the *Polygonum platycladon.* The name implies "flat branches," and they do, in fact, resemble green ribbon, or that seaweed called Laminaria. The shrub is practically leafless, and the strap-shaped twigs are jointed at short intervals. If you trace these downwards, you will find that they become thicker as you approach the main stem, which is rounded and quite solid. Allied are the Dock (*Rumex*), Rhubarb, Mühlenbeckia, a curious Riviera climber which I have mentioned in another chapter, and many small weeds such as Bistort and Knotgrass (*P. aviculare*). These differ in leaf and in habit almost as much as is possible, yet their affinities are revealed in every case by the little triangular fruit. Buckwheat (*P. Fagopyrum*), that is, "Beech-wheat," German "Buch-weizen," is so called from the same triquetrous grain, which resembles Beech-mast: Buck = Buch = Beech. "Book" is, of course, the same word.

The Water Germander, *Teucrium Scordium*, has been found at Nice, at Mentone and near Grasse. The flowers are pink, and the plant has a smell of garlic; a peculiarity shared by the Alliaria, a common British Crucifer. This plant is mentioned by Pliny.

Photinia is an evergreen shrub or small tree, having a thick glossy oblong leaf like that of the common Laurel Cherry (*Cerasus lauro cerasus*). There is no plant on the Riviera which attracts more attention than the Photinia. Every one wants to know what that shrub is whose leaves as they fade turn to such a brilliant red, lighting up every garden and shrubbery, just as the Sumach (*Rhus cotinus*) illuminates the hill-sides. Great corymbs of white flowers are produced, but those alone would hardly suffice to make the plant conspicuous in these gardens of the Mediterranean coast where flowers are so abundant. Strange as it may seem, this laurel-leaved evergreen can be grafted on the Hawthorn (*Cratægus*), so closely are they allied.

As common as the Photinia, or even commoner, is a small tree, the Myoporum, which does not at first sight appear to deserve a place among peculiar plants. It is a very ordinary-looking tree, with a few small speckled flowers; but pick a leaf and hold it to the light, it seems to be pierced with innumerable little holes. These are immersed glands. You see a few of them in the leaf of Hypericum, and a great number in the rind of an orange. On the bracts of Hop (*Humulus*) the glands are sessile, not hidden below the surface; and in many plants they are raised on a stalk, as in the calyx of Lythrum.

The structure of the ovary of Myoporum is interesting. A section of the fruit would lead one to suppose that there are three carpels, whereas there are but two. Eichler thus explains the anomaly: One dissepiment only is formed, instead of two, as in the Labiates and Borages. Thus, of the four ovules, two are isolated and two are in contact. Of these latter one is suppressed, while the other usurps the whole of that cell: thus, a three-celled ovary results, each cell with one seed.

Ophiopogon (Snake's-Beard; whence this peculiar name?) might aptly be called "plante à surprises." An ordinary grass, to all appearance, you may pass it by a hundred times without suspecting anything, until it betrays itself by bearing some beautiful blue berries: hence the French name "Herbe aux Turquoises." These fruits dehisce before they are ripe, like those of Mignonette (*Reseda*). On examining the herb, you learn that it belongs somewhere near to the great Lily and Asparagus alliance. The grass-like foliage and open fruits are not the only peculiarities of this plant. The roots are like a string of beads (moniliform). I have seen the same structure in the root of a Bignonia. The filaments in the flower of Spider-wort (*Tradescantia*) are moniliform; every botanist has made use of these to observe the circulation in the protoplasm. Another very perfect necklace on a small scale is formed by the cells of Nostoc, a gelatinous Alga which appears on gravel walks after rain. There is a larger bead at intervals.

Gardeners out here use the Ophiopogon, as we do Thrift (*Armeria*), to form a border. A few years ago we had some tufts of it which a tame goose used to crop quite close. I could not get that unbotanical bird to understand that it was not a grass; and the result was that I never had the plant in flower.

Diospyrus kaki, common in the Nice gardens, will not fail to attract the attention of strangers. It is a small deciduous tree of the Ebenaceæ. Seen from a little distance, the kaki is not very unlike an orange tree, and the resemblance is increased by the large globular yellow fruits. These are sometimes sold as cheap as half a franc a dozen. Notice the persistent tetramerous calyx. Another Diospyrus, the Persimmon, is less common here. This is a taller tree, with much smaller fruits. "The longest pole knocks the Persimmon."

The last plant mentioned in the Bible (Rev. xviii. 12) shall also be the last of this chapter. John's "Thyine wood" is thought to be that of *Callitris quadrivalvis*, an Algerian conifer allied to the cypress. Solomon's

"Almug" may possibly be the same. The famous gum sandarach, worth its weight in gold, is the product of this tree. The hard dark fragrant wood was highly valued. "It is stated that Cicero had a table made of it that cost £9,000." I first saw the Callitris in Colonel Evans's garden on the Cimiez hill.

CONE OF CALLITRIS QUADRIVALVIS

27

Wayside Weeds

NOT all of our Northern weeds are able to endure the Summer on the Riviera. But we recognise most of the grasses. The Shepherd's Purse (*Capsella*) also defies the heat and drought. Plantain (*Plantago*), again, and Nettle, with the Dock (*Rumex*), its antidote; Milfoil and Clover, and the vulgar tribe of Hawkweeds (*Hieracium*); the tough *Sisymbrium* with its appressed pods; these and some others appear to be fire-proof, as they are indifferent to frost and snow. The humble Knot-Grass (*Polygonum aviculare*), though spread over the habitable world, objects to spend the Summer in Nice (sensible plant), for I presume the Winter is not too much for its constitution. *P. aviculare* is represented by a perennial species which Ardoino calls *P. Romanum*.

FLOWER OF ARISARUM

The Daisy (*Bellis*) is as common here as in the North, but the Dandelion (*Taraxacum*) does not seem quite at home. Its place is occupied to a great extent by the *Urosperm.* This Composite is of a much less glaring tint; the dark brown centre relieves the monotony of the yellow; the same rich colour is repeated in the border of each floret; and the neatly fitting involucre adds to the effect. The pappus, while yet unripe, is not unlike a paint-brush. By the suppression of two or three internodes a whorl of leaves is often formed on the axis. This plant is interesting as showing the transition to the opposite leaves which appear in many Composites.

In April and May *Lepidium Draba* forms white-topped forests by the wayside everywhere. This Crucifer appears now and then on our south coast. A yellow-flowered plant of the same order, *Diplotaxis tenuifolia* D. C. (*Sisymbrium L. Brassica* Boiss.), *Riquetta* the natives call it, is even commoner, though it does not cover large patches of ground like that last mentioned. The leaf is very pungent; it is used to flavour salad. I should think that a little would suffice. This weed patiently endures any extremities of drought, and flowers almost the whole year round.

Mr. C. Bicknell informs me that in Italy the popular name Richetta is applied to *Eruca sativa* Lamk.

Of the Pinks (Caryophylls) perhaps the most widespread is the delicate little *Gypsophila* (or Tunica). It can thrive more than 3,000 feet above the sea. I must apologize for including this charming Caryophyll among Wayside Weeds; I did not intend it for an insult, as the Irishman said when he called Mr. Balfour a perjured villain. This same Gypsophila decorates the ruins and the tombs of Rome. The red and green carpet of *Saponaria ocymoides* is not so common, for it requires a little moisture. But the Italian Catch-fly *Silene Italica* may be found on every bank, with its sticky stem and withered white flowers. The petals of this *Silene* are always shrivelled up. You would suppose that the plant were about to perish: but just at sunset, when the invalid goes indoors if he values his life, the folded petals straighten out, and a five-rayed star displays itself. If you ask why this Catch-fly closes in the day, the answer is that a man does not wave his umbrella unless he wants a cab. The plant is not fertilised by bees and butterflies that flutter in the sunshine, but by night-flying insects; as soon as these are on the wing the *Silene* spreads its corolla to attract them.

The wild *Verbena* springs up on the garden path, and in spite of your utmost vigilance the gardener destroys the sacred herb. A neglected flower-bed is soon grown over by the *Heliotrope*, a greyish annual, which has neither the colour nor the perfume of the cultivated plant. A still more disappointing plant is the *Amaranth*, which grovels in the gutter. How does it happen that this ignoble weed has appropriated the classic name? Can this be the flower which Pliny recommends for making wreaths and garlands, the unfading Amaranth, praised by poets, sung by bards? It has been suggested that the real Amaranth is *Helichrysum orientale*, Tournef, still extensively cultivated in Provence for making funeral wreaths. This is the flower which we call "everlasting," French

"Immortelle." The wild plant, *H. Stœchas* D. C., from which this is supposed to be derived, is almost common enough on the Riviera to be called a Wayside Weed. The flowers are of a brilliant yellow, and this little Everlasting deserves its Greek name, which interpreted means "Sun Gold." It owes its attraction to the petaloid scarious phyllaries: the leaf is linear, white beneath, with the edges rolled back. The Italian, with an infelicitous appropriateness, applies to these plants the name "mortorie."

A downright Weed, a regular "Unkraut," as the Germans say, with the full force of the pejorative prefix, is the curious *Arisarum vulgare*. On the red soil of the Mt. Vinaigrier it grows so thickly in some places that you might suppose it to be a most abundant crop of some carefully cultivated vegetable. The natives call this Arum a "little lamp." To see the resemblance, you should turn the livid spathe on its back, then the curved spadix represents the wick. Arisarum has been likened, still more appropriately, to a cobra with hood erect. It must be almost impossible to eradicate this weed; for when the spade cuts through a corm, it only makes two plants of one.

Some people object to the odour of the Garlic (*Allium*), but there is no one who does not admire the pretty white umbels of *A. Neapolitanum*. It resembles our British *A. Ursinum*, but is not so strong-smelling. Great quantities of these flowers are sent from Mentone to London and Paris, where they are in great demand about Easter time.[24] It is said that people who reek of garlic do not take cholera. This pachydermatous microbe, which laughs at our most potent drugs, potions, and specifics, cannot endure the smell of garlic. There might be a gleam of hope for suffering humanity if this principle could only be carried out: Discover the particular perfume for which a given microbe has the greatest repugnance, and cultivate a taste for it. Then, instead of nostrums we shall have nosegays, and for serious cases strong scents will be prescribed. Thus for cholera garlic; for the spirillum of gout, asafœtida; for still more pestilent bacteria, still stronger odours will be indicated.

Many of the Riviera Wayside Weeds are less striking than those already mentioned, but not less interesting. *Oxalis corniculata*, though but a lowly herb, would almost be called a "flower" in our own country, where it is at home on the south coast. There are plants of the same genus very common in gardens here, and so often met with in the open country that I suppose they must be pretty well established. The flowers are white or red or yellow, and showy enough to be above the rank of Weeds. One species, I think it is *O. cernua*, has eatable tubers. This Oxalis is cultivated to a certain extent on the Riviera; I have seen patches of it here and there; and the tubers are for sale

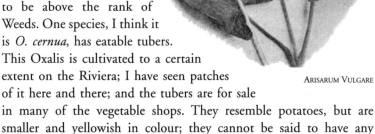

ARISARUM VULGARE

in many of the vegetable shops. They resemble potatoes, but are smaller and yellowish in colour; they cannot be said to have any particular flavour.

Mr. Bicknell ("Flora of Bordighera") confirms my statement that *O. cernua* is naturalised here. It is commonly met with (he says) under olives and lemons along the Riviera, and is well established in various places near Bordighera and Ventimiglia, in Val Borghetto, and above Ospedaletti on the road to Coldirodi. The same author quotes Professor Henslow to the effect that this is a remarkable instance of a plant having undergone a complete change of season in flowering. *O. cernua* is a native of the Cape of Good Hope, and flowers in the Winter, *i.e.* July: but throughout the whole of the Mediterranean border, where it has been dispersed since 1806, it blossoms from November to April.

Oxford Ivy (*Linaria Cymballaria*) is not included by Ardoino in the Flora of the Riviera, but it grows near Nice in places where no one could have planted it. If herbs of this sort spread upwards on a wall, as they often do, I believe that the seeds are carried by ants. It is well known that this Linaria is able to thrust its seed-cases into a chink of the wall; but this does not altogether explain the phenomenon.

When the English botanist has examined the more conspicuous of the Wayside Weeds, he will find that many a small plant has escaped his attention. For instance, it is easy to overlook such an unpretending flower as the *Campanula Erinus*.

I will conclude this chapter with an anecdote *à propos* of the so-called *Hemp Nettle*, a Wayside Weed which is commoner here than at home. I once won a wager over this Labiate. It was on this wise: Some forty or fifty of us were enjoying a holiday in Derbyshire. It was a Natural History excursion. Most of the people were intent upon rocks and fossils, faults and anticlinals; but there were a few plant hunters among the party. Mrs. G., in particular, was an accomplished field-botanist; she was a schoolmistress, and a neighbour of mine. Some of the excursionists were bringing flowers to this lady to learn the names. I said to a geologist walking beside me, "Mrs. G. knows the British flora well; I believe that she could name any plant with her eyes shut"—a rash statement. The fossil-collector offered to wager his geological hammer against my vasculum that she could not do it. I recklessly accepted the challenge. Mrs. G. was unwilling to make the attempt; she did not think it possible to name a plant without seeing it. But we persuaded her to try.

While her husband was tying a handkerchief over her eyes, the other man went to the roadside to select his plant. The odds seemed very heavy against me, so I said to Mrs. G. in German (too many people know French): "If you can't make the plant out, call any Latin name you like, and I'll swear that it's correct: the man knows nothing about Botany." Mrs. G. was shocked, as a lady ought to be, at this unscrupulous suggestion. "Ich hatte eine bessere Meinung von Ihnen,

VASCULUM AND HAMMER

Herr Professor!" she answered reproachfully. "Surely," I said, "a gentleman may perjure himself to save a lady's botanical reputation." "And his own vasculum!" she rejoined.

Meanwhile the geologist had picked his plant. When I saw what he was bringing, I knew that my vasculum was safe; opposite leaves, square stem, swollen nodes, spinous calyx: Mrs. G. will never miss those tangible characters. And so it was; as soon as her fingers touched the plant, she said, "Galeopsis Tetrahit!" The members of the Natural History Society were surprised and delighted; but Mr. G. took it as a matter of course, for he regarded his wife as a sort of sorceress who could perform almost any miracle. If she had taken her shadow off the ground and proceeded to fold it up, he would simply have felt in his pocket for a piece of string to tie round the parcel. As for that geological hammer, is it not used in our house for breaking coal, even unto this day?

Notes:

[23]   In England the flower is passed off as a Star of Bethlehem.—T. H.

MORICANDIA ARVENSIS

28

The
Judgment of
Paris—I

"Judicium Paridis."

THERE was held in Nice, a few years ago, a "Concours de Beauté." Ladies from different parts of Europe submitted themselves to be stared at, and prizes were awarded to those Professional Beauties who obtained most votes. The thing was hardly in good taste, not to say anything stronger about it.

Let us institute a "Concours de Beauté" in which the competitors shall be, for the most part, natives of the Riviera: a competition where the winners will show no arrogance, and the losers feel no disappointment; a contest which shall cause no scandal and give rise to no offence. We shall pass in review the Beauties of Bank and Brae, of Hedgerow and Hill-side, of Mountain and Meadow, and award the prizes without prejudice. I propose to take the different families in their natural order; or, rather, in the order given by the Floras, which, as every botanist knows, is not strictly natural.

The Buttercups (*Ranunculus*) are the first to present themselves; but we shall dismiss the brazen Beauties at once. They stand no chance against their cousins, the Hellebores. *Trollius*, in spite of her rustic embonpoint, is a handsome flower. This and the charming Columbine (*Aquilegia*) are abundant in the Maritime Alps. But there can be no doubt that in this family the prize must be awarded to the Peony. This flower may be almost said to rival the Rose. The Queen of flowers has perfume, it is true, but there exists a perfumed Peony. You may find the wild Peony in many places near the coast. It grows at Thorenc, and at Caussols, above Grasse, and on the Mt. Baudon, just behind Mentone. But there is a spot, within a drive of Nice, where the Peony is so abundant that it covers the hill-side. When these plants are in flower in early May the effect is magical; the Riviera has no finer sight to offer. The locality is above Vence, on the road to Coursegoules, but a long way on this side of that mountain village which hangs on the flanks of Mt. Cheiron.

It is likely that before many years are out the Peony and many other conspicuous wild flowers will disappear from these uplands. The gardeners from the coast ascend with carts during the Summer, and carry them away in quantities, for they have, unfortunately, a marketable value.

If the town of Nice were in want of a symbol, surely the Peony should be selected, for this plant is dedicated to Apollo Paion, hence its name. "Phœbus the Healer" is, or ought to be, the patron deity of Nice.

One other plant allied to the Buttercup deserves an honourable mention: the *Athragene*, a climber of the Clematis sub-order, with large drooping lavender-coloured blossoms. We do not often see the flowers, for they come out early in the Spring, before we have migrated to the mountain region where they live. Once or twice I have been in time to find a few remaining.

Not far from the Buttercup family comes the *Magnolia*, a Transatlantic Beauty. The flower is not amiss, only there is too much of it. Like all else American it relies on bigness; but beauty and bigness do not coincide. We may admire a giantess in a platonic sort of way; Minerva may be as tall as you please; but Venus does not stand higher than a man's shoulder. With this compliment we will permit the Magnolia to return to the banks of the Susquehanna. The most interesting thing about the tree is the suspended scarlet seed.

The Crucifers are not among the showiest flowers, yet the rich colour of the *Moricandia arvensis* would be hard to match. This rare plant adorns the sea rocks west of Monaco, and the cliffs at Ventimiglia.

It is one of the most highly organized members of the Cress family, adapted to fertilization by long-tongued insects. The petals are brought closely together, so as to imitate the narrow tube of a sympetalous corolla. A similar structure is figured by Kerner in the flower of *Matthiola varia.*

One of the prettiest of the Pink family is *Silene quinque-vulnera,* or "Five wounds"; so called from the spot of red on each petal. This Silene is an annual. I have found it as far north as Berthemont.

If we except the Cistus, there are no families of striking beauty until we reach the Mallows. I think the honours are divided between the lovely *Lavatera maritima* and the rare *Lavatera trimestris.* The former plant lives on the sea rocks between Nice and Mentone. It does not seem to be found at Cannes, but it grows as far inland as Le Bar. I transplanted one into my garden, and it succeeded perfectly. The *Trimestris* has very large pink flowers. I have had the luck to find this great rarity on more than one occasion. The plant may be easily known by the enlarged disc which covers the carpels.

The shrubby *Polygalas* are among the commonest Riviera garden plants. They are considered fairly well able to resist the Summer drought. But I have noticed that they are the first shrubs to perish in a neglected garden.

In the *Flax* family I must award the palm (Fenians forgive me!) to an orange-flowered woody species, *Linum trigynum,* which is fairly common in gardens. It is botanically interesting because it has three instead of five styles.

Of the Geraniums and Pelargoniums, wild or cultivated, I personally prefer the little *G. sanguineum,* which you may find in most shady places a short distance from the coast. But I do not pretend that this flower deserves the prize of beauty; it is a case of sheer favouritism. By the way, could anything be more inappropriate, more ill-chosen, more objectionable than the specific name of this amiable and delicate little plant?

We pass on to the Pea Flower Tribe. The Riviera has four times as many species of Leguminous plants as Great Britain possesses. Among the small herbaceous flowers, surely the *Coronilla varia* is most, if not the most, attractive. In the mountains it abounds, but on the coast it is not common. Nevertheless, I find a few specimens every year in the outskirts of Nice. *C. varia* is so conspicuous that you cannot easily pass it by.

Among the woody Leguminosæ, the choice is difficult. The claimants are so numerous that one is at a loss: the *Wistaria*, with its lilac festoons, the *Robinia* with its mass of white, the great golden Broom (*Spartium*), *Cassia*, with its scarcely bilateral flowers, and small rounded pods, common in gardens. These and others can hardly be denied. But my choice shall fall upon a small South American tree, the *Erythrina*. An interesting species, though the natives seem to despise it, I suppose because the great red flowers are not produced in the middle of the Winter season. Some of the gardeners' books do not even mention the Erythrina. The flowers are said to be ornithophilous (fertilized by birds), but they must be more or less independent, for I have found fruits now and then. The trunk is light and spongy, the leaf not unlike that of a Laburnum, but with armed petiole. Branches covered with flowers are often sold in the market for a few sous.

It is said that the Erythrina may be taken out of the ground, just as you would the bulb of a hyacinth, and kept during the Winter in a dry place. Acting on this information, I once tried to pull up one of these small trees. Be not too censorious! It was growing on some waste ground, and there were other extenuating circumstances. However, it held too tight.

The *Rose* may be considered as "hors concours." In the allied Apple family I give all my votes in favour of the Quince (*Cydonia*). And if fruit trees are allowed to count, the *Peach* may stand as champion of the Almond tribe without much fear of defeat. But from an ornamental point of view the Peach is almost too abundant in some districts of the Riviera; the mass of red is quite oppressive to the eye. At Hyères, for instance, it is said that the Peach tree is supplanting the Orange. The *Spireas* are represented by a small white-flowered shrub without which no garden in these parts is complete. The popular name is "Italian May." If there were a prize for producing the greatest possible number of blossoms, we might award it to this praiseworthy little plant.

In the Saxifrage family, the Maritime Alps possess a plant of great beauty and rarity, the famous *S. Florulenta*. It was discovered by an

Englishman on the verge of the perpetual snow near the highest crests of the mountains. As no further specimen was found by any one after this for a space of thirty-six years, the Florulenta began to be regarded as a mythical plant. But at last the Abbé Montolivo, enthusiastic botanist of Beaulieu, and other native explorers, confirmed the Englishman's discovery; and the plant is now constantly brought in by the chamois-hunters, who sell it for half-a-franc. When you are fortunate enough to find a rare plant of which few specimens exist, it is better not to inform the general public of the exact locality, for the less people know about botany, the more anxious they will be to tear it up, if it be in the least degree ornamental.

If guides and shepherds once find that a plant is worth sixpence, they will make havoc of the species. But the Florulenta is safe from extermination, growing, as it often does, on rocks which are inaccessible to human foot. This rare Saxifrage has a peculiarity which is not mentioned in any botanical work which I possess, viz.: that the terminal flower of each inflorescence has five instead of two carpels.

CASSIA

JACARANDA MIMOSÆFOLIA

29

The Judgment of Paris—II

*"Flowers,
My earliest visitation and my last."*
MILTON

IN the last chapter I commenced to pass in review the Natural Orders represented on the Riviera, and to inquire which is the most ornamental plant in each. I now return to Mount Ida and resume the task. The *Epilobes*, which have conspicuous flowers, grow, for the most part, in torrent beds and on stone-slides. *E. angustifolium* (*E. spicatum*), a garden plant in England, is found in the Fenestra valley, with two other species of almost equal beauty. The Fuchsia is much less common in the Nice gardens than one might expect. I suppose the air is too dry. Many persons think that the irrigation of the Nice valley by the water of the recently constructed Vesubia canal has increased the amount of moisture in the air: and it may be expected that, as this water is more extensively used, a still greater change of climate will result. In this case certain plants and insects may be able to maintain themselves, which at present thrive only in the damper air of Cannes.

This Vesubia canal is a wonderful work. It starts from the torrent at St. Jean la Rivière, close to a narrow gorge, which is strongly fortified. Here the road branches to the Sanctuary of Utelle. This picturesque spot is now easily accessible from Nice since the Ciaudan has been pierced and the Vesubia valley can be entered from the Var.

Astrantia is the pride of the Umbellates, and as abundant in the hill district as it is handsome. *Benthamia* has no rivals in the Cornel family. The fruit of this rare garden shrub is not unlike a strawberry in outward appearance. The *Scabious* which I prefer is a salmon-coloured species abounding in the stony cornfields at Caussols, above St. Vallier.

Now for the Composites. The Thistleheads have a gigantic champion, the Artichoke (*Cynara Scolymus*), cultivated here, not for the beauty of its great blue flower heads, but for the succulent bracts of the involucre.

Among the Corymbifers I am partial to the Milfoils (*Achillea*), of which a very pretty yellow species grows above St. Vallier (*A. Tomentosa*), and another (*A. Ageratum*) on the coast west of Vence Cagnes.

But taking the white foliage into consideration, *Cineraria maritima* may be accounted more ornamental. The honey of this species must be very plentiful, for I have seen as many as fifty bees on one plant at a time. This is the "Pardon Plant" of St. Honorat. Notwithstanding the specific name, this Cineraria may be found at some distance from the sea. I have not been able to ascertain why it is called "Pardon Plant."[24]

If we must have a flaring yellow Composite, you cannot well improve upon *Bupthalmum*. I moderately admire the plant, ugly as it is; but I cannot exactly say what redeeming point it has. As in the case of a person who is more or less attractive in spite of a tip-tilted nose and bright red hair, we are constrained to exclaim, "Quelle jolie laide!"

Of the Ligulates, next after the delicate Catananche already praised, I would place either Chicory (*C. Intybus*) or a Tragopogon with a dark violet flowerhead: I think it is Ardoino's *T. australis*. This grows on the Levens common together with a yellow species; and in the same spot there is a curious plant with yellow disc and purple ray, probably a cross between the two.

The showy Gentians are mountaineers; mostly the same as those found in Switzerland, so that I need not describe them. The commonest, and perhaps the prettiest Convolvulus is *C. Althæoides*. Its later leaves, deeply cut with narrow segments, differ so much from the earlier ones that you will hardly recognise the plant when it has grown a little. I admire also in this family a beautiful blue-flowered species (*Ipomœa Learii*) which overruns some of the gardens in Alassio. Let us add the cultivated shrubby C. *Cneorum* with white flowers and silvery leaves. Our British *C. Sepium*, though eclipsed by the bright colours of these Southern flowers is nevertheless "very decorative," as they say in French; especially when you see it wreathing the dry stem of an Arundo, and supplying just that variety of outline and of colour which is wanting to these giant reeds. The common Ipomœa, were it not an annual, would be preferred to all other climbers of its family; but it is troublesome in a garden, for it may fail where you wish it to grow, and sowing itself elsewhere may completely smother some valuable shrub.

Cerinthe (why called "Honey-wort?") is the most beautiful of the Borages; this flower is confined to two or three localities near Nice. A proxime accessit may be awarded to the deep blue Lithosperm (*L. purpureo-cæruleum*), a plant easily confounded with the equally common Alkanet. It grows wild in England below the overhanging cliffs near Mary Church, Devonshire, and in a few other spots.

Lungwort (*Pulmonaria*), with its red and blue flowers and spotted leaf, will reward any one who takes the trouble to place it in a shady corner of his garden. Latin authors call the Myrtle "bicolor": why so? There are plants such as Pulmonaria, Melampyre, and Latania, to which the epithet were more appropriate.

Among exotic Borages the shrubby *Echiums* will surprise and delight the English botanist.

The most remarkable garden shrub of the Solanum family is the

Trumpet Tree (*Datura arborea*) with great white pendulous blossoms. It is not perfectly hardy. *Paulownia* would be more missed from the Riviera gardens than any other species of the Figwort (*Scrophularia*) order. A flowering tree is in some degree the property of the public. The owner cannot keep it entirely to himself; however high the wall, we catch a glimpse of it. Not very many plants of this family are cultivated here, in the south of Europe. I calculate that, even including the shrubby Veronicas, not more than one per cent of the garden plants belongs to the Scrophs. Our Northern Foxglove (*Digitalis purpurea*) is replaced by *D. lutea*, a much less ornamental plant, with small yellowish flowers. Another flowering tree, the *Jacaranda*, may represent the Bignonias. Most people, if they see only the leaf, will take it for that of an Acacia. The tongue-shaped fruit is curious.

Your favourite Labiate? The question is not easy to answer, for this is the home and focus of the family, and they abound. Nevertheless, I give the preference to a British plant, for there are few more graceful wild flowers than *Melittis*. It flourishes a few miles inland in cool and shady spots, and is partial to hazel copses. I think that I have found it as near the coast as the ruins of St. Martin, about a quarter of an hour's walk above the town of Vence. This is, by the way, an excellent place for a picnic. I call Melittis a British plant because it grows in certain localities in the south and south-west of England: but it is probable that many British botanists have never seen the plant. Do not confound it with the perfumed Melissa, which it resembles only in name.

One admires the shrubby Teucrium which we have in almost all the gardens here. But its beauty lies rather in the silver-grey lining of its matted foliage than in its roofless bluish flowers. For these are somewhat too utilitarian, the lower lip, being found useful as a perching place for bees, is abnormally developed, while the upper lip is altogether suppressed.

The Wall Germander (*Teucrium Chamædrys*) is so common that one almost forgets how pretty it is. Here we have one of those sensible little herbs that face all their flowers one way, so that you may have a better view of them. I suppose the Wall Germander thinks that there is no harm in making the best of himself; so long as he does not become too obtrusive. This again is boldly claimed by Bentham as a British plant.

Other authorities admit that it is a garden escape. But it is certain that this Teucrium can live in England, and for this reason it should be commoner in our gardens. Hooker calls *T. Chamædrys* "a famous old gout medicine." M. John Briquet has published in Geneva a work on the Labiates of the Maritime Alps.

The cultivated *Salvias* are of every shade: white, purple, blue, rose pink, and fiery red.[25] *S. glutinosa* of the mountain region is an exception to Grant Allen's rule that yellow is not the colour of highly organised flowers. The yellow of this handsome Salvia is not, however, the buttercup yellow, but a more delicate tint. No flower of this genus is better adapted to show the abnormally developed connective and the swivel arrangement of the anthers with which the bee plays his game of quintain.

Passing to the Endogens, the Orchids are the first that attract attention by their beauty: and among them *Serapias* takes the lead. It is worth a journey to the Esterel to see the splendid *S. cordigera*. *Ophrys lutea* is not difficult to find at Cap St. Hospice and at Mentone. It may be described as a Bee Ophrys with a yellow border to the labellum.

The sweet little *Spiranthes* with twisted axis is common on the outskirts of Nice.

Limodorum (*Orchis abortiva* L.), leafless, livid, bluish, is more conspicuous though less attractive. This also is fairly common here.

In the chapter on the Vallon des Fleurs I have mentioned the grand *Barlia longibracteata*. We have found the rare *Orchis papilionacea* (*O. rubra*), the Butterfly Orchis, in flower on Cap Ferrat on May 15th. Moggridge considers that the resemblance of this lovely flower to Serapias is for the most part only superficial. I have never seen either the spotted leaf or the beautiful pale yellow flowers of *Orchis provincialis*. Although this species is rare near Nice, it is given by Mr. Bicknell as very abundant under the chestnuts in certain districts of the Italian Riviera. One little gem I am fain to include among the fairest of the Orchid tribe, though it is a long cry from the coast to the grassy slopes (pelouses) of the Colmiane above St. Martin Vesubia, where we so often lingered to admire it. I mean that bit of sunset on a stalk, the *Nigritella*.

The most remarkable Iris is *I. tuberosa* (*Hermodactylus*): the flower is almost black. Early in March it is sold in the Nice market. The peasants say that they bring it from the Var, but they are either unable or unwilling to give the exact locality. This rare plant has been found in the Magnan Valley, but I doubt if it exists there now. There is a third locality near Grasse, which has lately been searched in vain. *Crocus versicolor* may be found on the Mt. Vinaigrier towards the end of January.

I will not presume to say which *Narcissus* is the most beautiful. The yellow and white *N. Tazzetta* abounds in the low-lying meadows all along the coast. *N. poeticus* is so plentiful at Levens, and on the peaty grassland above Grasse, that it forms white patches when in bloom which may be seen from afar. Fortunately for this latter plant, it has but a small commercial value, so it is not removed in quantities by the gardeners and florists. It does not flower early enough in the Spring to command a good sale; this is the reason why it escapes persecution. The Poeticus is said to avoid a calcareous soil. Two beautiful species, *N. aureus* and *N. papyraceus* (*niveus*), are found quite close to Nice, but, as they are rare, I will only add that they do not grow due south of the town.

The Riviera boasts twelve or fourteen species of Narcissus, including one which is called after Cavaliere F. Panizzi, a botanist of San Remo.

Pancratium is praised by those who have seen its white flowers on the sea-shore between Bordighera and Ventimiglia.

Three *Lilies* grace the hill-sides at some little distance from the coast: these are *L. bulbiferum* (the Orange lily), *L. pomponium,* and *L. Martagon.* The first is the most striking, and in certain places by far the most abundant. The peasants bring in great double handfuls of them. I have observed that in this species a large proportion of the flowers are staminate with rudimentary carpels: this fact is not recorded in Müller's work on the fertilization of flowers.

Of the wild *Tulips* I have seen three: *T. præcox,* which abounds all round Nice, and particularly at Cimiez; *T. Clusiana* less common here; and *T. australis* which we have gathered above Vence, and again farther inland at an elevation of 7,000 feet.

The Rose Garlic (*Allium roseum*) is one of the prettiest and commonest among the twenty native species. Bulbils are formed in the umbel: these fall and take root. The genus *Ornithogalum* boasts *O. Arabicum:* perianth white, carpels a glossy black-green, buds a rich cream colour. When I found this magnificent plant on the Pessicard hill, near Nice, I supposed it to be a garden escape; for even in this land of flowers one is surprised to find a wild flower of such striking beauty. The Star of Bethlehem is also cultivated. In mid-May we have bought a large bunch for a couple of sous. It would be in great demand if it flowered before the strangers leave the Riviera.

The lily-like Phalangium (*Anthericum liliago L.*) is as beautiful as it is common, though its pure white blossoms can hardly be compared with those of the Star of Bethlehem just mentioned.

Notes:

[24] The juice of *Cineraria maritima* has been used in London hospitals as a remedy for ophthalmia.—T. H.

[25] The flowers of *S. albo-cærula* have a marked scent of pineapple. *S. gesneræflora* is very striking: flowers scarlet. *S. Sessei*, the tallest of the genus, has involucrate flowers of a spendid red. The beautiful blue *S. patens*, common in English gardens, does not thrive on the Riviera.—T. H.

30

Rare and Local Plants

VITEX Agnus Castus is a shrub with graceful palmate leaf and clusters (verticels) of violet flowers. It grows here and there on waste ground along the coast, and, being deciduous, is easily overlooked in Winter; but in the Summer no botanist would be likely to pass it by.

Vitex was recorded from Cap Martin as late as 1863. I do not know whether the plant is still to be seen in that locality, but it has disappeared from the neighbourhood of Nice. It used to grow in the Magnan valley, but this torrent bed has been explored of late years from source to sea by Mr. H. Bourdillon without finding any trace of it. This enthusiastic and most athletic botanist is, in spite of his name, an Englishman.

Many years ago I found this remarkable palmate-leaved shrub in a wild place between the road and the sea near the right or west bank of the River Loup; but I could make nothing of it, for it was not in flower. Perhaps it may still be found in that spot. At any rate there is a place on the same part of the coast where it does certainly still grow in considerable quantity. At Vaugrenier, between Antibes and Cagnes, where the high road and the rail both run close to the sea, the Vitex forms a kind of hedge by the roadside. There is a swamp just here. This locality is not mentioned in the books, but three others are given: Antibes, Chateauneuf, and Foux de Mouans between Grasse and Cannes.

The fragrance of this shrub is alluded to in Plato's Phædrus. The leaves, dried and powdered, are credited with the same virtue which gives its name to the genus Artemisia. Hence the epithet "castus."

Vitex Agnus Castus has but one relative in Europe, or at any rate in this part of Europe, namely, the wild *Verbena*, a plant accounted sacred from the earliest times. We cultivate several plants of the same order: for instance, the Scented Verbena (*Aloysia triphylla*), which becomes almost

Serapias Cordigera

a tree in this climate; and the *Clerodendron*, a small Japanese shrub fairly common in Nice. But the most striking species of the Verbena family grown in the gardens here belong to the genus *Lantana*. These are climbing, or rather trailing, shrubs, with wrinkled leaves and many-coloured flowers, which change their tint as the flowering advances. Lantana has a peculiar smell.

The Stemless Cudweed (*Evax*), or as Linnæus called it, the Pygmy Filago, is a plant which I have found in one spot only, though I do not say that it is rare. This Composite forms little rosettes on the bare ground at Antibes, between the railway station and the fortifications. It is easy to identify.

When I lived at Cimiez I used to see upon the ruins an exquisite little Primulaceous plant, *Asterolinum stellatum* (*Lysimachia linum-stellatum* Linn.), an annual like the last. This minute herb may or may not be counted rare, but you can search a good many places without finding it. The full beauty of the little gem is not apparent without a magnifying glass, for it is frosted over with small stars which the naked eye can scarcely see. Asterolinum is (inadequately) figured by Gillet et Magne. But, neither in this Flora, nor in any other that I possess, are the little stars mentioned. Nevertheless the specific name proves that they did not escape the attention of the great Swedish savant.

While I am writing of Cimiez, I will mention a plant which appeared in my garden there, and which may be truly considered rare. I have, in fact, marked it with a capital R: *Crozophora tinctoria* (Croton Linn.), an annual plant of the Euphorbias, which a botanist will easily recognise by the fruit. It is almost useless to search for a plant of this sort, for you can never tell where it may turn up. Crozophora has a greyish tinge, and the leaf is furnished with two glands.

In the pebbly torrent bed of the Magnan, and also in that of the little stream which issues from the Vallon Obscur, Nice, I have found the *Acanthus* more than once. It seems likely to become established on the Riviera. In gardens it is common enough. *Acanthus mollis* is the plant in which Goethe first observed the dissemination of seeds by projection. The rivers of this coast are stony, like the Arcadian Crathis, but, unlike that classic stream, they are not full of fish. Though the angler may be disappointed with these streams, they are for the Botanist an admirable hunting ground. Here we find many a plant which cannot exist upon the sun-baked hills; here also we may often gather mountain species, such as the *Saponaria officinalis*, whose seeds have been carried down to the warmer coast region.

The Greeks called a violent, headstrong torrent of this sort a "scraper," "Kharadra"; and rightly, for it lays bare more ground than it can occupy. "Kharacter," or as we spell it "Character," is the same word; for it is the mark which the will has scratched or engraved upon the plastic elements which it controls. The Romance word, "Torrent," allied to "torrid," implies that the ground is burnt bare, as it were. Any one who looks down upon the Paillon or the Var from the hills near Nice, will appreciate the force of these two words.

M. Burnat says, "Dans les Alpes Maritimes on trouve à quelques pas de la mer certaines espèces montagneuses: par exemple, *Primula grandiflora, Betonica hirsuta, Cerinthe minor, Erinus alpinus, Anemone Hepatica*, etc." He mentions also a few Alpine plants which descend into the Olive region, below 800 metres. The nearer the snowy summits, or in other words the more abrupt the slope, the greater the number of Alpine species which invade the lower regions. Thus the Rhododendron actually reaches down to the level of the Lago Maggiore.

I shall now mention an extremely rare plant which my daughter was fortunate enough to find on the southern slope of the Mt. Vinaigrier: *Vaillantia Hispida.*

It is a small annual of the Stellate Order (Rubiaceæ), allied to the Galium. The leaves are in whorls of four; the fruit has three tips, and is covered with white hair. It was on April 28th, 1890, that we found this treasure. It is now in the possession of Mrs. Harrington Balfour, who has kindly lent it to me to refresh my memory. As this is the only locality on the Riviera where the plant occurs, and it is so scarce that in many years botanists are unable to find even a single specimen, I will describe the spot. If non-botanical people were likely to take advantage of the information, I would be careful not to give particulars of the locality; but this Stellate is so small that even a botanist may easily overlook it, and so inconspicuous that it is not likely to be persecuted by the general public. If you miss the Vaillantia, you will be compensated by one of the finest views in Europe; a view which, once impressed upon the memory, can never be effaced. The panorama embraces the land-locked harbour of Villefranche and St. Jean, reaching out into the sea; then the Nice valley, and the long line of coast extending to Antibes; beyond this, the Islands, the Esterels, and the more distant mountains of the Moors. As you turn towards the west and north the view is bounded by the snow-clad Cheiron and the confused masses of the Alps.

Ascend the old Villefranche road until you reach the Col. Here the road to the right (the Route Forestière) runs along the Mt. Alban and the Mt. Boron, whereas the turn to the left leads by a rocky path past a kind of reservoir up to the higher coast road, which it joins at a spot called the Quatre Chemins. Near the top of this rocky path the Vaillantia was found.

Linaria Pelliseri, a rare annual, bears the name of Bishop Pelliser, of Montpelier, who was put to death for his adherence to the reformed religion. This martyr of progress is mentioned by Kingsley in his essay on Rondelet. Let this humble Linaria be counted ever among the number of the sacred plants!

There is no corner of the Riviera but has some special flower or shrub. On the sea cliffs there hangs a very pretty little tree, *Anthyllis Barba Jovis*. The silvery pinnate foliage is covered with down; the flowers are pale yellow. This Anthyllis is planted in many of the gardens here. There are half-a-dozen specimens by the little footpath which runs along the eastern side of the Promontory of St. Jean from the village of St. Jean towards the mainland. The cliffs here, though it would not be pleasant to fall over, are not steep enough to protect the plant against any one who is determined to carry it away. At Monaco, where the precipice is steeper, the Anthyllis has a safer refuge. I think that I have seen this shrub in the Esterels, close to the station of Trayas. Our British *Anthyllis vulneraria* is not common on this coast, but I used to find *A. tetraphylla* on the ground now covered by the new Cimiez boulevard.

Petite Afrique, between Beaulieu and Cap Roux, but nearer the Cape, has an Asphodel (*A. fistulosus*), easily known by the pink line on the flower, and the hollow sterns and leaves. It grows plentifully on the stony slope of the railway embankment within a few yards of the high road. I believe this beautiful plant to be extinct in Nice. The only specimens that I knew of in this district were destroyed in widening the new boulevard of Carabacel. I hope that botanists will be satisfied with admiring this Asphodel at Petite Afrique without uprooting it.

Leuzea conifera is a very curious composite, with a single cone-like capitulum. From the top of this protrudes an absurdly small tuft of purple florets. The leaves are whitish beneath. Altogether the plant has a singular appearance. I have found it in three places: on the limestone rocks by the "Two Brothers," near St. Martin Vesubia, some 4,000 feet above the sea; on the south slope of the Mount Chauve; lastly in the Vallon Obscur, Nice. It is rare in this last locality, and you cannot count on finding it there. So conspicuous a plant is easy to find in any place where there are even a few specimens.

LEUZEA CONIFERA

In this same valley I have gathered a Lythrum; not our British plant, Tennyson's "Long Purples," but a smaller species, *L. Grafferi.* Ardoino calls it "assez commun," but it is certainly rare in the Nice district. Before leaving the "Dark Valley," I will mention two more flowers worth notice: *Hypericum androsæmum* and *Samolus Valerandi,* the former of which cannot be called common.

Simethis bicolor is absent from the eastern Riviera, and for the western region Ardoino gives but one locality, Cap Croisette near Cannes. We found it in the Estérel, not far from Trayas station. Rare as is the Simethis out here, it is rarer still in Britain, where it is confined to a single spot about half-way between Bournemouth and Poole on the borders of Hants and Dorset. From the name of this locality it has been called the Branksome lily.

These are a very few of the Rare and Local plants which might be enumerated. I will conclude with the Nice Snowflake (*Leucoium Nicæense*). It is distinguished at once by the split spathe. This plant has a more limited geographical distribution than almost any other. Nevertheless, it is not absolutely confined, as Ardoino says, to the coast

VITEX AGNUS CASTUS

district between Nice and Mentone, for I have found it west of the Var. It is abundant on the Mont Vinaigrier, the Mont Alban, and the Mont Boron; in fact everywhere to the east of Nice down to the sea rocks. The Nice Snowflake is much persecuted, but I think that it is in no danger of extermination, for it grows in some places which are little frequented and are not mentioned in the books. It is supposed not to flower before the Equinox.

Professor Penzig ("Flora delle Alpi") gives the following list of plants peculiar to the Maritime Alps:—*Viola nummularifolia, Iberis garrexiana, Silene cordifolia, Dianthus neglectus, Trifolium balbisianum, Moehringia papulosa, M. dasyphylla, Saxifraga florulenta, S. cochlearis, S. lantoscana, S. lingulata, Primula Allionii, Plagius virgatus, Achillea herba-rota, Potentilla saxifraga, Senecio Persoonii, Micromeria piperella, Euphorbia canuti, Pinguicula leptoceras, Phyteuma balbisii, Campanula stenocodon, Asperula hexaphylla, Lilium pomponium, Fritillaria involucrata, Allium narcissiflorum,* &c.

Tribulus terrestris

31
Dry Fruits—I

IN a certain Grammar School, or rather Lycée, for it was in France, there was a very backward boy whose father dealt in Dry Fruits. When this boy was called a "duffer" by his comrades, he always answered, "I don't care, I'm clever enough for the Dry Fruit business." When his Latin verses would not scan, and his master explained to him that there was no hope in this world or the next for a boy who makes "false quantities," he thought within himself, "If it comes to the worst, I can fall back upon the Dry Fruit line." And finally, when he failed to pass his examination, and was compelled to go home without that precious little document which the British Passman calls a "Testamur," he exclaimed in the bitterness of his heart, "Tant pis, I shall have to deal in Dry Fruits!" I know not whether the term is still in vogue, but formerly "Fruit Sec" was said of a person who was not likely to set the Thames on fire.

Let us go, just for a few moments, into the Dry Fruit line. I do not mean those preserved peaches and candied apricots which we see at the confectioner's. The Dry Fruits I wish to call attention to are very different from these. They have never been imported or exported by any one. Stranger still, no one has ever bought or sold them, and probably no one ever will. Just think how few things there are in this world which you cannot either buy or sell. Another remarkable fact about these Dry Fruits is that no one, however hungry, would think of eating them.

The first specimen which I shall take is in the form of a Maltese Cross, or rather, Star: an ornamental little object which a jeweller might use as the model for a charm or a breloque. It grows upon a small prostrate plant, the Caltrop (*Tribulus terrestris*), a resident alien, so to speak, a forlorn and friendless herb, whose nearest relatives dwell within the tropics. Tribulus is sometimes called Beancaper, though it bears no resemblance either to a bean or a caper. I found this plant some years ago upon the stony roadside at the spot where the Promenade des Anglais, Nice, crosses the Magnan, as close as possible to the sea. For the knowledge of this locality I am indebted to Dr. E. Sauvaigo, Director of the Nice Library; an assiduous botanist, who is always ready to oblige strangers with information about the flora of the district.

On the place where this plant used to grow, a sea wall has been constructed, and a garden-bridge. If these improvements have caused the Caltrop to disappear, it will probably be found by the round tower a little farther on. The leaf is opposite, stipulate, and pinnate, without terminal leaflet; the flower, yellow.

I cannot believe that this inoffensive plant is identical with the classical "Tribulus" or Caltrop, which Virgil, in his first Georgic, enumerates among the worst plagues of agriculture: the mischievous Rust which discolours the blades of corn; the Thistle, sign of neglected ground; the rough growth of "Lappæ," perhaps the Burdock (*Arctium Lappa*), which disfigures the damp pastures with its great coarse leaves; the unfruitful Darnel (*Lolium*) and the barren Brome. Tribulus does not belong to the army of weeds which invade the cultivated ground: on the contrary, it is content to root among the pebbles of the beach, only just beyond the wash of the waves. Nor is it fair to liken the ornamental little seed-case to the formidable Caltrop, an instrument of war armed with great iron spikes, intended to impede the advance of cavalry. It has been suggested that Virgil's Tribulus may be the *Centaurea calcitrapa*. This

Composite is found on the Riviera a short distance inland, but it is not very common.

From "Tribulus" comes "Tribulation." But what has the little plant to do with sorrow and distress? The connection is not apparent at first sight. I think that it is thus: corn was threshed with an instrument resembling in form the fruit of the Caltrop, "Tribulus." Then the blows of adverse fortune came to be spoken of as "Tribulation," for they were compared to the heavy crushing strokes of the flail-like "Tribulus."

The various functions of the spines which cover many of these small Dry Fruits are not discussed in any botanical work with which I am acquainted. Of course, it is well known that these prickles or burrs or hooks may serve to spread the plant by catching in the wool or fur of some animal, the seed being thus carried to a distance. In the Mortola Gardens, near Mentone, you may see the *Martynia*, or Grapple-plant, with its extraordinary fruits. These are furnished with long curved grappling hooks, resembling the tusks of a mastodon.

But I think that the fruit prickles may serve other purposes than "getting a lift" from some passing quadruped. Why should they not act like the hairs on a caterpillar, and make the object an unpleasant morsel for a bird to swallow?

A stone-fruit like the cherry may take no harm by being swallowed; but in cases where the seeds have no hard covering they would be digested, and thus the plant would lose, in fact it would be slowly exterminated.

In the Riviera gardens a common shrub is the *Sparmannia*. The fruit resembles a sea-urchin, or a rolled up porcupine. It would go hard with a bird which got one of these fixed in its throat. The Sparmannia forms its fruit only in favourable seasons, and in a good situation. The brightly coloured stamens are sensitive, like those of the Barberry (*Berberis*) and some other plants. When the filaments are touched near the base they move inwards. Sparmannia is allied to the Linden (*Tilia*). Of course this little vegetable hedgehog may serve a double purpose: it may travel on the back of a sheep or a goat, and so disseminate the plant; and the prickles may also be defensive.

Under the Olive trees everywhere you may find a little Medic (*M. denticulata*), with spiral prickly pod. The so-called "Calvary Clover"

(*M. intertexta*) has a pod of the same sort but larger. Now a bird, however hungry, would hardly try to eat this little legume, even if it were not armed. The single minute seed, for I think that there is but one, would not be worth while. It follows that the spines are not defensive. Locomotive they probably are; but I think that they may also have a quite different function, namely, to prevent ants from dragging the pods down into their subterranean store-houses. I have seen the insects attempting to pull in these prickly Medic pods, in fact you may often find round the entrance of an ant burrow quite a collection of these Dry Fruits which the ants have been compelled to abandon after taking the trouble to bring them from a distance. How is it that so intelligent an insect miscalculates the size of his hall door?

This pod does not dehisce (open) to release the seed, for in that case the ant would have no difficulty in carrying the grain home to his little larder; but the rootlet and stemlet (plumule) protrude while the seed remains protected by the hard dry pod. Thus you always notice these seedling Medics growing up from a prickly appendage which is attached to the base of their stem.

Among the Medics two other curiosities are worth mention; first, *M. orbicularis*, which you may find in any Olive grove. The spiral pod resembles an accordion. Next, *M. scutellata*. The fruit is similar in structure, but the whorls lie one within the other, reminding one of a Chinese puzzle. Who will explain to us the purpose of these plants in producing such complicated structures? For purpose there is. A herb which went to such expense of sap without obtaining any advantage by it would soon be distanced in the race for life.

The Scutellata is not exactly common, but in the Nice district it can generally be found without much trouble. At Cimiez it is plentiful.

These two botanical conundrums exhibit perhaps the strangest development of the leguminous pod. But the same natural order has other forms worth notice. For instance, the *Tetragonolobus*, often classed under Lotus, a bright yellow flower, which does not deserve so cumbersome a name, has a four-winged pod. You may find it in the damp places all along the Var. I have also gathered it at Carras, near Nice, close to where the tram stops, and in a ditch by the high road at Tourettes. It prefers moist ground. Scorpiontail (*Scorpiurus*), on the

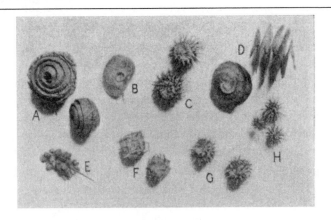

GROUP OF MEDIC FRUITS:
A. SCUTELLATA, B. FRUTISCOSA, C. NIGRA, D. ORBICULARIS, E. LUPULINA, F. TRIBULOIDES,
G. DENTICULATA, H. MINIMA

other hand, grows where the ground is dry. It is fairly common. The plant derives its name from the curious curly pod. The leaf is simple (unifoliate): either it is a flattened-out leaf-stalk (phyllode), or else the terminal leaflet only is developed. To appreciate the delicate veining on the thin disc of the *Trigonella* you must hold it to the light. This genus seems to prefer the Italian side of the frontier.

FRUIT OF TRAPA

32
Dry Fruits—II

THE short stumpy pod of the Chick Pea, or Ram's Head Pea (*Cicer Arietinum*), is another Dry Fruit unfamiliar to most of us. This pulse is commonly grown on the Riviera. In India it is known by the name of "Gram." The crop has a striking appearance, on account of its grey-green colour. It stands about as high as Sainfoin (*Onobrychis*) or Lucern (*Medicago sativa*). The herbage is sticky, and secretes so strong an acid (oxalic) that the shoes are spoiled by walking through a field of it.

There is a curious legend attached to the Ram's Head Pea. When Joseph and Mary were fleeing with the infant Christ from the Massacre of the Innocents, and were hard pressed by Herod's soldiers on their way to Egypt, they begged each plant and shrub to hide them. The Chick Pea churlishly refused. Not only this, but the malignant plant actually produced, by the cracking of its dry pods, a noise which attracted the attention of the pursuers, and well-nigh betrayed the hiding place of the Holy Family. When the soldiers had gone past, and the danger was over, the Virgin, justly incensed, cursed the impious pea plant.

If the Chick Pea were permitted to speak in its own defence, it might very well plead that it is not easy for a plant scarcely a foot high to shelter two grown-up people and a baby, not to mention the mule: "A l'impossible nul n'est tenu!" But, at any rate, the sticky and spiteful little vegetable might have abstained from making a noise so as to bring the soldiers to the spot.

We must admit that the Chick Pea richly deserved the Virgin's malediction. Cursed or not, this pea is insipid to the last degree. Yet as a food it is considered nutritious, and when roasted it will sustain life longer than any other substance; at least, so they say. I wonder if this is the pulse which we read of in history as forming the sole diet of those fierce Arab conquerors who swept northward over Palestine, and westward along the coast of Africa.

The Chick Pea is ground and mixed with Chicory to the extent of fifty per cent. This is not regarded as an adulteration; on the contrary, it is said to improve the flavour of the coffee. The "Ram's Head," with curling horns, may be seen, with a little help from the imagination, by holding the young seed at a certain angle. From Cicer is derived the name of the great Roman orator.

If we turn to the Cress flowers (Crucifers) we shall find some interesting variations of the shorter pod (silicule). Woad (*Isatis tinctoria*) grows plentifully all along the Var beside the high road. I have also found it below the village of Peillon, and in the mountain district near Duranus, at the top of that fearful precipice the "Frenchman's Fall."

But the headquarters of Woad ought to be the village of *La Gaude*, which is called after the plant. It is an axiom of Philology that "g" and "w" are, in certain cases, interchangeable. Thus "guard" and "ward," "guarant" and "warrant," "Gauthier" and "Walter," "Gaude" and "Woad," &c. I have passed through the village of La Gaude, but omitted to notice whether the patron plant is specially abundant there. I think that had it been so, the fact must have struck me. La Gaude has also been derived from a Gaelic word for wood. This is the famous herb with which the ancient Britons are supposed to have dyed their bodies. The yellow flowers are not altogether unsightly. The pendulous fruits resemble little vegetable violins: unimaginative persons might perhaps liken them to luggage labels.

We are engaged upon the Crucifers. If you wish to see a very pretty one, you have only to take a walk on the Mont Alban, or the Vinaigrier, or almost any other hill near Nice, and you may pick on every bank and terrace the lemon yellow *Biscutella lævigata*, sometimes called Buckler Mustard. The word means "double shield," Latin "scutum"; Italian "scudo," the coin; French "écu"; and it exactly expresses the outline of the fruit, which resembles a pair of coins placed side by side. The flowers appear in the first week of the year, and go on through the Spring. Nice may be proud of the Biscutella, for it does not appear in the Cannes district. I suppose that it prefers a calcareous soil.

A lovely butterfly lives upon this plant, the Southern Orange Tip, or Glory of Provence (*Euchloe Euphenoides*). The Northern insect (*E. Cardamines*) is much rarer here. On this same plant another choice species lays its eggs, *E. Belia*, which has the underside of its wings decorated with nacreous markings. This butterfly is fairly abundant, but inexperienced collectors do not notice it on the wing, because of its resemblance to the Bath White (*P. Daplidice*). If you spend the Winter in Rome, and visit the ruins of the Colosseum, you will find the Biscutella growing plentifully all round the arena.

ANTHOCHARIS EUPHENOIDES, THE GLORY OF PROVENCE

At the corner of the Place Massena rosaries are sold, made of the curious horned fruits of the Water Chestnut or Water Hyacinth (*Trapa*) strung together. The quadrangular seed-cases of the Eucalyptus are treated in the same manner. The Water Chestnut, as its Latin name implies, floats on the surface of some marsh or swamp. The lower leaves resemble roots, the upper form a rosette. The stalks of these are inflated, so as to make the plant more buoyant. If you cut off the blade of a leaf, and, detaching the stalk from the plant, pull the little green spindle under water and release it suddenly, it will spring up into the air like a salmon. Trapa does not grow in the Var swamps. Mr. Bicknell informs me that these rosaries are made of *Trapa Verbanensis*, a species known only in the Lago Maggiore, opposite Arona, in the bay of Angera.

Under the *Casuarina*, everywhere, the ground is strewn with the rounded or oblong fruits of these curious trees. I mean the larger ones, about the size of a walnut, for there are two kinds. The carving is plain enough, yet very neat and regular. How well finished is the work turned out by Nature's lathe! And how simple are the materials: carbon and a little water, that is all! With these few elements she will produce a thousand times ten thousand specimens of any given pattern, and each one true to the original design and faithful to the archetype.

The Casuarina is an Australian tree which may be known at once by its resemblance to an Equisetum. The Australians call it "Beef-wood" or "Iron-wood"; and still more absurd names are applied to it, such as "She Oak"[26] and "Botany Bay oak." Two species are very common in the gardens here. One has a drooping habit; the long thin leafless jointed striate twigs hang down like green whipcord; or shall we liken them to the tresses of a mermaid's hair? The staminate tree, when it flowers in Autumn, becomes tinged with gold or bronze; the minute inflorescence on the pistillate tree is bright red. When the wind passes through the branches of this Casuarina, it makes a strange melancholy sighing sound. The other species (*C. stricta*) is a tall erect tree with the habit and the aspect of a Conifer; in fact, it is commonly taken for some sort of Pine tree.

The aborigines of Australia made forks of this wood to eat human flesh with: these were handed down from father to son. The precious heirloom was reserved for cannibal rites, and might not be used for any other purpose. It is curious that while a kind action may be done informally, an elaborate ceremonial must always be observed when men are intent upon anything particularly wicked.

We have now examined a few of the Dry Fruits which are to be found at every turn. Those who care for curious and beautiful objects will find many another which I have not space to mention. There is, for instance, the graceful urn of the Campion (*Lychnis*); the exquisite little basket of the Aristolochia suspended by its slender cords; the ridiculous pod of the Thunbergia, which seems to imitate the head and beak of a duck in the act of quacking. These, and a hundred more, will repay the trouble of collecting. I say "collecting"; why not? People collect stamps and coins and curiosities of all sorts. The Dry Fruits of the Riviera form a collection as yet unhackneyed; and, to the botanist at least, abounding in interest and instruction.

Notes:

[26] A corruption of *sheok*, the name given to this tree by the natives of Australia.—T. H.

FRUIT OF CASUARINA

33
Perfumed Plants

"Redolent murræque crocique."

THE "Little Corsican" used to say that if landed blindfold on his native island he would be able to recognise it by the perfume of the flowers. I think that one might say the same thing of the Riviera. There is among the Olive groves an aromatic fragrance which is so familiar to us that we should know it again if we were to breathe it after whatever lapse of time. How much more then if we have inhaled this balmy air in early life? There is something pathetic in the grim soldier, who has been the terror of Europe, familiar with the roar of battle and the dread sounds of war, thinking with fond regret of the sweet-scented hill-sides of his early home. There comes a time to each of us when we look back on days which are hardly any longer to be called a memory, but rather a faint dying perfume of the past.

The disciples of Empedocles were wont to grow aromatic herbs as a preventive of disease. Here we need not to cultivate them, for Nature has assumed the task.

Let us inquire from what plants these "odours of Edom" are exhaled. Firstly, there is that little Crucifer, the honey-scented *Alyssum maritimum* which sprinkles the stony ground, distilling sweetness from its myriad small white flowers. Then Thyme and Mint and other Labiates abound, shedding, as we walk over them, a stronger and more penetrating perfume. Here and there the neighbouring Orange grove sends a waft of rich scented air to mingle with the breath of humbler plants. And when we come upon a bit of broken ground, we are wrapped in the resinous exhalations of the Aleppo pine.

The particular odour which Napoleon preferred is said to be that of the *Cistus Monspeliensis*, a white-flowered shrub, with sessile viscous leaves, which occurs here and there on the Riviera. The leaves of the little Yellow Marigold (*Calendula arvensis*) are also highly aromatic, likewise those of the Calamint so common here. Notice the spreading cymes of this plant, which reveal to us the secret of the verticillaster or false whorl in the Labiates. Southernwood (*Artemisia abrotanum*) is indigenous, but I never found it. *Euphorbia spinosa* has delicately perfumed flowers, and those of the Smilax are used to flavour drinks.

These are the all-pervading perfumes of the Olive hills: but we must add many an aromatic shrub, such as the Myrtle and the Rosemary. Nor must we forget the Roses, the Jasmin, the Violets, the so-called Geranium (*Pelargonium odoratissimum*), the Tuberose (*Polianthes tuberosa*)—

> "The Tuberose, with her silvery light,
> That in the gardens of Malay
> Is called the mistress of the night,"

and the other sweet-scented plants which are cultivated all along the coast. Lindley states that the fading flowers of the Tuberose emit sparks on the evening of a sultry day.

The Bay Tree (*Laurus nobilis*) is said to give its name to Vallauris, the "Vale of Laurels," near Cannes. So Laurentum in Latium was famed for its Laurel groves. Here dwelt the younger Pliny, and hither in the second century fled the plague-stricken Romans, seeking the protection of the spicy air. The allied Camphor Tree (*Laurus Camphora*) is not very common in gardens, and those which I have seen do not look flourishing, but in the Pallavicini park at Pegli, near Genoa, there stands a specimen with a trunk at least three feet in thickness, *teste* E. M. Holmes, F.L.S.

The aromatic *Chenopodium ambrosioides* is subspontaneous at several points along the coast.

There are some odours which are not usually considered pleasant, but which I am not ashamed to say that I enjoy. For instance, that of the large coarse yellow Composite *Inula viscosa*, a plant so common on all waste ground that it may be said to take the place of our Ragwort (*Senecio Jacobæa*). If you bruise the leaves you find that the plant is strong-smelling. But in certain conditions of the weather it gives out,

Eriobotrya japonica, the Loquat

without being touched, a pungent odour which is far from being disagreeable. I am not quite sure that I dislike even the smell of Rue (*Ruta*).

Of our sweet-scented British plants, Melilote is common: Anthoxanth lends its perfume to the hay, as in the North; but Woodruff (*Asperula odorata*) is wanting, or rather it occurs in a part of the mountain district which is not often visited. However, the Melissa, sometimes called "Balm," a lemon-scented Labiate, forms an excellent substitute. This delightful plant is commoner near Nice than any one would suppose who did not watch for it when walking out. Without its small white flowers you might easily mistake it for a Lamium. It comes as a pleasant surprise to find that a herb which you have taken for an ordinary wayside weed requires but a gentle touch to shed a balsamic odour all around.

One of the sweetest of the exotic garden shrubs is the Pittosporum. The "fleurs embaumantes," white, yellow, or red, perfume the air to a considerable distance. If it be true that Peris live on perfumes, a single Pittosporum ought to support a large number of these amiable creatures. These small trees are planted all along the Promenade Anglaise, Nice.

Olea fragrans and *Orchis fragrans* merit their specific name. The latter plant is common enough in grassy places near the coast. Of the rarer variety *coriophora* it will be sufficient to say that the French call it punaise! an opprobrious epithet which is only too well deserved. In the first week of June we have found *Orchis fragrans* in flower on the Pessicard hill, Nice.

Its overpowering and nauseous sweetness is a drawback to the universal Ligustrum (*L. Japonicum*). The odour is like that of the closely related Privet, but still more unbearable. The flowers appear in July. There is a palm, fortunately not grown on the Riviera, which is so highly perfumed that when it comes into flower no one can remain in the neighbourhood. The only way to deal with plants of this sort is to cut off the flower buds. The Ligustrum and the Plane (*Platanus*) are a source of great discomfort to residents on the Riviera.

It is strange and hardly credible that the people who gather the Orange blossoms are liable to be prostrated and even rendered insensible by the strength of the perfume. The perfumes at Grasse are said to have "an exasperating effect" on the nervous system.

I have perceived in some gardens a most agreeable odour, which it was difficult to trace to any particular shrub. I was told that it proceeded from an *Escallonia*, perhaps *E. rubra*. The plants of this genus are all more or less aromatic. In one of Mr. Hudson's delightful Natural History books the vinous perfume of certain *Œnotheras* is praised. "*Œno*" is of course "oinos", wine.

About the scent of the Loquat (*Eriobotrya*) flowers, a difference of taste exists. Persons whose opinion is entitled to the highest respect liken it to the smell of drains! Others delight in it. For my part I like these trees, and planted a good many of them in the garden of the last house which I occupied. The perfume reminds me of the British hawthorn. The French name is "Bibassier," or "Néflier du Japon." This handsome evergreen is a native of China and Japan. It is a favourite with Indian gardeners. The Loquat comes up freely from the seeds that are thrown away when the fruit is eaten; it stands unmerciful pruning, and, if planted as a hedge, can be made to form a perfect wall of verdure. Often of its own accord the tree will take the shape of an umbrella, and give an admirable shade. The flowers appear in November, the fruit in April and May. In 1882, some were ripe at the end of March. The tree was introduced into Europe by the French in 1874. Strange as it may seem, the Loquat can be grafted on Hawthorn and on Quince.

The scented fern (*Cheilanthes odora*) used to occur below Eza. It grows as a rule on dry walls in the mountain region. Near Pigna and Buggio, north of Bordighera, it is said to be abundant. The odour is but faint.

I must now mention some plants which are not exactly "perfumed"; and to begin with there is one whose acquaintance you are bound to make if you happen to have a garden and to spend a few moments weeding it. I allude to that rankest of all rank smelling weeds, the *Fetid Chenopod*. There is scarce a yard of ground without this nasty plant; if you touch it you must wash your hands. *Eucalyptus pendula* has an odour which some people consider very disagreeable.[27] Professor Penzig says, "Add the awfully scenting flowers of Ailanthus and of Ceratonia."

The extraordinary Dragon Arum (*Dracunculus*) is a flower which should certainly be grown in the corner of a garden farthest from the house. The spathe is three or four times as large as that of the ordinary British Arum, and of a deep port-wine colour: a beautiful object, but the smell is not to be expressed in words. It is worse than the Carrion Plant (*Stapelia*), and that is bad enough. If you cut out the spadix, you may bring the flower into the house and admire it with impunity. A gardener near us grows a good many of these Arums, but they do not seem to be in much demand. They thrive in the open air. On the banks of the Cephisus this plant reaches a height of six feet, the spathe alone measuring close on a yard. The Oriental Cashmere pattern on carpets

FROND OF CHEILANTHES ODORA, THE SCENTED FERN

and shawls is traced by Professor Jacobsthal to an imitation of the form of this gigantic spathe. It is said that snakes will not approach the plant.

Another "Perfumed Plant," the fungus called Clathrus, was found by my daughter on the Mount Boron. Beautiful and curious though it is, we did not bring it home. Yet another fetid fungus I have more than once perceived near Nice: one does not care to gather it. The English name is more forcible than elegant.

A propos of this plant, Dr. Alfred Russel Wallace told me an amusing story. Near one end of his miniature Botanic garden, in Parkstone, stands a pillar-box. People posting letters here were annoyed by a pestilent smell. They supposed that the drains were out of order. Or possibly they imagined that the great Naturalist had brought home from the Malay Archipelago, or from the Valley of the Amazon, some evil weed that was poisoning the air. So they reported the matter to the Post Office. At last the complaints became so numerous that the Postal authorities sent an official to call upon Dr. Wallace and request him to discontinue the nuisance! He explained that the undesirable plant was there when he took the house. He had done his best to eradicate the mycelium, but the obstinate Cryptogam was more than a match for the distinguished man of Science.

Notes:

[27] The most pungent scent of any tree in my garden is that possessed by *Oreodaphne Californica* (Laurineæ). Bruised leaves held to the nostrils produce violent and continued sneezing, the olfactory nerves remaining insensible to other odours for at least half-an-hour. The fruit of the Chinese pepper, *Xanthoxylon alatum*, is also extremely pungent.—T. H.

34
Springtide

"Hic ver assiduum."

IT is not easy to say exactly when the Spring commences on the Riviera. The Hazel (*Corylus*) flowers with us at home in February and March, but out here it loosens its catkins to the breeze, and protrudes its pink styles as early as the middle of December. Before the old year has passed away the next year's buds are opening. There is no period of the year when wild plants are not in flower on the Riviera. I have gathered a long list of flowers on Christmas Day. But the greater number of these were such as one sees the whole year round.[28]

The time of flowering differs so much from year to year that it is difficult to fix a date which may be counted on. Elevation again, or what is almost the same thing on this steeply sloping coast, distance from the sea, makes a great difference. By walking a very few miles inland you will find plants in full flower which are long over on the coast. Moreover, when east winds prevail in a given season, ground sloping west will be

THE HUMMING BIRD MOTH, MACROGLOSSA STELLATARUM

warmer, and have the vegetation more advanced. But when the equally cold mistral is more frequent through the Winter, as happens sometimes, the east exposure has an advantage. I have heard it stated that we have had more east wind of late years, and less mistral. It is said that the natives like the mistral. I doubt if any one enjoys these icy *gusts*; but the proverb says, "De *gustibus* non disputandum"!

Besides the Hazel, there are several wild plants which I have seen in flower before the year was out: for instance, the Fragrant Coltsfoot (*Petasites*). Not being aware that this plant is common here, I took the trouble to bring some from a distance for my garden, and afterwards I found it growing wild just outside the gateway. The natives have the good taste to mingle the vanilla-scented lilac flowers of the *Petasites* with their bouquets. A wild Narcissus flowers sometimes at the end of December, but I do not know whether it belongs to late Autumn or to very early Spring. I think that Hellebore not unfrequently flowers in mid-December: I have found *Coronilla Emerus* in flower as early as December 9th, and both Primrose and Hepatica towards the end of the month.

As early as the first week of January we sometimes have the following in flower: Figwort Buttercup (*Ranunculus Ficaria*), Almond, and Primrose: about the middle of the month the wild Anemone (*A. coronaria*) and the Snowflake (*Leucojum*) appear in favourable seasons: in the last week we have *coronilla Emerus*, Hepatica, and the beautiful *Lavatera maritima* on the rocks close by the sea. Crocus, Orchis, Iris, Cytisus, Polygala, Biscutella, Honeysuckle (*Lonicera*), and many others often flower in January; and on warm days through the Winter one sometimes sees the Red Admiral (*V. Atalanta*), the Cabbage White (*P. Brassicæ*), and the Humming Bird Moth (*M. Stellatarum*). The great blue-black Carpenter Bee (*Xylocopa*) often appears before the month is out; and on one occasion we took the gorgeous Cleopatra on Mount Vinaigrier as early as January 28th. The insect appeared much too fresh for a hibernated specimen.

The Humming Bird Moth just mentioned is commoner here than any other Sphinx. The French name of the insect is *Porcelaine*. It sucks honey without perching, and has the swift flight peculiar to its family, but it is not crepuscular, it flies in the full sun like a bee or a butterfly.

Barlia longibracteata, with Carpenter Bee

Stellatarum constantly hibernates, coming into the house for shelter. They hide in all sorts of places, and appear on the window pane when warmer weather wakes them up again. I have heard a furious buzzing under my pillow, and found a Humming Bird Moth with his wings rubbed quite bare from struggling to get free. He knows quite well that frost and cold do not last long out here, so he does not think of allowing himself to be extinguished, but "when gloomy Winter has put forth his squalid countenance," he finds some sheltered corner and waits till it is over.

One often sees this moth hovering about the flowers of a gaily coloured wall paper: this looks as if the sense of smell were wanting. You need no microscope to observe that the singularly bright little eye of this insect is a perfect hexagon. My son has often found the tailed green larva on the yellow Beadstraw (*Galium*). *A propos* of Galium, I notice that the Rev. W. Tuckwell, in his delightful "Tongues in Trees," supports the spelling "Bedstraw," as if the plant had been used to stuff mattresses. But the form "Beadstraw" is more poetical and quite as likely to be correct. "Bead" (M.H.G. beten) meant "prayer." To tell (M.H.G. zählen) one's beads was to count one's prayers. Now a pious peasant who had no rosary to hand might find the Galium useful for this purpose. As the stem is passed through the hand, the fingers will be arrested at each node by the whorl of leaves, and a long stalk of Beadstraw would involve a good many Pater Nosters and Ave Marias.[29]

The yellow Galium is considered in this district to be a sovereign remedy for diarrhœa. You do not drink it as a tisane, nor eat it as a salad. It is for external application only: you wear it under your feet inside the socks! The feeling is not unpleasant, *experto crede*, provided you do not have the stalks too thick and too dry. Still "avoir du foin dans les souliers" is one thing, and to have Beadstraw in your socks is quite another.

Some of these Sphinxes are hardly to be told from Humming birds when on the wing. Bates, writing of a Brazilian species (*M. Titan*) says that it was only after many days' experience that he learnt to distinguish one from the other. Not only the natives, he says, but even educated white men, firmly believe that this moth changes into a Humming bird, in fact that the two creatures are one and the same.

The Stellatarum does not sit and sulk on a railing like a good many moths, he hustles about busily, so long as there is light to see the way from one flower to another. He is not silly enough to commit suicide in a candle, nor greedy enough to be caught gorging on a sugared tree trunk; he can even resist the temptation of rotten apples soaked in rum! When other moths are indulging in these luxuries he has retired to rest in the crevice of a rock. Though his appetite is good, he must be called abstemious: in fact, to judge by the pace of his flight, he must keep himself in perfect training, whereas his close relatives, the plethoric Burnets (*Zygæna*), can scarcely carry their large abdomens from a scabious to a thistle top. It is not surprising that this brisk little insect should be regarded as lucky, and receive the title of "Bonaventura." His scientific name, "Long tongue of the Stellates" or Madder family (on which the larva feeds) may be appropriate enough; but if I had to baptize the moth, I should be disposed to give him some such name as "Faustus" or "Hilaris" or "Lætus."

The great black Carpenter bee (*Xylocopa*) is represented in some beautiful coloured diagrams by Professor Dodel Port, which I possess, as sucking honey quite correctly from a Salvia; but, as far as I have observed his conduct, he is an unscrupulous robber. I have watched this bee rifling flower after flower of Honeysuckle and of Salvia; in every case he cut through the base of the corolla at once, without making any attempt to get at the honey in the legitimate way. There are few wild flowers which seem large enough to admit the body of this great bee; and not many cultivated ones, unless it be Acanthus, Justicia, Paulownia, Cobæa, and some of the Bignonias.

The little Sun Lizard has no fixed time for appearing; whenever the sun shines strong upon the wall, and the air is not too keen, he creeps out from his crevice and begins to bask as usual.

Appropriate to early Spring is the legend of the Almond, which runs thus:—When St. Patrick went to reside in the monastery of Lerins, his sister might not follow him, so she remained on the mainland where the town of Cannes now stands. Taking leave of her brother, she asked him when he would come to see her. "When the fruit-trees are in blossom," he replied. Before the Winter was over she grew weary of waiting, and one day, as she looked wistfully toward the prison-house of her brother, she besought the trees to flower. But one feared the frost, another shunned the biting breath of the mistral, while a third was unwilling to be conspicuous by flowering while all other trees were bare. But the Almond, pitying the lady's solitude, bravely put forth its bright petals from the bud. A spray of the untimely blossoms was sent over to the island. Patrick, surprised and pleased, remembered his promise, and hastened to obey the sweet summons of his sister. The Almond, proud of the sister's gratitude and of the saint's approving smile, has ever since that time flowered earlier than any other tree.

Notes:

28 I am disappointed if I have fewer than 450 species in flower in the open border at La Mortola in the month of January.—T. H.

29 A distinguished botanist, to whose authority I willingly defer, assures me that a stalk of Galium could not be used as a rosary. Might it not, however, have obtained its name from its likeness to a rosary? Thus *Scandix pecten* resembles a comb, *Stellaria* a star, *Capsella* a purse, the replum of *Lunaria* the moon and so forth. Many plants were dedicated to the Virgin Mary. The Beadstraw may have been one of these. In any case it seems to me that Our Lady's beadstraw and Our Lady's mantle are more poetical and euphonious plant names than Swine's-cress and Treacle-mustard.

XYLOCOPA VIOLACEA, THE CARPENTER BEE, AND NEST

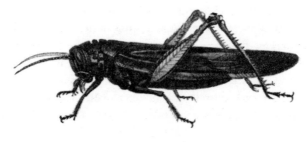

LOCUST

35
Early Summer

"Nunc formosissimus annus."

IN February appears the Grape Hyacinth or Starch Hyacinth (*Muscari*), with its close cluster of dark blue beads. I have seen it as early as the 8th. There are certain flowers which mark a stage in the course of the revolving year, just as there are events which make a period in the little cycle of our lives. When the first specimen of Muscari is brought in from some sheltered spot, the weary invalid may take it as a welcome sign that the sun is gaining power, and that the forces of the Winter are in full retreat.

On old book-stalls and in the window of some village stationers, you may often see curious little books with ornamental binding. They explain the "Language of Flowers": The Wallflower is puffed up with pride; the drooping Violet is a symbol of humility; the blazing poppy threatens anger; the Myosote, uncurling its blue flowers by the river side, promises the most devoted affection; and so forth. This "Language of Flowers" is almost the only one not yet included in our school curriculum. We cram our pupils with languages, living and dead, classical and modern, Aryan and Semitic, polysynthetic, agglutinative, and inflectional. But the "Language of Flowers" does not count for promotion to a higher form, nor does it carry marks in any competitive examination. The British parent is still of the same opinion as that Bourgeois of Alphonse Karr's, "who does not wish to take his son's mind off his studies by having him taught Botany." Yet there is indeed a "Language of Flowers," and those alone who learn it can interpret the whisperings of the springtime, can translate the great epics of the fields, and read the lessons of the changing seasons.

The "Language of Flowers" has no Grammar or Gradus, no Dictionary or Delectus, no wearisome rules of Syntax or of Prosody: it has not yet taken its rank among the instruments of educational torture. But the time is at hand: those queer little books with a gilt garland on the cover and a coloured bouquet for a frontispiece are doomed; no one will buy them now, for the scientific wiseacres have decreed (at Cambridge for instance) that children must begin Botany by the study of Chemistry, and that an urchin who does not know a daisy from a buttercup must learn vegetable histology with the aid of a compound microscope.

Now to return to the Grape Hyacinth: you will not find it mentioned in any of those pretty little books on the "Language of Flowers." It would never do to include the Muscari, for the offer of this flower in Eastern countries involves (if we are to believe the German writer Museus) a statement of affection so emphatic as to offend polite ears.

MUSCARI RACEMOSUM, THE
GRAPE HYACINTH

March brings the Swallows. I have seen them as early as the first day of the month, but these may have been stragglers. I think that they do not generally return until the third week or later. These are some of the dates on which I have seen them first: March 1st, 19th, 25th; April 1st, 21st. Of course, the swallows may be flying for some time on the Riviera before one catches sight of them. In the ancient Roman calendar the arrival of the swallows is marked on February 24th, the only natural history fact,

I believe, which is to be found in their calendar. In England, the swallows reappear about April 19th. The Riviera date is, as we might expect, intermediate.

The Mole Cricket belongs also to this month. I have marked the following dates: February 23rd; March 2nd, 22nd, 26th. Several butterflies emerge. *P. Machaon* (the Carrot Swallow-tail) is on the wing. The French appropriately call this butterfly the Queen, for there are in Europe few rivals to dispute her sceptre. A second Swallow-tail (*P. Podalirius*) appears before the end of March, floating and hovering over the fruit trees everywhere. The Camberwell (*V. Antiopa*) sails past among the willows. *Thais* swarms in the reed brake, and with it you often find the earliest Fritillary, *A. Dia.* The yellow *Colias Edusa* begins to race along the clover tops, and the little *P. Phlæas* commences the merry dance which the Blues and Skippers (*Hesperidæ*) will take part in later on. The Bath White (*P. Daplidice*) appears very early.

The Peach Blossom lights up the valleys early in the month, and about mid-March the Cherry flowers: I have seen the Peach out on the 1st, and the Cherry as early as the 6th. Next in order of flowering comes the Plum. The buds of the Horse Chestnut (*Æsculus*) and Walnut (*Juglans*) open, and the white petals fall from the flowers of the Sloe. The peasant, armed with a long rod, clambers barefoot up the Olive tree; and all day long you hear a rattling sound as he clears the bright black berries (drupes) from the twigs. Squatting on the ground, the women and children fill their baskets with the fruits.

The streams flow red, for they have been dyed a rich claret colour by passing through the Olive mills.

April boasts the fleeting Cistus. I have seen it in flower at the end of March. Professor Allman says: There is no spot too dry and shadeless for these beautiful shrubs. Their season of flowering is in the later Spring and early Summer, when they display day after day in unlimited profusion their large and rose-like white or purple flowers, and mingle the balsamic odour of their leaves with the aromatic exhalations of the Labiate. But the life of the Cistus is a short one: in a few hours the corolla has fulfilled its function. Opening to the morning and to the noon, the petals soon fall to the ground, and long before the setting of the sun there is nowhere to be seen, over all the hill-side, a vestige of the great blossoms of white and purple which had but an hour before spread such a glory over the landscape. And day after day does the young corolla open its petals to the morning and cast them to the ground before the evening in uninterrupted sequence, until the advancing Summer brings the period of flowering to an end.

The *Locust* rises with a whirr, and flies a few yards heavily: then, overweighted by his clumsy body, he plunges headlong into the first green thing he meets.

Cleopatra flashes past with orange wing, startling and delighting every eye. Its pale green mate escapes the notice of all but the experienced collector, as she flutters over the Buckthorn (*Rhamnus*) bushes. I have twice seen this butterfly before the end of March, and once even as early as January. The Quince hedges (*Cydonia*) flower in the first week of April; and there is no more lovely sight. My latest date is April 15th, the earliest the day before the equinox. The wild Gladiolus flowers as early as the 6th, but sometimes not until the 28th. The fig leaves begin to show at the end of each curving branch, and the Judas Tree (*Cercis*) is lined out with red. In the suburbs of the town you hear "Chapeaux de Paille!" for the sun is strong, and the trees as yet give little shade.

Springtide is over, and with May the perfect Summer days set in. On the 10th or 12th, sometimes even as early as the 2nd, the *Fire Flies* light their little lanterns in the damp and shady spots, and before long they flit about in countless multitudes, making the evening hours bewilderingly beautiful. "Véritables étincelles vivantes, elles voltigent le soir autour des buissons, et présentent un charmant spectacle." The cherries ripen; the peasants say that "the fireflies turn the cherries red."

On all sides song is heard and sounds of gladness, for "the flowers have appeared on the earth, and the time of singing is come, and the cooing of the turtledove is heard in the land" (Sol. Song ii. 12).

We speak of "merry England," but what do the Northern people know of merriment? The Provençal might still say of them as the French queen does in Schiller's play:

"Ihr kennt nicht das Vergnügen, nur die Wuth!"

Here every village has its garlands hung across the "Place," and every street has flowers festooned from house to house. On Sunday evenings all through the merry month of May, the young folk dance round and round under these garlands of flowers, and sing and laugh until the air resounds with their rejoicing, and one almost forgets, as one looks on, that toil and sin and misery exist. This is the Mois de Marie, the bright and happy month sacred, as is meet and right, to Mary or Maia or Diana the sweet Virgin, type of womanhood and Queen of Heaven.

It may be true, as Canon Hole asserts in "Nice and her Neighbours," that these festive people are the slaves of a childish superstition. But I hope that the day may be far distant when a dry and gloomy Calvinism shall rob these south European nations of their glad May dances, and condemn them to a life as dull and joyless as our own. The Ligurians have no monopoly of bigotry; and if we must have a superstition, a bright is better than a gloomy one.

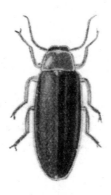

FIREFLY, LUCIOLA

36

Sunshine and Shade

"Nobis placeant ante omnia sylvæ."

DURING the greater part of the year shade is sorely needed on the Riviera. To increase the amount of shade would lengthen the period during which it is possible for us to remain on the coast. But these seaside towns lay themselves out for the Winter visitors, and make little effort to attract or to retain more permanent residents. People who linger beyond the conclusion of the season must take their chance of sunstroke, and are compelled to suffer other serious discomforts.

Of course many of the landlords cannot help themselves. The strangers who come out only for the Winter months want every ray of sun. If the garden contains anything higher than a hollyhock, they grumble. The unlucky proprietor must roast all Summer in order that he may have a chance of letting his house in Winter. In the end a race of human salamanders will be evolved in Nice, whose skulls will be sun-proof, as the nose of a Neapolitan is smell-proof.

Some years ago one of the local papers complained of the want of shade, and likened Nice to a calcareous desert sprinkled with enormous barrack-like buildings painted a blinding white and exposed to the full fury of the sun. Since that time a great number of trees have been planted, and many of those then planted have begun to give shade.

Frequenters of the boulevards are now perfectly protected from the sun; but those who prefer excursions in the country are less fortunate.

At Genoa two things are wanting, as the saying runs: trees on the land and fishes in the sea. (There is also a third desideratum, for which, lest I be guilty of a "diffamation," I must refer my readers to their Baedecker.) Nice is not quite so badly off as this, yet the country roads are treeless to a great extent.

I am convinced that the Plane (*Platanus occidentalis*), the only tree now planted, is not suited to a health resort. The hairs from the hanging globular clusters of fruit are a serious drawback. At certain seasons of the year the roads are lined with these, and whenever there is wind they are carried into the eyes and nose and throat. There is no avoiding these spicules, and they are peculiarly irritating. The Plane is not only a source of great discomfort, but of actual danger to all who suffer from the throat and lungs. The bark is said to be poisonous. The tree is utterly unworthy of the exquisite lines addressed to it by the poet Clough.

The French are very fond of these trees: there are said to be 26,000 of them in Paris.

It is easier to condemn the "Bachelor Plane" than to say what tree should take its place.[30] To multiply quite unproductive trees for shade alone cannot be right. Is there no tree which affords both shade and fruit? The Walnut (*Juglans*) is a good-sized tree: the wood is valuable for cabinet work, and we make gun stocks of it. Now, it is clear that all things which help human beings to destroy each other must be of the utmost importance. There is a great demand just now for Walnut wood. The French complained lately that the German government had bought up all the Walnut wood in France. The leaves are said to have the valuable property of keeping off flies, and the shade *appears to be* excellent. But no one out here will rest under a Walnut tree. It is the universal opinion in this part of the world that you will take harm if you do so. I am not one of those who hasten to make light of these popular ideas. If the balsamic odour of the Pine Forest is invigorating and refreshing, why should not the exhalations of some trees have a contrary effect? This is a point which might well occupy the attention of scientific men.

To Dellius, needing rest from war and politics, the poet recommends a quiet lounge

> "*Where the huge Pine and Poplar silver-lined*
> *With branches interlaced have made*
> *A hospitable shade.*"

And Horace is right: the Abele (*Populus Alba*) gives an admirable shade, and is altogether preferable to the bark-casting Plane. By the Var

NICOTIANA GLAUCA

and also at the mouth of the Loup there are some noble trees of this species, whose height is given in the text books as double that of the Oak.

Tityrus, as every schoolboy knows, reclined in the shade of a Beech tree. But there are not many Beeches on the Riviera; at least I have seen one only in Nice, and that stands in the grounds of the Villa Liserb, Cimiez, close to the house. Near Caussols above St. Vallier there is a beech wood which contains only stunted and scattered trees. The best have been cut down for firewood.

The hatred of the Spaniard for trees is proverbial: the result is that on the denuded table land of Castile the wind is, they say, so keen that it will kill a man without blowing out a candle. The Ligurian does not exactly hate trees; but he is quite indifferent to them, and rather glad of a pretext for cutting them down. My landlord at a former house was threatening a tree which stood opposite to his window. It was a Nicotiana (*N. glauca*), allied to the tobacco, with yellow tubular corolla and glaucous entire leaves. The plant is very common here, but this particular shrub, or rather tree, was the largest I have ever seen of that species, so I attempted to intercede for it. This Nicotiana, I said, was probably the finest on the Riviera, and an ornament to his property. But the shrub was doomed: the landlord feared, forsooth, that robbers would climb up by it and enter his window!

If a negro is ordered to cut down one of the giants of the forest, he will sometimes hesitate: "There's too many jumbies in it." There are, unfortunately, no jumbies in any of the Riviera trees; or rather the natives see no jumbies in them. These "plages ensoleillées," like the rest of Europe, are "entgöttert," to use Schiller's word.

When will each town and village once again possess its sacred grove? A shady spot which no human hand may desecrate, where plant and bird may find an inviolate asylum; a true Arboretum, dense and tangled; no gravel walks, no trim parterres, no "bedding plants," no close-cut grass. We want something which shall bring the townsman into contact with Nature, and help him to understand that feeling which Goethe expresses in his noble opening lines of the "Iphigenie auf Tauris":

"I enter now with awe and reverence
Your sacred shade, ye ancient lofty trees."

The sacred grove attached to every town should not be that piece of land which can be had at the lowest price, but rather, to use Nathaniel Hawthorne's words, that spot where the sense of beauty is gratified by a lovelier shade than elsewhere, and a more exquisite arrangement of lake and wood and hill.

A portion of every country must be "field" (German "Feld") or cultivated ground where the trees are "felled"; but it is also necessary that a certain proportion of every country should be "wild" (German "Wald"), as were once the "Weald" of Kent, the "Wolds" of Yorkshire, and the Cots-"wolds" of Gloucestershire. If this law is disregarded, a retribution follows. The outraged Dryades may not revenge themselves as did the nymph in Lowell's pretty poem "Rhæcus," but the punishment is not less certain. The climate is destroyed by *déboisement*, and in some cases a country is rendered uninhabitable. Other mischief follows the wholesale cutting down of trees. At Trieste, for instance, the shipping has been repeatedly injured by storms of wind from the north-east since the unwooding of the Karst.

The Maritime Alps are now being rewooded at a great expense; and not a day too soon, for I read lately in the report of the Alpine Club that the forests of Pine and Larch (*Larix*) on the mountains north of Nice were disappearing rapidly. And I am assured by a person who has known the Riviera for a long series of years that this "déboisement" has coincided with a change of climate for the worse.

How unsightly, how desolate, are barren rocks, compared with pine-clad slopes! Look northward from any point of the Nice valley, and you will see a triangular hill which forms the southern shoulder of the Férion. On the same ridge, a little higher up, stands the Deserted Village. This triangular hill-side was a short time ago so completely denuded that it bore the name of Bare bones, "Costa Pelada"; but now, rewooded, its verdure strikes the eye at once.

The British government has done well to stop the cutting down of trees in Cyprus; the Gladstones of the island must seek some other recreation. This, like all other mischief, is quickly done and slowly remedied. The process of devastating a country was called in Greek "temnein gēn," or "koptein tēn khēran," both of which expressions have reference to cutting down trees.

Our own country abounds in trees; but we must not take too much credit for the fact. We plant them as a shelter for pheasants, and we allow them to remain because we do not need them for firewood. England will be well-wooded so long as coal is cheap.

Dresden, of all the towns I am acquainted with, sets the greatest store by trees; though the felling once a year would need to be counterbalanced by a good deal of planting. At Whitsuntide the whole town is a bower. Saplings and branches are piled up and sold in the markets and open places; and as we buy Holly and Mistletoe at Christmas, so the Dresdener purchases a young Silver Birch or Fir tree, which he puts up in some conspicuous spot, or close by the door-post of the lady he admires. The tramcars come along under the shelter of four trees fastened to the corners; and the Elbe steamers, which run to the Saxon Switzerland, look like well-wooded islands.

Trees may not make a Paradise, but we can hardly conceive a Paradise without trees. Milton, it has been observed, fills the Garden of Eden with flowers, but Genesis mentions only trees.

Notes:

[30] Good trees for the public streets are *Acacia Julibrissin, Robinia, Paulownia imperialis, Sterculia platanifolia, Ulmus Americanus, Gingko biloba,* the Horse Chestnut, *Brachychiton populneum, Ailantus,* and the Black Walnut, which I have planted at Alassio and Ventimiglia.—T. H.

37

Gardens and Gardeners

I ONCE read an amusing story of an unfortunate knight who was taken prisoner by a sultan in the East, and to save his life turned gardener. He became in fact, to alter the title of Molière's play, a "Jardinier malgré lui." The Pacha required a gardener, and he would have no bungling native; a European must be found. The servant of the knight sees a chance of saving his master's life, so, fibbing nobly, he declares him to be an accomplished horticulturist. The prisoner is spared on the condition that he lays out a European garden.

What shall the soldier do? He is profoundly ignorant of plants; he cannot tell a privet from a pine tree. Now there is no profession (unless it be the scholastic) in which a man can succeed without knowing anything whatever. A gardener is expected to understand something about his business. However, this prisoner took heart: he summoned to his aid those powerful genii "Aplomb" and "Toupet"; he set his fifty labourers to work, and made a desperate effort to look as if he had some idea what he meant to do. It is not easy to look as if you knew all about a thing that is inscrutable. Parsons manage it, and doctors; sometimes a schoolmaster partially succeeds.

Well, our amateur gardener went at it, as they say, "de la tête et du cul, comme un corbeau qui abat des noix"; like a jackdaw knocking down walnuts. He felled the palms and tamarisks that gave a pleasant shade, he rooted up the aromatic herbs that perfumed the evening air; he abolished the grassy places, and made bare gravel walks. One purpose he kept steadily in view, namely, to leave nothing as he found it. Nature must disappear, as far as possible. Then he traced fantastic flower beds, in which no native plant must show. He cut and carved; he filled up here, he dug and delved and devastated there.

The Pacha was delighted with his garden, because it was something new and singular, and had cost a great sum of money. The Pacha's garden is not the only one of this sort.

Why should the wild flowers disappear? Dr. Smee, prince of gardeners, "could not find it in his heart," he said, to extirpate them from his beds and borders. How much more here in Nice should they be allowed to live? for we may say of the Riviera, as Byron does of Italy, "All thy weeds are flowers." Sir Thomas Hanbury admits to his botanical paradise at La Mortola about 350 indigenous species.

The native gardener has a great objection to plants which grow spontaneously. You will intercede in vain for a Gladiolus or a Grape Hyacinth (*Muscari*): "Cà c'est de la saleté!"

A neighbour had received from America a small Guava shrub (*Psidium*). After some time this Guava threw out a few little knobs. Two gardeners were on their knees examining these. "It is going to fruit," said one. "No," answered the other, "it has not flowered yet." The first gardener maintained that some trees produce fruit without flowering. The other denied this. I listened with interest to the argument. The first man was hard pressed: at last he said, "How about the fig tree? This fruits every year, and no one ever saw a flower on a fig tree." This settled the dispute, and gardener number two laid down his arms.

A learned commentator censures Epictetus for mentioning the flower of the fig tree, and adds, "The philosopher had forgot that fig trees do not blossom, and is less excusable than the English translators of the Bible (Hab. iii. 17), to whom fig-trees were not so familiar"!

I may explain for the benefit of very unbotanical readers that the fig has as many flowers as any other plant, but we do not notice them, because they are enclosed in the succulent receptacle which becomes what we call the fruit. This is really an infructescence. In Dorstenia the "fig" is open, and the flowers are exposed to view.

I have often examined the Caper (*Capparis spinosa*), to ascertain whether it can propagate itself in this climate; once only I found a half-ripe fruit.[31] The question is how the plant spreads, for the peasants do not seem to cultivate it. They know the use of the Caper, however, for they pick off all the flower-buds that are within reach. I asked a gardener if he had ever noticed a ripe fruit. By the word "fruit" of course

VILLAGE OF LEVENS WITH MT. VIAL

I do not mean anything eatable. Botanically speaking, a fruit need not be eatable. He took the flower which I held in my hand, parted the tassel of stamens, and looked where the ovary should be. "No," said he, with a sagacious air, "that flower cannot produce any seeds, because it has no pod." Now the "pod," as gardeners call it, of the Caper flower is stipitate, that is to say, it is perched upon a particularly long stalk, so that it occupies the position usually held by the stigma. That is why the gardener failed to find it. A little knowledge is a dangerous thing!

The Niçois gardeners' rendering of plant-names is very amusing: "Habrothamnus" becomes "Brotanus," "Heliotrope" is "Vanille," and so on. Our English gardeners also play some strange tricks with Greek and Latin, and even with English, words. A gardener in the Nottingham Arboretum told me that he had just been planting an "Edger Golly." I made him say the word again: no variation. Did he know the botanical name? No, not he! Then I asked to see the plant. What was it? "Je vous le donne en vingt." A "Hedge hog holly." Too many consecutive aspirates.

How can we wonder that a gardener should be puzzled by some of the botanical names. What is an illiterate person to make of "Mesembryanthemum"? We cannot blame him much if by means of metathesis, crasis, and other grammatical expedients he simplifies these sesquipedalian terms. After all this is the self-same process by which our modern languages have been enriched. "Eleemosune" is far too long: German reduces it by half, "Almosen," three syllables instead of six; French cuts these down to two, "aumône"; even this is too much for the busy Englishman, he can tolerate but one syllable, "alms." If our ancestors curtailed "paralysis" into "palsy," "fidelity" into "fealty," and so forth; why should an ill-starred gardener be expected to say "Mesembryanthemum" when he refers to that thick-leaved plant with a flower that reminds one of a Composite?

"Quarter Sessions Rose" has a more familiar ring than "Rose des Quatre Saisons"[32]; and surely "Pilligorum" has a more homely English sound about it than the classical "Pelargonium"!

Notes:

[31] Mr. C. Bicknell states that the rare *Capparis rupestris* ripens its fruit. Hanging over the door of the church of St. Siro, in St. Remo, there is a plant which produces abundant fruit.

[32] So "Glory to die John" for the rose "Gloire de Dijon."—T. H.

38

Grassy Places

A Review of the Region

"Happy they
Who in the fresh and dawning time of youth
Have dwelt in such a land, tuning their souls
To the deep melodies of Nature's laws."

ALFORD

GRASSES are well represented on the Riviera, for very many species may be found here: nevertheless our English greensward is not common. The rainless season dries it up. For this reason the hotel-keepers find it easier to sow fresh grass each Winter than to keep it alive during the Summer by constant watering. So just about the time when the first frost-bitten strangers begin to make for the south, we see a sparse preraphaelite herbage sprouting in front of the hotels. This "gazon," as they call it out of courtesy, never quite succeeds in hiding the nakedness of the soil. Nevertheless, in well-kept gardens, there are lawns which will bear comparison with ours.

There are extensive "Grassy places" of a swampy sort at the mouth of the Var; but the nearest approach to an English meadow in the Nice valley is a field as yet unbuilt upon as you go from Carabacel towards St. Barthélemy. It is bright with Beadstraw (*Galium*), and many another flower that is familiar to our eyes, and the stream that waters it is fringed with yellow Flags (*Iris*). But the lovely Butomus of the Thames and Trent is hardly to be seen on the Riviera. Were it not for the great Reeds (*Arundo*) which form its western barrier, this meadow might remind us of our Northern home.

Rank meadows such as this are not characteristic of the Riviera. On the contrary, they are rare, for there is little level ground.

There is no common that I know of in the immediate neighbourhood of Nice. But at Levens, twelve miles to the north, stretches a lofty table-land, carpeted with the greenest herbage: a "Grassy place" extending for miles without tree or hedge or wall. "Du véritable gazon anglais, doux commne du velours, et d'un vert qui n'a pas son pareil" to use the words of Doctor Antonio. On the east rises the Férion; to the north, beyond the deep and precipitous valley of the Vesubia, stands the dark mass of the Vial. This is the mountain whose black crags you see behind the Mont-Chauve as you look up the Avenue de la Gare from the Place Masséna. To the south lie mapped out clearly the promontory of Antibes and the Ile Ste. Marguerite; to the west a multitude of mountains, rank beyond rank, like Titans marching to a war.

The Levens common is not studded with golden Gorse (*Ulex*), like many of those in England and Ireland; but in Spring the western part of it is covered with Narcissus (*N. poeticus*). Mixed with these is the Bellevalia (*Hyacinthus Romanus L.*), a rare plant with dirty-white perianth, petaloid filaments, and blue anthers. In Autumn, as we return from the mountains to the coast, we find this "Grassy place" lighted up by the blossoms of the Colchicum. Rarely is such a sight as this to be enjoyed.

The naturalist who drives up to Levens by the St. André Gorge, back by La Roquette and the Var valley, will not regret his excursion.

Grass, like many other things, is the more valued the rarer it becomes. In Norway every tuft of herbage that hangs in the crevices of the rocks is gathered in with care. Even the stray blades which spring up on the thatch of the cottage are not despised. On the Riviera also, where "Grassy places" are few and far between, no scrap of herbage is wasted. Even the grass which lines the roadside is often rented by some landless peasant to feed his rabbits or his goat, and throughout the Maritime Alps the sickle of the toilsome villager spares no green herb that grows by hedge or ditch or watercourse. Each bank is bared, not a flower is left, even the Clematis is torn from the hedge: a desolation, and a sad sight for the botanist. A peasant living close to us in the outskirts of Nice fired on an old woman who was taking a few handfuls of grass.

It is difficult for us who live where grass abounds to estimate its value, but where the sun is strong and grass is scarce men set great store by it. Of all the honours granted by the Romans for noble deeds in war, the most difficult to obtain, and that which conferred the most dignity, was the "corona graminea" or crown of grass. Now, those things on which man's life depends are ever sacred: or shall we say that they were accounted sacred in ancient times, and must be so again? Each dread epidemic that sweeps across Europe warns us that water is holy, whether priest-blessed or no. Why is tree-worship found in every clime where trees can grow? Because in times before the dawn of history, beyond the ages of bronze and stone, the tree supported human life. Dim memories of the distant past, inherited through a thousand generations, cause us to look on trees with pleasure and delight.

And so it is with grass. Our ancestors may have fed their cattle in some verdant glade. A "Grassy place" was to them the means of life. The sight of grass rejoiced men in the shepherd state, for it meant rest and plenty, its absence was hunger and despair. Therefore to us, their descendants, each "Grassy place" is pleasant still; therefore the crown of grass was held in higher honour than the diadem of gold.

The village of St. Vallier, above Grasse, instead of clinging to the mountain side, like most of the Riviera hamlets, stands in a grassy plain which extends up to the very walls of the houses. At harvest time you may count on this common hundreds of corn stacks, for all the farmers of the district store their grain here until it can be threshed. Seen from the hills above, this meadow, with its tent-like ranks of piled up wheat, resembles an encampment; but the rich study in green and gold suggests more peaceful thoughts.

Still higher up, at Caussols, 3,800 feet above sea-level, yet within easy reach of Grasse, and overlooking the coast, is a stretch of grass some three or four miles long, as green as any in the Emerald Isle, and level as the surface of a lake; a *tapis vert* on which no money can be lost, but much health can be won. The herbage looks all the greener and fresher from being surrounded by a barrier of the barest rocks. In St. Vallier, and in the strange Rasselas Valley of Caussols, the well-to-do bourgeois of Grasse and of Le Bar have country houses where they take refuge from the summer heat.

FENESTRA, COL AND LAKE

As we ascend still higher from the coast, grass becomes gradually more abundant, until at last we reach the wide-spread mountain pastures where the sward is embroidered with Alpine flowers. On the *Baus della Frema*, for instance, we are at 8,000 feet, that is, twice the height of Ben Nevis, yet within a walk of St. Martin Vesubia, which village is within a drive of Nice. This indeed is a "Grassy place" which has few equals in snowy Alp or cloud collecting Apennine. The sloping green is sprinkled far and wide with Edelweiss (*Gnaphalium leontopodium*, Stella d'Italia). In no other place that I have heard of is this starry symbol of the snowy summits so enormously abundant. There are acres of it, as easy to pick, unfortunately, as buttercups in a meadow. No climbing is required. Butterflies are swarming. A small fritillary (*Melitæa Cynthia*) chases his mate which wears a lighter livery. A pale green Colias (*C. Phicomone*) scuds along, keeping near the ground lest the breeze should carry him away, then darting suddenly downwards to the shelter of the grass when he needs to rest his wings. A little farther up the ridge, among the patches of snow, you may catch the strange *Aëllo*, a primeval butterfly, and *Callidice*, if you can run fast enough. It is said that Aëllo appears but every other year. Perhaps the Summer at this altitude does not last long enough for the insect to go through its transformations in the space of one season.

Beyond these snowy crests lies Piedmont. Around us are peaks unnumbered and unnamed as yet. In front floats Corsica; not as you see the island from the hills near Nice, but standing high above the sea, the mountains distinctly outlined with their snowy tops. This is a "Grassy place" to be remembered, not only for itself, but by reason of the lovely spots we pass as we approach it from below. After these Alpine pastures the sun-burnt coast looks bare: "The grass faileth, there is no green thing" (Isa. xv. 6). Yet we find fresh verdure here and there. Even the desert has its "Grassy places" (John vi. 10), where those who will may rest and be refreshed.

The enchanted region which I have thus rapidly sketched from coast to crest may, for botanical purposes, be divided into three zones or districts. First, the Coast to a little over seven miles inland, but not rising much above 2,500 feet; next, the Mountain country beyond and above these limits; lastly, the Alpine, from a little over 5,000 feet. Each has its special Fauna and Flora and its peculiar charms. Yet how few strangers have explored even the first of these three zones! How many leave the Riviera unconscious of the wonderland that lies so near them!

39
Flocks and Herds in Provence

WE read in Luke ii. 8 of shepherds on the hills of Palestine keeping watch over their flocks by night. Were these shepherds working, or resting from their work? In other words, were the sheep feeding, or were they sleeping in some fold or enclosure? It seems natural to suppose that both the flocks and their guardians were at rest, for we are not in the habit of regarding the sheep as a nocturnal animal. But there is a difficulty; if those shepherds of Bethlehem were sleeping, how could they see that Angel and that "Heavenly Host"? Now, a shepherd, like any other mortal, must sleep at night if he works all day. His dogs will guard against wild animals. I am inclined to think that these men were not resting, but at work. If Christ were born, as some theologians maintain, not at Christmas, but at the vernal Equinox, when the sun has gained power, the supposition would be much strengthened that the flocks were feeding by night, and the shepherds wide awake.

Whatever the custom may have been in Palestine, the sheep on the hills to the west of the Var feed by night during a great part of the year, that is, during the whole Summer and far into the Autumn: in fact, they avoid the sun as long as it has any heat. At daybreak the shepherd appears on the ridge of the hill, outlined against the sky. He has chosen a spot where it is possible to descend. A narrow track winds down the cliff. Soon the grey line of sheep is hurrying along the face of the mountain. A constant rattling is heard as the stones slide and fall which are set in motion by the feet of the animals. Here and there, where a dangerous leap has to be taken, the shepherd has built up a kind of rude causeway to make it easier for the weaker ones. But the goats scorn any such assistance: they go bounding down the face of the rock, paying little attention to the path. It may happen that the head of the file has reached the valley before the last stragglers have left the mountain top, for there are often hundreds in a single flock. Galloping along the level ground, they make for the fold and disappear. The shepherd also goes to sleep. In the evening he leads them out again to spend the night upon the mountain.

Goats are mingled with the sheep. For some reason or other the shepherds in these parts desire to keep as many as possible of these destructive animals. I suppose that they are more profitable than sheep. But the law allows only a certain proportion: I think it is half-a-dozen goats to a hundred sheep. This law is not strictly obeyed. The peasants say that sheep will not graze by themselves on the mountains. If there are no goats to lead them on, they huddle together and refuse to move. This is why a given number of goats must be mixed with each flock of sheep. In Switzerland also the sheep are led to and from the pastures by goats; and in South Africa the sagacity of the goats sometimes saves a flock of sheep which are in danger of being destroyed by a storm.

It is curious that the goat should be taken as a type of wickedness (Matt. xxv. 32 and 33), whereas the sheep is the symbol of innocence. Perhaps the former animal gives more trouble to the shepherd. Many a time we have seen the goats stray into a field of Sainfoin (*Onobrychis*) when the more obedient sheep have scampered home to the pen. The shepherd encourages this trespassing, and does not permit the dog to interfere. But he is called to account by the owner of the crop, and has to pay for his dishonesty.

Some of these shepherds are very well off, and own as many as two thousand sheep. For the Summer they rent a tract of mountain in the Maritime Alps: in the Winter they migrate westward, and hire a piece of land in the Crau or in the Camargue. Sometimes they convey the flocks by rail, but they generally travel by the road. In this case donkeys or mules are provided to carry the lambs which may be born during the journey.

The Crau is a barren, stony region on the east side of the Rhone delta. To the north is the Durance, and to the south-east the Berre swamp. The town of Arles may be said to preside over this desert. After the Autumn rains some scanty herbage springs up on the Crau: on this the flocks subsist throughout the Winter. The almond is almost the only useful tree which can live upon this barren plain.

Here it was that the fabled fight took place between Heracles and the Ligurians; and these are the stones which Jupiter rained upon the enemies of the Sun God, when the hero had shot all his arrows and was almost overwhelmed by numbers.

The Camargue—"Caii Marii ager"—is the delta of the Rhone. An extraordinary region, consisting of swampy flats and reedy mud-banks, where fever reigns, and where the mirage cheats the eye. These marshes are the haunt of the Ibis, the Flamingo, and the Pelican, and in the shifting channels of the stream the Beaver builds his house. These animals are said to do so much mischief to the dams that a reward is given for killing them.

On the drier ground are herds of half-wild cattle destined for the bull-fights of Languedoc; and it is said that there are also some hundreds of white horses, the descendants of those left there by the Saracens. This is the Winter resort of the innumerable flocks which graze during the Summer in the Maritime Alps and the mountains of Provence. The very similar marshes between Ravenna and the mouth of the Po are described with much eloquence by Hugo Bassi in Harriet H. King's inspired poem, the "Disciples." The patriot priest looks wistfully across that desolate region "where shore and sea and river lose themselves."

It would be interesting to ascertain what effect this nocturnal browsing has upon the sheep. And one would think that those Lepidoptera whose larvæ are night feeders, such as the Satyridæ, must suffer severely; but the butterflies of this family appear, on the contrary, to be very abundant.

The flocks in this district are so numerous that they seem to have reached the limit beyond which starvation must begin. One sees the sheep wandering to and fro, searching vainly for a blade of grass upon the rocky ground.

In the squalid Alpine villages to the east of the Var, great numbers of goats are kept. They are taken out every morning to spend the day upon some distant mountain side. It is a pretty sight to see them trooping back into the village at nightfall, each animal stopping when she comes to her owner's doorway. Besides these village goats, great flocks are driven up from the coast regions, when the grass fails there, to spend the Summer on the highest summits where the chamois has his home. It is

GORGES OF THE VAR

admitted that the numbers of these mischievous animals ought to be greatly reduced in the interest of the woods and forests of the Maritime Alps. The botanist, if he had any voice in the matter, would certainly vote against his enemy the goat.

At an elevation of some five or six thousand feet we come upon the "Vacheries," great sheds where the cattle are kept during the Summer. One of the labours of Hercules was to clear out the Augean stables, where the manure had accumulated to such a depth that no man could remove it. He turned a stream into the building, and thus accomplished his task. We are inclined to look upon this ancient fable as an allegory without any basis of fact. But the primitive and disgusting method is actually practised in the mountain pastures of the Maritime Alps. From time to time the sparkling torrent is turned through the filthy cow-sheds; the picturesque valley is made unsightly by the yellow and polluted stream, and the manure is wasted which might fertilize the fields.

With the milk from these Vacheries they make a kind of cheese, which is so rank that as it is being carried down the valley you can smell it almost before it comes in sight. I suppose that they consume this nasty stuff themselves, for it is not likely that any one could be persuaded to buy it.

In the first days of October the cattle are driven down by the snow from the heights where they have been grazing to pass the Winter in the reeking village, imprisoned in dark vaults beneath the houses.

In the beautiful district east of the Var there are no snug farmhouses scattered through the smiling valley. The whole population, together with the cattle, crowd into the dirty villages. Even the swine are kept in those cave-like stables under each house. Fowls fly in and out at the windows, and the refuse is thrown into the little stream which flows through the middle of the street. The population is sallow and goitrous, and badly tainted with cretinism. Some of these poor creatures cannot even speak, but utter hoarse grunts. They carry great weights like beasts of burden. I have never seen so much cretinism, unless it be in some parts of the Salzkammergut. The children are killed off by dirt and disease. Squalor and ignorance are branded upon everything. Most unlovely are these mountain villages to the east of the Var; they form a wretched contrast to the divine beauty of the scenery.

Perhaps the custom of seeking the shelter of the village every night dates from those early days when each little community was at war with its neighbours, when every stranger was a foe, and no man was safe who slept outside the walls. Possibly, also, before the days of guns, it may not have been easy for a man, without his neighbour's help, to hold his own against the wolves. Even now they sometimes scrape at the doors of the houses when the Winter is severe.

But what great and manifold injury does this custom inflict upon the peasantry! In the overcrowded village cleanliness becomes impossible; the very sense of smell is lost. Moreover, a man cannot live near the ground he tills. After his long day's work the peasant must trudge home, perhaps from the farthest confines of the district. A tired child clings to his back, and the wife follows, balancing on her head the baby in its wooden cradle, which has been lying all day under the shade of a chestnut or a cherry tree.

The French occupation has done a great deal to improve the condition of the people, but it will require more than one generation to educate the villages of the Maritime Alps, and bring them level with those west of the Var. We wish these people greater cleanliness, and some small share of knowledge and enlightenment. But they possess one thing which we might envy them. Theirs is that natural and simple life, in which alone is found whatever happiness this world admits.

Long may these kindly mountaineers preserve their arcadian simplicity, uncontaminated by the so-called civilization which is now beginning to invade their sequestered valley.

40
Wild Animals

"Triste lupus stabulis."

THE most remarkable of the larger wild quadrupeds are the boar, lynx, wolf, and chamois. The Boar is still hunted in the Esterel. Within the memory of persons now living, crops were devastated by this animal above the village of Clans, in the Tinée valley. I can remember a boar, I suppose the last one, being killed in the Var swamps.

Two Lynxes have been shot, of late years, near St. Martin Vesubia. One was attempting to make off with a hide from the outskirts of the village, when a peasant brought him down. "Il laissa la peau," as the saying is. The other was killed by a chamois-hunter. I was offered the skin for a few francs. The lynx is particularly hated by the shepherds, for he is said to destroy more sheep than he can eat. They call him "the blood-sucking wolf."

Wolves are still abundant: but in Summer they retire to the inaccessible snowy summits. Of late years they have been driven backwards farther from the coast. I can very well remember when the postman dared not venture, at certain times of the year, up the Vesubia valley, beyond the village of Lantosca, that is, a little over twenty-five miles north of Nice. I saw a man, not long ago, who had a litter of young wolves in a basket. He was taking them down the valley to claim the reward that is paid for the destruction of these animals. The hunter receives twelve francs for a male wolf, fifteen to eighteen for a female, and six for a young one. Formerly the male wolf or lynx had a price of two pounds upon his head, and the female three pounds. A couple of huntsmen, brothers, living lately in the Tinée valley, killed between them over one hundred and fifty wolves, and not far from one hundred lynxes.

In the old hard-fighting days those men were fittest to survive who most resembled wolves. All nations therefore honoured the wolf. He

VILLEFRANCHE, TOWN AND HARBOUR

represented an ideal, and we always do honour to our ideals. Lupa was the foster mother of Romulus. Lycaon, the Wolf-King and impious cannibal of Arcadia, was one of the most ancient Kings of Greece, if not the very earliest; for he is fabled as the son of Pelasgus. Fierce as wolves were the founders both of Greece and Rome. And was not Alfred the Great a son of "The Noble Wolf"? The third Evangelist is "St. Wolf." I need not mention the hero of Quebec or the unfortunate patriot of '98. The greatest German poet is "Wolfgang" von Goethe: Mozart is also "Wolfgang." Apollo, the sun-god, was "Lyceus," swift and strong as a wolf, that is: and from his temple was named the "Lyceum," by the banks of the Ilissus, where Aristotle taught. (The derivation from a root "luk" = light is nevertheless more reasonable.)

But it was not enough to be as prone to bloodshed and as ruthless as a wolf. The man who could actually transform himself into a wolf had obviously a great advantage over those enemies in whom there still lingered some traces of humanity. In this transformation the Teutonic races were the greatest adepts: they reached the lowest depths of ravening ferocity. The Were-wolf, Loup Garou, or Gerulphus, was common in the Middle Ages. Gervasius assures us that in England he frequently saw men change into wolves. "Vidi frequenter in Anglia homines in lupos mutari."

Beware of persons whose eyebrows meet, for that is considered to be a sign of the Were-wolf, or Gerulphus. Indeed, there is still a good deal of the wolf about many people, beetle-browed or not. The callous indifference of vivisectors to the torture of helpless animals cannot otherwise be explained. Better perhaps the wolf than the fox, for against Reynard strength and courage avail nothing. Isegrim is on the whole less dangerous.

There is a French saying that "Jamais loup n'a connu son père." We are informed by African travellers, Burton and others, that the whole Negro race is still in this primitive stage of morality: "No child knows its own father, and each man counts his sister's children to be his heirs." This lupine morality prevailed among the Picti, the ancestors of the present North Britons, to the great scandal of their more respectable neighbours, the Scoti or Irish Gaels. It is thought that all races, at an early stage of their history, traced their descent thus through the mother.

The superstitions relating to wolves would fill a volume. I will mention one only. Be careful to keep a sharp look-out when wolves are in the neighbourhood, for if a wolf sees you before you catch sight of him, you will thenceforth lose your voice. In Virgil's ninth Eclogue, Mœris, when pressed to sing, makes this excuse: "Lupi Mœrin videre priores,"—"The wolves saw me before I set eyes on them." Young ladies troubled with nervousness may find this hint useful when the hostess insists upon a song.

The Ibex, if not exterminated, is so rare that I have never seen one.

Chamois are brought every year in considerable numbers to St. Martin Vesubia. From the windows of the hotel at the Madonna di Fenestra, the chamois may frequently be seen threading their way among the precipitous rocks. This spot is a great resort for men who take a savage delight in killing this beautiful and harmless creature. The upper part of the Fenestra valley, though geographically in France—in fact it is absolutely cut off from Italy during eight or nine months of the year—belongs politically to Italy. I have been told that when hunters from the French villages trespass in these regions in pursuit of chamois, the Italian game-keepers, if they catch them, do not always confine themselves to confiscating their guns. A solitary poacher in those wilds might be roughly dealt with.

A hotel-keeper in the village of St. Martin Vesubia had a young Chamois, which was so tame that it would climb on to his shoulders. One day it came into the church, through the open window, during service. Sometimes when this animal was at play it would lower its head so as to bring the curved tips of the horns under an imaginary enemy, and then give a sudden and very rapid upward stroke. A newspaper was ripped to pieces with one loud report or crash. If used in this way, against another animal, be it a wolf or a rival buck, these hooked horns must inflict a terrible wound.

It is said that the chamois eats during the Summer a great quantity of a plant which grows in the Alpine region. This does not mingle with the other food and digest, but forms a compact mass, which remains in the stomach of the animal until the Winter, when it serves as a store in the absence of other food. The hunters call this small aromatic plant "Genepie." I succeeded in obtaining a piece, and found it to be a species of Artemisia (*A. mutellina*, see Gillet et Magne, Flora). The natives attribute valuable properties to this little herb. I believe that in some parts of Switzerland the term Genepie is applied to an Achillea.

41
Myoxus
Somniculosus Glis

THERE are in Europe three species of Dormice: first, the little animal about the size of a mouse, which school-boys keep in their lockers. I need not describe this: it appears to be common here, for I asked my gardener to get me one, and he brought, in a short time, a family of them imprisoned in a flower pot. The native name is "Loir," the scientific is *Myoxus Avellana*.

The second species, *Myoxus Nitela*, I am not so well acquainted with: but there is in the valley of the Vesubia, at 3,000 feet, and higher up, an animal which they call "Rat Fleuri." This is almost certainly the Nitela. It has elegant light and dark markings, and a tuft at the end of its tail: size about that of a rat. I have seen them close to the village of St. Martin Vesubia, and they have been brought to me shot; but I have not

MYOXUS NITELA (ON THE RIGHT), MYOXUS GLIS (ON THE LEFT)

succeeded in obtaining one alive, though I have offered a good price.

In the work by Vérany, on the Zoology of the department, *Myoxus Nitela* is not included, though the two other species are given. I have therefore reason to believe that the presence of this little rodent has not before been noticed in this district.

The third species, *Myoxus Glis*, abounds in the chestnut trees of the Vesubia valley. Some specimens, which were sent to the Regent's Park Zoological Garden, were labelled "Myoxus Dryas," if I remember rightly.

The body of this little animal is about six inches long; the tail also measures six inches, and is furry from base to tip, so that it is able to cover itself up when it goes to sleep. The fur on the underside of the body and legs is white. The animal is nocturnal: towards evening you see them appearing on the chestnut trees or under the eaves of barns. A friend asked me where to look for them. I advised him to search in his attic, and there he found a nest full of young ones: these are now in the Zoo.

Farther down the Vesubia valley there are larger Loirs, with a tinge of red in the fur. Possibly this may be the true *Myoxus Glis*. In this case our smaller, darker ones must be either a variety or a fourth species.

If you try to catch a Myoxus, or introduce your hand into the hole where he lives, he bites fiercely, and the bite is very painful. But if taken young, they are easily tamed, and make interesting pets. We kept a number of them in a recess covered with wire gauze: it is about six feet high by four broad, and fairly deep; a regular "glirarium." It is fitted with ladders, and a rope hangs from the top: up and down this they run with perfect ease; in fact, they are so completely arboreal in their habits that they seldom visit the ground.

These animals are of extraordinary activity: I have seen one spring from a chestnut tree to a telegraph wire, run along this at full speed, erect, not after the manner of a sloth; then dart into another tree which stood in the path of the wire. When confined in a small cage they turn somersaults with great rapidity, just as squirrels do; in fact this Myoxus comes very near to a squirrel both in habits and appearance. It is difficult to learn anything about them from the natives: they are eatable; that is the only fact they know or care to know. Accordingly they shoot great numbers of them; I suppose that if they did not do so, few chestnuts would be left, or walnuts. In Herculaneum the cages have been found in which these animals were kept and fattened, for they were considered a delicacy by the Romans.

When they hear any one coming, they run to the cage door to be let out; then they climb all over us, as they would on trees. They will spring fearlessly through the air from one person to another, and they do this very gracefully. One, which we did not consider a good jumper, sprang from one chair-back to another; I found the distance to be three feet, that is, six times the length of its body, and I judge, by the ease with which he took the leap, that he could clear a much greater distance. When at liberty in a room they scamper about, and run up and down the curtains, but they do not try to escape. It is better not to let them loose in the daytime, for, in seeking to avoid the light, they get into inaccessible places.

We feed them on chestnuts, walnuts, hazel nuts, and acorns; taking the shells off the nuts so that they may not have too much practice in nibbling. The untamed ones will bite their way out of almost any wooden cage, and are not in the least degree interesting to keep. They thrive very well on biscuits, and are fond of sugar. We give them also bits of orange, raisins, figs, and fruit of all sorts. Myoxus requires plenty of water; he cannot live, like a rabbit, without drinking. They never refuse a piece of cake, and one of them is quite a connoisseur of sweets. My son treats him to cough lozenges, though the little quadruped does not show any signs of weakness in the throat and lungs.

The German name for the animal is "Siebenschläfer," because it remains torpid during the Winter; but our tame ones have never been torpid. Finding provisions abundant, and the climate mild, they prefer to remain awake.

There must be several broods of *Myoxus Glis*: for a female born in the Autumn produced a young one in the cage the third week in April, and a litter of five more early in June. It is difficult to understand how those can live which are born in the Spring time, when there are no fruits upon the trees. The stores laid up by the old ones can scarcely be enough to supply the parents and two or three broods of young ones until next year's nuts are ripe.

Martial mentions the fatness of the Myoxus, and a German writer accuses them of gluttony: "er friszt so lange er fressen kann." But I do not think that they spend as much time eating as a rabbit or a guinea-pig.

One of our Loirs grew excessively corpulent as Winter approached. Ignorant of his sex, and misunderstanding his motives, we put him in a comfortable cage by himself, and furnished him with every delicacy. He disappointed us, however, as Joanna Southcote did her faithful followers. I believe that this extraordinary obesity was simply the natural preparation for the Winter's sleep which would have overtaken him in the colder mountain air.

Cuvier states that these animals become torpid at a temperature of about 10 C. When the mercury rises to 12 or 14 they revive. But the increase in warmth must be gradual: sudden heat kills them. It is remarkable that if the temperature falls much below 5 C. the Loir awakes and becomes active, so that intense cold has the same effect as heat.

They make several distinct noises. First a buzzing sneezing sound when they are angry. The wild ones buzz whenever any one approaches them, the tame ones only at each other when they fall out. They also utter now and then a loud plaintive piping noise, for no reason that we can discover; and they can also produce a sort of gentle twittering like a bird. The males have sometimes an unpleasant musky smell. The only other drawback of these little animals is that they are so pugnacious. One pair will live in peace, however. Though quarrelsome, they are very timid, and I doubt if they could be successfully managed by any one who did not handle them gently.

My son has one which hangs at full length by its hind feet from his finger, eating nuts which it holds in its forepaws. It will remain in this strange position as long as you keep it supplied with the kernels of hazel nuts, and you may carry it about the house thus. These animals do not dislike hanging head downwards; on the contrary they will eat and even drink while suspended without being taught to do so.

42
Small Quadrupeds

THE Mole is by no means confined to animal food. A peasant in the hill district showed me a store of turnips partially destroyed, as he said, by Moles. They will eat potatoes, and, Buffon says, also acorns.

It is marvellous that these subterranean animals can survive the frequent irrigation which must fill their burrows with water. The fields are often drenched for many successive days and nights, and so skilful are these people in the art of swamping the land, that they will leave no dry spot anywhere, however much the ground may rise and fall. This artificial deluge is a serious drawback to the Summer resorts in the beautiful Vesubia valley; and I believe it is the main cause of the cretinous, goitrous, and unhealthy condition of the inhabitants.

It is well known that Moles are able to swim; but swimming would not help them very much. An English naturalist states that to avoid drowning they will even climb up into trees. A "Moldiwarp" among the foliage of an elm would surely be ill at ease (like a lawyer in heaven!). The front paws of a Mole seem badly adapted for climbing, but the instinct of self-preservation will sometimes compel animals to do things which one would not think possible. An earthworm is a very unlikely creature to go up a tree, yet millions of them do this every year in Brazil when the Amazon overflows its banks. The hungry natives gather them from the tree-tops, where they are found sticking like those fishes which Horace mentions in his second ode.

"Mole" in the Bible is variously translated: chameleon, ibis, salamander, centipede, and swan!

Rodent.—At an elevation of over six thousand feet, a small Rodent, whose name I do not know, came out from under the roots of a larch-tree, and allowed us to take it up and put it down again more than once. Nor did it show any signs of fear. If this little animal is so indifferent to danger, how does it escape being eaten by hawks and weasels? Why is it not quickly exterminated by its natural enemies? I imagined at first that this creature was ill, or for some reason unable to take care of itself, but on another occasion we found one of these same animals on a mountain called the Tournairet at an elevation of over seven thousand feet; and this one was as familiar as the other. Here is a problem for naturalists. That tame mouse of Thoreau's was attracted and rewarded by eatables: but this little Ligurian fellow had no mercenary motives. He refused bread and all other delicacies: indeed, he did not seem to care about civilized food.

Mouse trap.—*A propos* of rodents, Gilbert White cites from an old book a description of a mouse-trap, which neither he nor any one else is able to understand. It is, in fact, a conundrum without an answer. Waterton also describes several ingenious contrivances. The Riviera mouse-trap is both simple and effective. I hope that no one, reading my account of it, will be compelled to say, in the Niçois dialect, "Capisi pas." Take an empty flower-pot, a short rod of iron or hard wood, a thick piece of board large enough to stand the flower-pot on, lastly, a bit of Arundo-stem: a piece of Elder-wood, with the pith removed, will do just as well. Now fix the iron rod upright in the middle of the board, and place the pot mouth downward on the board, with the iron rod passing through the hole which is in the bottom of the pot. Next cut your wooden tube, Arundo or Elder, to such a length that if placed vertically under the pot it would just allow the rim of the latter to rest on the board. To set the trap, remove the flower-pot from the iron rod, slide the tube over the rod, and place a bit of crust or cheese-rind close to the foot of the rod, so as to prevent the tube from touching the board: it should be raised about an inch. Thus the pot, when placed mouth downward on the rod, will hang with its rim just above the board, leaving space for a mouse to pass under. The mouse pulls away the bit of cheese: this allows the Arundo-tube to slide down the rod, and the pot, which is supported by the tube, falls and rests upon the board. Of course the hole in the flower-pot must not be large enough to let the Arundo-tube slip through.

Weasel.—A douanier gave me an interesting account of a battle which he said he had witnessed between a Weasel and a viper. The two animals fought fiercely until they were out of breath; then they retired, each one to a certain plant, of which he ate a leaf or two. By this they were so refreshed and renovated that they were soon able to renew the battle with redoubled energy. After each "round" the combatants returned to these same plants to be cured of their wounds and reanimated for the fray. So intent were they upon the struggle that the customs officer was permitted to approach quite near. Being curious about the herb to which the Weasel had recourse, he pulled it up while the pugnacious little animal was engaged with his adversary. Now when the Weasel returned, wounded and bleeding, to the magic herb, lo, it was gone! While he searched here and there in vain for the antidote to the poison that was working in his veins, the serpent, restored to health and strength, returned to the attack, and conquered easily.

I asked the douane-man to show me those two plants. One of them he found without much difficulty by the border of the little torrent where we sat. This was the vulnerary or "simple" which had cured the wounds inflicted by the Weasel. I was naturally much more anxious to know the sure and certain remedy for snake-bite. Was it some deadly weed rising rank and poisonous from the foam of Cerberus, and potent, on the *similia similibus* principle, to counteract the venom of the viper? Was it Hemlock with spotted stalk, or Henbane, or the shrieking Mandrake? No one will ever know; for the douanier could remember neither the leaf nor the blossom of the herb which he had pulled up from the ground. Perhaps it was that mysterious charm which Hermes of the golden rod gave to Odysseus to preserve him from the spells of the enchantress Circe:

> *"Its root was black, its flower resembled milk;*
> *Gods called it* Moly; *difficult for men*
> *To dig it; but the gods can all things do."*

Or was it perchance the divine *Soma*, sacred to the great god Indra? *Allium magicum* claims to represent the Moly of the ancients. I have grown this plant, and can certify that the bulb is not black; so the claim must be disallowed.

VILLAGE OF LA ROQUETTE

Strange that it is so hard to find this herb which cures the snake-bite, heals the sick, and remedies all human ills! What are the botanists about? Dull fellows, with all their learning they cannot even tell us whether it is exogen or endogen, acrogen, or thallogen. Alas for these dark days! The Moly no longer grows in the sunlit Isles of Greece, nor can you pick the sacred Soma by the Ganges bank or on the Coromandel coast. The spot where I sat chatting with the douane-officer was surpassingly lovely; but even in the beautiful valleys of the Maritime Alps you may search in vain for that mysterious plant, whose secret is known only to the Weasel.

43
Birds

IN the Spring of 1892 a number of large birds passed slowly over the outskirts of Nice. They flew in a leisurely manner towards the north-east, and at no great elevation, so that we had a good view of them. I considered them to be Vultures, as Eagles are not gregarious; and an English resident, who was still nearer to them, formed the same opinion. He told me that there was great commotion among his poultry, and that the pigeons flew in at the bedroom windows for safety.

As I watched these great birds of prey, wheeling and sailing overhead, I thought what a sensation they would have caused in ancient times! What anxious speculations, what omens of good fortune or forebodings of disaster!

Those Vultures seen by Romulus and Remus were probably birds of this same species.

The Griffon Vulture is common in the Pyrenees, the Sierras, Sardinia, and Sicily. Seebohm states that it is less abundant in the Alps. But Vérany includes the bird among those "qui vivent sédentaires dans le département des Alpes Maritimes," and he mentions it as nesting near Tenda. The Griffon Vulture has been known to wander as far north as England. The flight of this species (says Seebohm) is very majestic: they float and soar without apparent effort, as if they disdained to flap a wing, wheeling round and round in grand sweeps.[34]

Birds and beasts of prey were much bolder before the days of guns. In countries where the natives do not possess firearms these creatures have even now but little fear of man. Bates relates that the Urubu Vultures on the Amazons are not afraid to enter a house. "My cook," he says, "could not leave the kitchen for a moment on account of their thievish propensities. Some of them were always loitering about, watching their opportunity; and the instant the kitchen was left unguarded, the bold marauders marched in, and lifted the lids of the saucepans with their beaks in order to rob them of their contents." There is no impossibility about that good old story of Tanaquil and Tarquin. If a Vulture will take the lid from a pot on the kitchen fire, an Eagle might very well snatch a man's hat from his head, if he happened to mistake it for something edible.

Near the village of St. Martin Vesubia an Eagle one day took a chicken which was at our very feet. The mother of this chicken, a large hen of a very good breed, seized the Eagle by the wing, and almost prevented him from rising. The courageous fowl was dragged along the ground: if she could have held on a few seconds longer, or if we had not been too much surprised to move, the Eagle would have paid for his temerity. The bird on this occasion swooped from north to south. This would prevent his shadow giving warning of his approach. I wonder if birds of prey habitually take this precaution.

In the spring of 1898 a postman going from Sospello to a neighbouring village was attacked by Eagles, and so seriously injured that he died not long afterwards.

Ant Eater or Wryneck, French Torcol. This bird is about the size of a sparrow. It lies on the ground by an ant-path; places its tongue, which is cylindrical and almost as long as its body, in the way of the insects, and draws them in when they adhere to it. The plumage and markings of the Ant Eater are well adapted to make the bird inconspicuous when it has settled on the ground to feed. The native name is "Fourmilier." I believe that it is commoner on the hills than by the coast, and I have been told that it nests in a hollow tree.

It is difficult to observe the habits of this or indeed of any other bird, because the incessant persecution makes them wild. Every feathered thing is ruthlessly shot down; even little fly-catchers, not much bigger than a bumble bee, are blown to pieces *à bout portant.* Between the cruelty of this "chasse" and our fashionable pigeon-shooting there is little to choose. Both show a brutal indifference to suffering, a contempt for Nature, and an incapacity for any higher recreation. The natives have a great appetite for all kinds of small birds. There is hardly a peasant who does not trap them, even when the law forbids. They are said to eat even swallows. No wonder that the birds which warble in the olive-groves have no life in their song. They twitter in a half-hearted manner as if they expected every moment to be their last.

A naturalist (Mr. E. Lockwood) saw the following "small game" exposed for sale in the market of Nice: blackbirds and thrushes, hawfinches, goldfinches, mountain finches, with here and there a woodpecker, Sardinian warbler, and jay. These (he says) constitute the ortolans of visitors, just as short-toed larks and wagtails pass for ortolans in India. Strings of robins and chaffinches were also hanging up, and a kite, perhaps the last of his race, which some fortunate *chasseur* had brought down. Even the insignificant size of the goldcrest does not save it from destruction.

M. Vérany thus protests against the shooting of insectivorous birds: "Elle est absurde, et même très nuisible, la chasse que sans pitié on fait, surtout dans la campagne de Nice, aux oiseaux à bec fin, qui sont les insectivores par excellence."

Lesser Bittern.—One of these was found in our yard. The servant imagined that we had purchased it, and, as we keep a great many strange creatures, she was not very much surprised to see another novelty. "What does the new bird eat?" she asked. The Bittern was soon captured. He was injured either by a shot or by a stone. My wife attempted to doctor him, but the ungrateful creature very nearly pecked her eye out. We gave him a frog, but he could not, or would not, eat.

Bats are not scientifically classed with birds, but I will follow Victor Hugo's example and number them among them among the fowls of the air. He says of the Bat:—

"La chauve-souris, triste oiseau!
Sœur du hibou funèbre et de l'orfraie avide."

So Hood in the "Haunted House,"—

"The startled bats flew out, bird after bird."

Why do these "sad birds" fly about in midday during the Winter in this district? Has the ancient curse been revoked, and are the daughters of Minyas reconciled to Bacchus? The native name is "Rattapinnata" or

Winged Rat, analogous to the German "Fledermaus," and our old-English "Flittermouse."

There is towards the eastern end of the main Boulevard in Nice a wonderful Bird Cage. I often pass that way on purpose to look at it. This cage is of wire gauze, and tubular, forming a long loop which runs from the window of an entresol all round the garden, passing under the shade of the palms and Dracænas, and among the shrubs. Swarms of small birds disport themselves in this aviary, going indoors to feed when they are hungry.

Sir Thomas Hanbury kindly sends me the following Notes on the Birds of the Riviera:—

I have been asked as to the birds I have observed frequenting my garden and the neighbourhood. The subject is a large one, and it is impossible to do justice to it in a short notice; besides I cannot claim to be an ornithologist; and except in my garden and woods, where no gun is permitted, the birds are persecuted in so merciless a manner as to render them difficult to approach for purposes of identification and study.

Birds of prey are seldom seen at La Mortola, an occasional kestrel or sparrowhawk at most. The eagle owl (*Strix bubo*) is found in the near mountains; it and other species of Owls would be of the greatest service in relieving the country of the excessive abundance of rats and mice; but I have failed in my efforts to induce the peasants not to destroy these useful birds.

The Corvidæ in this part of the coast are represented by the raven; the crow, rook, and jackdaw being unknown. Once only have I seen a flock of choughs (*Corvus graculus*), and they being fired at soon disappeared.

The Hoopoe is common in the month of March, on its way from Africa northwards, and the same may be said of the quail in the month of May, when they arrive in a very exhausted state.

The splendid-plumaged bee-eater (*Merops apiaster*) is a rare bird of passage. I have only seen it once, when a flock of ten visited my garden in the early morning. The night jar, or goatsucker, I have noticed on a single occasion, as also that remarkably gorgeous bird, the golden oriole. The dipper (*Cinelus aquaticus*) is common on the banks of the upper part of the river Roya; herons, bitterns, and

VILLAGE OF LANTOSCA

kingfishers are occasional visitors to this swift-flowing stream, and come even, in mistaken quest of food, to the dry slope that forms my garden.

The blackbird, the robin, and chaffinch are Winter visitors only, retreating to cooler and moister spots in the mountains when the breeding season arrives; not so the blue thrush of the Mediterranean, which remains the whole year, and, though a very shy bird, evinces an extraordinary liking for buildings, frequenting ruins or roosting in an outhouse if not disturbed.

The blackcap is the commonest bird in my garden, and the one I most appreciate, for its lively habit and sweet song; unmolested it becomes almost fearless, and it is charming to see it in the month of February, when, perched on the flower stem of the Aloe, it sips the nectar flowing from the lovely blossoms.

Nightingales arrive in April, and nest in large numbers in my garden, singing day and night during the breeding season: they exhibit extraordinary tameness and confidence, resuming their song almost at once if purposely interrupted by clapping of hands or other noise. The parent birds and their offspring leave for the north when the Summer heat begins.

The swift, the swallow, and the martin are abundant, and appear on this coast a few days earlier than in England; the sand martin, however, remains the whole Winter, but is not common.

The Alpine swift is to be seen for a day or two early in the Summer on its way to Switzerland. I consider its flight exceeds in velocity that of any other bird.

The cuckoo is common enough in April and May, but prefers the mountains. The cuckoo's mate, or wryneck, is heard in the Spring, by its repeated sharp note, oftener than it is seen.

The red-legged partridge is common on the mountains. I have seen one specimen of the flamingo, said to have been shot in the valley of the Roya.

Space does not permit of giving more than the names of other birds frequenting La Mortola, such as the goldfinch, yellow wagtail, wren, golden crested wren, redstart, tits, stonechat, siskin, and lark. Nor can I describe the many kinds of gulls and divers that frequent the rocks on the sea shore of this cape.—T. H.

Notes:

[34] Sir Thomas Hanbury is sceptical, he suggests that these great birds may have been Herons! I see them (he says) every Spring for one or two days: but I cannot conceive the reason of their coming, as there is nothing for them to eat on our part of the coast. They descend the valley of the Roya, and go westward towards the Var, returning disconsolate to the lakes and rivers of the mountains.

Sir Thomas's note is interesting: but surely it is not very difficult "to know a Hawk from a Hernshaw," as the saying runs.

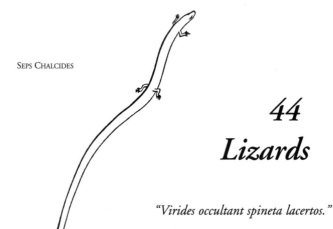

44
Lizards

"Virides occultant spineta lacertos."

AT least half-a-dozen species of lizards occur on the Riviera: the lively and ubiquitous Wall Lizard (*Lacerta muralis*), two species of Gecko, the Green Lizard (*L. viridis*), the splendid Ocellata, and the queer-looking Seps. Risso enumerates several varieties of that inveterate sun-worshipper the bright-eyed little *Muralis*. The manners and customs of these lizards are more curious than might be expected. I watched a pugnacious little saurian one day which had taken up its post on a low broad-topped stone wall. When another lizard appeared, he drove him away. All the others fled: no one seemed a match for him. The little tyrant had the wall to himself. When a claimant turned up, he had only to arch his neck and assume a threatening attitude, then the other immediately showed the white feather. After a while, I saw a rather small one crawl up and trot along in a jaunty manner towards the champion. I expected to witness a terrible fight, for it was evident that this little fellow was full of pluck; but lizard number one pretended not to notice him, and shammed to be quite intent upon fly-catching. The new-comer actually walked across the back of the other, although there was plenty of room to pass. He pocketed the insult, and did not budge. Lizard number two now took a short turn on the top of the wall, just to inspect the domain, as it were; then he returned, and this time, instead of passing over the back of the other, he calmly walked underneath him! Now, to pass under a lizard, you must disturb him considerably, for his abdomen touches the stone on which he stands. Even this outrage was not resented. One could not help thinking of Pistol and Fluellen and the leek.

It is a question whether this animal can hear sounds. A friend of mine thought that the Ligurian lizards will listen to whistling; he treated them to a mixture of "Home, Sweet Home" and "Rule Britannia," and persuaded himself that they enjoyed it. Mr. G. H. Brian, Sc.D., F.R.S., states that a green lizard, running up the trunk of a cork tree, would stop to listen when he whistled gently. There is a story of a lizard which would come out from its hiding-place on hearing the adagio to Mozart's quartet in C. If this lizard was a Niçois, he must have had a more classical taste in music than the other natives of these parts, to judge by the pieces one hears in the Jardin Public.

A lizard with two tails lived for some time close to our sitting-room window. We determined to catch him and keep him as a curiosity; but he made himself scarce. I have never seen another. Lizards without any tail are extremely common, especially where there are boys about. Virgil says that lizards avoid the midsummer sun. I do not remember any occasion when it was too hot for these little salamanders on the Riviera, though it is often much too warm for a human being. But I have never (thank heaven!) spent the whole Summer in Nice. So I inquired of the natives whether the Wall Lizards disappear at any time during the Summer or Autumn. I was assured that they are always to be seen.

Perhaps in the latitude of Rome and Naples the habits of the lizards may be different, for I am unwilling to believe that Virgil is mistaken in so simple a matter.

It is natural that as we approach the tropics we should begin to find traces of the conditions which prevail in the torrid zone. Now, in some hot countries insects and reptiles go into a Summer sleep during the dry season, and the trees shed their leaves. As we might expect from the heat and drought of the Summer, there are traces on the Riviera of this period of repose. The Laurustinus (*Viburnum tinus*) for instance, the Giant Euphorbia (*E. dendroides*), and some other shrubs, lose their leaves in the latter part of the Summer and put forth new ones in the Winter.

GECKO AND WALL LIZARD

It is difficult to observe this phenomenon, and to draw up a complete list of the plants and animals which become torpid, for it happens just at that time of year when the coast district of Liguria has become almost uninhabitable for northerners, and when even the natives are fain to take refuge in the mountains. The term "æstivation," the opposite of "hibernation," is sometimes applied to this Summer sleep of plants and animals. In elementary botany the word has, of course, a different meaning.

I have alluded to the common *Gecko*, or Fanfoot, in another chapter. The native name is "Lagramua," but for some inscrutable reason it is commonly called a "Tarantula." Cold weather makes these creatures torpid. A number of them roll up together into a ball, and lie hid in the crevices of an old wall. The toes are flattened, and have on the underside a series of plates like those on the back of the sucking-fish. By means of this structure it can cling to a smooth wall, or to the ceiling. It moves noiselessly, and some species utter a mournful sound; at least the books say so. My daughter tells me that she has often heard them squeak like a mouse.

Prince Bonaparte, "Fauna Italica," thus eloquently commences his article on the Gecko: "Vedi un esempio dell' ingratitudine degli uomini. Quest' innocente animaletto, chiamato Tarantola, intento di continuo a purgare i luoghi in cui vive, e sono quegli stessi in cui viviam noi, da ragni, da zanzare, e da un infinità d'altri insetti molesti, non ha saputo trarre altre ricompense dai beneficj che ci rende fuori che calunnie e persecuzioni." (This harmless little creature, which clears our houses of vermin, reaps nothing but ingratitude.)

One is inclined to suspect that the Gecko is able to adapt his colour to that of the wall on which he lives. It is sometimes almost impossible to see them until they move, and even their eyes appear to take the tint of the stone.

I have seen but one other living creature that imitated the surface of rock or stone so successfully: that is Briseis, a butterfly of the Satyridæ. When this insect settles on a stony spot, and raises his wings, so as to expose the under surface, and completely hide the colours on the upper side, it becomes practically invisible. You may come within a few inches, and still fail to distinguish the butterfly. *Satyrus Hermione*, again, when perched on the trunk of a chestnut tree, may defy the sharpest eye. From what enemies is the Gecko thus carefully concealed? No quadruped can reach him as he clings to the vertical cliffs by his adhesive toes. Either he fears some bird, or, what seems to be more likely, he finds the disguise useful to beguile his prey.

Another species of Gecko occurs on the Riviera. It is lighter in colour. I have been told that the sea-rocks east of the port of Nice are good places to look for it.

"You unsanctified son of a house lizard!" was the remark addressed by Miss Kingsley to a clumsy negro who had upset the boat and capsized her into some very dirty water. The provocation was certainly sufficient to make the most good-natured person say something emphatic, and the fair traveller was equal to the occasion. If the "house-lizard" here alluded to was a Gecko, we may infer that this unfortunate little animal is in bad odour wherever he is found.

The Green Lizard is widely spread in the south of Europe. It is common enough in the neighbourhood of Nice, but not very easy to catch. *Lacerta viridis* is much larger than the Sun Lizard. I have never seen one in a town or village. The native name is "Lambert."

This species extends as far north as Jersey. Gilbert White speaks of a "beautiful green lizard" occurring in Devonshire, and also on the sunny sand-banks near Farnham, in Surrey. But it is not certain whether he refers to *L. viridis* or to the greenish variety of the Sand-lizard (*L. agilis*), a much smaller animal found near Poole, in Dorset. The green lizard is easily tamed, and will eat out of the hand, and drink from the hollow of the palm. If enclosed in the hands, it likes the warmth, and makes no effort to escape.

The Ocellata is larger still, a miniature crocodile with his gaping mouth and wriggling gait. Nothing can be more beautiful than the colours of this animal just after he has changed his skin. They appear to be marked with burnished gold. When captured they bite bravely, but are not strong enough to hurt. The peasants accuse the Ocellata of eating grapes. I do not know to what elevation this species extends, but I have seen it at 3,000 feet, or a little over.

The Blind Worm (*Anguis fragilis*), here as elsewhere taken for a snake, is abundant at the roots of the Bamboo.

A very curious creature, something like a Blind Worm with legs, occurs here and there on the Riviera. The scientific name is *Sēps Chalcides*. I have seen this lizard in captivity, but I have never been fortunate enough to find it wild. It frequents damp places or swamps; the embouchure of the Var would be a good place to look for it. The brothers Gal, who keep the natural history shop in the Corso, Nice, showed me one which they caught at Beaulieu. It cannot be very common, for many of the natives are not aware of its existence. In Sicily, where this harmless little animal is abundant, it is regarded as poisonous and destroyed by the natives. When frightened, it clings to the decaying stem or leaf of some marsh plant, hoping thus to escape notice. It is very timid, and no provocation will make it bite. Seps is viviparous. The Niçois name of the animal is "Aguglioun de prat." The Italians call it "Cicigna" or "Cecella."

In the "Prometheus Unbound," Act iii., Scene I, Shelley mentions the Seps:—

"All my being,
Like him whom the Numidian Seps did thaw
Into a dew with poison, is dissolved,
Sinking through its foundations."

On this passage, a friend, who is a brilliant lecturer on English Literature, gives me the following note: Shelley alludes to verse 763 of Lucan's "Pharsalia," where the army of Cato, passing through the Libyan desert, is plagued by poisonous snakes—worst among them the "exiguus Seps," which fixed its fangs in the leg of one Sabellus, and inflicted a fatal wound, so that his body seemed to dissolve and putrefy: "membra natant sanie."

Visitors to the Riviera need not be alarmed: there is nothing evil about the "exiguus Seps" excepting his ill-omened name. Dr. Alfred Russel Wallace assures me that there is no poisonous lizard in the Old World, and only one in the New. Shelley's "Numidian Seps," if indeed so deadly a reptile ever existed, has certainly no connection with our innocent little lizard. The Greek root "Sep" or "Sap" means "corruption": hence we have "sapro-phyte," a plant which lives on decaying organic substances, as do many Fungi; and "anti-septic," that is, "against decomposition."

HYLA ARBOREA, THE TREE FROG

45
Tree Frogs

"Spina viret; venter, pars maxima corporis, albet:
Limosoque novæ saliunt in gurgite ranæ."
OVID

THE Tree Frog, *Hyla aborea*, really a toad, is a noisy and obstreperous little creature, whether he sits in an Agave and performs a solo, or croaks in a hoarse chorus at the margin of some tank or reservoir. The din is deafening if you come too near; still it is one of those natural noises to which one is easily reconciled.

The sleepless stranger may take comfort from the fact that things might be worse by far. He may thank his stars that the Riviera Frogs, though they sing out lustily, are not so stentorian as the Brazilian ones. We read in Wallace, "Travels on the Amazon," that one of these Transatlantic disturbers of the peace "makes a noise something like what one would expect a Frog to make, namely, a dismal croak; but the sounds uttered by the others were like no animal noise that I ever heard before. A distant railway train approaching, and a blacksmith hammering on his anvil, are what they exactly resemble. They are such true imitations, that when lying half dozing in the canoe, I have often fancied myself at home hearing the familiar sounds of the approaching mail-train, and the hammering of the boiler-makers at the ironworks." Talk about *tapage nocturne!*

Green Frogs are not invariably green (if I may be permitted to speak thus), any more than a blackbird is invariably black, or an etymology invariably true. They can be of a beautiful turquoise blue. These cerulean Frogs are of great value: I think that as much as a hundred francs has been given for one. They are to be obtained from a man who keeps a crockery shop in Mentone. He has a "speciality" of blue frogs. People accuse him, so I hear, of dyeing the epidermis of the animals by making them swallow some pigment. The pottery man denies this: he says that they are quite natural, like a green pink or a twelve inch waist.

Perhaps this ingenious person, if he finds that the public appreciate his novelties, may produce, or rather discover, Frogs of any desired tint to match a lady's costume; scarlet frogs for an anarchist, orange for a unionist. Just think what a "shindy" there would be if an orange Frog were to appear in a ditch tenanted by the ordinary green home-ruling sort! What a splash and splutter; what a "row"!

The purchaser of a certain turquoise Frog has made a wonderful discovery, which, however I am disposed to accept *cum grano salis*. You feed the Frog on fireflies, which he swallows as we do oysters. They continue to shine in the interior of the Frog, which is thus beautifully illuminated, for the light glows through his translucent body the more easily as he has no ribs. He is, in fact, "éclairé à jour," an object of dazzling brilliancy, like Glycera's countenance "nimium lubricus adspici"; or like those brightly shining bottles we see at night in the windows of a chemist's shop.

To make the illuminated turquoise Frog absolutely perfect, he should be taught to croak in arpeggios.

St. George Mivart, F.R.S., has written a volume on "The Common Frog." He tells us many interesting things about the small saltatory reptile, which is not a reptile: how he has three eyelids; how he cannot breathe when his mouth is open; and so forth. But what would Mivart say to the illuminated turquoise frog? What new experiments would he try upon this *un*-common Frog?

There is probably no new experiment which could be tried upon a Frog, this never-failing resource of the physiological experimenter. It would take long indeed, says Mivart, to tell the sufferings of much-enduring Frogs "in the cause of science." We have tried what Frogs can do without their heads; what their legs can do without their bodies; what their arms can do without either head or trunk; what is the effect of the removal of their brains; how they can manage without their eyes and without their ears; what results follow all kinds of local irritations, chokings, poisonings, and mutilations the most varied. And each of these experiments is repeated a hundred thousand times.

For the particulars about the turquoise Frog I am indebted to the late Mr. E. Conolly, a Winter visitor, whose ready wit and whose stoical endurance of suffering are well known to the residents in Cimiez.

There is one question which I do not think that the men of science, with all their experiments "in the cause of science," can answer; one secret which we cannot wrest from the wretched little animal by all the torments of the laboratory, or by all the tortures of Torquemada. How does he find his way to water from any distance, and in spite of any obstacles? I have met the Tree Frog on a dry hill-side; there was no tank or cistern that I could see. But I am certain that the little fellow knew where to have a drink and a swim just as well as a thirsty Niçois knows his way to the buvette.

Darwin ("Voyage of Beagle") found in South America a little black toad with a vermilion belly. This animal was crawling about during the heat of the day on dry sand hills and arid plains where not a single drop of water could be found. The great naturalist supposed that this toad depends on the dew for its moisture, which is probably absorbed by the skin; for these reptiles possess great powers of cutaneous absorption. Thinking to give this little toad a great treat, Darwin carried it to a pool of water; but he was surprised to find that the animal could not swim, in fact it would have drowned if he had not helped it out again. If the green Frog has the same power of imbibing dew through the skin, we are able to understand how he subsists upon the dry hill-sides of the Riviera at a distance from the water.

An Englishman carried home a couple of green Frogs, and placed them in his hothouse. Before long they both disappeared, and found their way to a basin in a neighbouring garden. Here they lifted up their voices and croaked triumphantly, to the great surprise of the dwellers in that house. They were captured, and taken back to the hothouse, but as soon as ever they felt dry again they absconded, climbed over the wall, and turned up in the pond as before.

There is another little mystery about the green Frog. How can he perch with his tender body on the top of an Opuntia? If he attempted to jump on to a Cactus from some other plant, he might impale himself: he has too much sense to run a risk of this sort. It follows that he must climb up from the foot of the Cactus, as he is not able to fly. He must, therefore, thread his way through a labyrinth of spines which scarcely allow room for his body to pass. How would you like to walk a mile naked, squeezing your body between the very sharpest bayonet-points every inch of the way? Yet the Tree Frog can do this, and seems to enjoy it. Once securely seated on the Opuntia, or in the heart of an Agave, he is like a New Zealander in his pah, or a Scotch metaphysician entrenched behind the Absolute, the Infinite, and the Unconditioned; you cannot get at him anyhow.

46
Shells

THE following are a few notes on those molluscs which are the most closely connected with the everyday life of the people.

Tritonia is a large spiral shell, used as a musical, or rather, unmusical instrument. It is capable of producing the most discordant sounds; worse even than that hideous cycle-horn with which the "scorching" wheelman announces his approach, and scatters the terrified pedestrians. When an ill-assorted marriage takes place, or one which is considered to involve some scandal or disgrace, the Tritonia is brought to bear, and the guilty couple are treated every evening to a "sérénade

SPIRAL SEA HORN

assourdissante." Now and again the police are compelled to interfere on behalf of the unoffending neighbours.

In the country districts this primitive trumpet is sometimes used by a man who sells scented flowers to the distilleries. When the village children hear the more or less melodious sounds, they bring out the wild Jasmin flowers (Daisemin the natives call it) which they have collected for traffic with the perfumery man.

This is the ponderous sea-horn on which the Persian Prince in Moore's "Fire Worshippers" blew

> *"His signal deep and dread*
> *As those the storm-fiend at his rising blows."*

Shells, we read, were the original trumpets of mankind. The fishermen of Newfoundland blow a *Strombus gigas* as a foghorn: they must have plenty of practice, for this is the home of fogs, a veritable Niflungs region. This shell was formerly used in Wales as a dinner call. Among the miners of the Guernsey granite (diorite) quarries it served, more appropriately, as a blasting signal.

Tritonia is a Mediterranean gasteropod, but I do not know on what exact part of the coast the sailors find it.

I have alluded to snail-eating in another chapter. The species considered edible belong to the genus *Helix*. Those preferred by the natives are *H. aspersa*, *H. vermiculata*, and *H. nemoralis*. The first of these three is the common garden snail of which the thrushes are so fond. He makes havoc of our choicest plants, but the Frenchman turns the tables on him; for he is a favourite article of diet, especially on Good Fridays and fast days. *H. vermiculata* is not British. But *H. nemoralis*, the Belted or Girdled Snail, is our commonest land-shell. The diameter is about one inch; the colour varies from lemon to olive, and the brown bands are also very variable.

Labouring men eat *H. pisana* and *H. variabilis* boiled with beans. Pisana is one of the rarest and most beautiful of our British land-shells. It occurs in Cornwall and in Ireland.

H. operta, the glass snail, is considered a great delicacy by the Niçois, especially when it is found closed by its operculum. Most of the land-snails have lost this horny door; they are unable to "sport the oak," so to speak, and they shut themselves in only when the time comes to hibernate. Rabbit and "Cantaréu" (the native name of this snail) are dishes always ready in the rustic cabaret.

In the "Eight Communes" of the Ventimiglia district a law was passed imposing a fine of four lire on persons caught stealing snails from their neighbours' ground. If the thief was mean enough to pilfer them

<small>PREHISTORIC NECKLACE FROM THE CAVES NEAR MENTONE</small>

by night, the fine was doubled (W. Scott).

It is curious that the edible snail *par excellence*, the large *Helix pomatia*, is less esteemed by the Ligurians than the smaller species just mentioned. The coast climate is too warm for the Pomatia; it is brought in from the hills. This is the snail which the Romans ate, and which they are supposed to have introduced into Britain. It does not extend farther north in England than the midland counties. On the chalk downs it is particularly abundant.

The French and Italians are not the only people who appreciate these snails. The Swiss of the eastern cantons cultivate them in "snail-gardens"; and it is even whispered that the workmen of Didcot do not despise them. Passing strange, and a sad sign of national degeneracy that your true-born Englishman should feed on "cockled snails," as Shakespeare calls them. The shiny-black mussel, the corrugated cockle, the sewage-fed oyster, the carnivorous whelk, all these we may eat without loss of self-respect; but a snail fattened on bran and groundsel; no, never! Leave that to the foreigneering Frenchman. We blush for those workmen of Didcot!

A story is told of a town that was besieged. The defenders were starving; they grew thinner and leaner every day. One woman only showed no signs of distress; she remained as fat as an ortolan. People began to talk about witchcraft, and it would have fared ill with the poor widow had she not made a clean breast of it, and confessed that her life was preserved by snails, not sorcery.

VENUS' EAR

Sir Richard Burton, the oriental linguist and traveller, when a lad, had a bone to pick with an elderly French lady who lived next door. Wishing to pay her out without danger of detection, he collected an enormous number of snails and put them in her garden. Next morning the old lady was surprised to find a perfect plague of snails upon her plants and shrubs. But she was not in the least annoyed or disgusted. She gathered them carefully and carried them indoors to cook. A *bonne aubaine!* Burton's revenge was a failure. The distinguished Irishman found that if you have *maille à partir* with an elderly French lady, it's no use trusting to snails!

The diameter of Pomatia is given by Captain Brown ("Conchology") as a little under two inches, but Wood says that this species may grow to the size of a man's fist. What a dainty morsel, by St. Pansard, patron des goinfres!

The empty shells of this large species are used to illuminate most tastefully the village windows, balconies, and terraces during the Summer fêtes. On the window-sill you place a row of little damp clay mounds. On each of these you stick a shell, mouth upwards, and into every shell you pour a little oil, as Morgiana did into those forty jars. A bit of cotton serves as a wick. The effect of these little elf-lights is bewitching, and the cost is almost nil.

The French "Limace" and "Limaçon" come from the Latin "Limax." Varro derives "Limax" from "limus," mud; "Limax a limo, quod ibi vivit"; because it lives in the mud. But snails do *not* live in the mud, like eels. What muddle-headed fellows these ancient philologers were, to be sure! It is much more likely that "Limax" comes from "*lim*-us" because the animal is "s-*lim*-y." The northeners are fond of beginning words with an "S"; compare "niv" and "s-now." "Snail," old English "snaegl," is connected with "sneak."

The Ligurian fowls are as fond of snails as their masters. We used to gather double handfuls of that very small spindle-shaped species which covers the tops of posts and railings. These the hens swallowed, shell and all.

Associated with the remains of those prehistoric giants in the Mentone caves, shells among other ornaments have been found. It is remarkable that these shells do not occur in the Mediterranean. Some of them are from the Atlantic coast, others belong to a fossil species from Switzerland. A graceful necklace is supposed to have been formed by the shells of *Nassa neritea* combined with the vertebræ of a fish and teeth of a deer.

Venus' Ear.—These beautiful perforated shells abound at Antibes and at Villefranche. The mollusc is eaten in Japan. I do not think that they are large enough on this coast to take the place of the oyster.

The nacreous ornaments sold in Nice are mostly cut from the shell of *Turbo rugosus.*

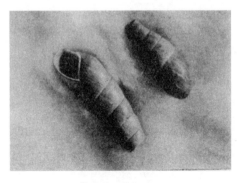

BULIMUS DECOLLATUS

47

Butterflies and Moths

"Et je suis si joli! Si tu voyais mes ailes
Trembler aux feux du jour, transparentes et frêles."
VICTOR HUGO, "Le Sylphe"

GREAT Britain has 65 or 66 species of Butterflies (*Rhopalocera*). I
believe that about 88 occur in the north-west of France. Kirby estimates
the European species at 300. Hofmann figures about 235. Of these over
140 are supposed to occur on the Riviera. My son found 109 near Nice
before he had been working very long.

There is probably no district in Europe where so great a variety of
insects can be found within so short a radius, or where so rich a
collection may be made. The Vesubia valley is a veritable "pays de
cocagne" for the entomologist; you may meet lepidopterists and
coleopterists from distant parts of Europe in the village of St. Martin
Vesubia.

CHARAXES JASIUS

Almost every British butterfly can be caught near Nice without any trouble, and some of our rarest species are extremely abundant here; for instance, the Queen of Spain (*A. Lathonia*), the Bath White (*P. Daplidice*), the Camberwell (*V. Antiopa*). The Black-veined White (*A. Cratægi*) will settle on damp ground in such numbers that you may take a dozen in one stroke of the net. The Fruit-tree Swallow-tail (*P. Podalirius*) is common everywhere up to nearly 3,000 feet.

In the mountain regions, Alpine and sub-Alpine species fly in swarms; for instance, *A. Amathusia* and the semi-transparent *P. Apollo*. The female of this latter insect is able to emit a buzzing sound. I heard this very distinctly on one occasion: the Apollo when gently transferred from a flower to my hand did not fly away, but continued to stridulate. Darwin found in South America a butterfly of the genus Papilio, which made a clicking sound, audible at a distance of twenty yards.

Some of the Northern insects are represented by Southern species. For instance, the Glory of Provence (*Aurore de Provence*) or Southern Orange-tip (*A. Euphenoides*) is much commoner round Nice than our *A. Cardamines.* The White Admiral (*L. Sibylla*) is absent, and its place is taken by *L. Camilla*, which lives upon the honeysuckle (*Lonicera*). The Comma (*V.C.-album*) is less frequently met with than the allied *V. Egea.* Of these we took about a dozen in one afternoon at Vence. It is not easy to understand the Spring brood, Summer brood, and other varieties of this insect. Again, the Brimstone (*R. Rhamni*) is so rare that I have seen but one taken in five or six years, whereas *R. Cleopatra*, its representative on the Mediterranean, is one of the commonest insects from the coast as far north as Lantosca or Bollena. The male Cleopatra may be attracted and captured by waving a light green muslin net. This is of course the colour of the female. Dark green will not do.

Another point which must strike any one who compares the Northern Lepidoptera with those of this district is the great size and beauty of these latter. The largest European species are *Jasius, Machaon, Podalirius, Circe*, with its sober uniform of black and white, and *L. Populi.* We have all these except the last. The gigantic moth *Saturnia Pyri* measures six inches across the wings. When it flies into your room and upsets your candle you might easily mistake it for a bat. One often finds the great, shaggy, brown cocoon on walls and tree trunks.

If insects from this district are measured against individuals of the same species from the north of Europe, a striking difference is frequently apparent. Thus, we have found specimens of *S. Carpini*, measuring an inch more than the type.[34] In an unbearably hot corner of the mountain district, a variety of *Satyrus Dryas* occurs, which is so much larger and handsomer than the type that one can hardly believe it to be the same insect. Even this great prize could not tempt us to pay a second visit to the fiery furnace where it flies. A magnificent variety of *Lycæna Arion* is to be found near Nice. Other instances might be given.

SATYRUS CIRCE

Many of the butterflies of the Maritime Alps are so local that you may live within a short distance of the spot where they abound, and yet seldom see them. Thus the coal-black *Satyrus Actea* swarms in a particular part of the Fenestra Valley, but is rare elsewhere. *Melanargia Syllius*, a kind of Marbled White, is extremely abundant on the sea rocks east of Nice, but to the west of the town you will find scarcely a single one. *Lycæna Orion* is so plentiful at the north end of the St. André gorge that you can catch as many as you wish; but I know of no other locality nearer than Levens. Cannes has almost a monopoly of the beautiful *Thais Polyxena*; Nice of the lovely *Euphenoides*; Hyères has the *Jasius*, king of European butterflies, and also the exquisite little *Thestor Ballus*.

The rare and valuable *Thecla Roboris* is confined to a spot not many hundred yards in extent. This butterfly is purple without streak or spot. *P. Alexanor* does not extend above St. Martin nor below Bollena. It is so rare that only one other locality is known in France, viz., Digne in the Basses Alpes. We have thus in the Maritime Alps three out of the four European Swallow-tails; the fourth, *P. Hospiton*, is confined to Corsica.

The distribution of a butterfly is governed by that of its food plant, and this depends in great measure on the nature of the soil. Elevation is a less important factor. *Satyrus Arethusa* does not reach the elevation of 3,000 feet in the Vesubia Valley, but it is plentiful at Caussols, above Grasse, at 3,800 feet. The Painted Lady (*V. Cardui*), whose larva eats the thistle, is universal, like that weed, and seems to care nothing about elevation. You may see it battling, with ragged wings, against the mountain breeze, 8,000 feet above sea-level. Other Butterflies appear, like that page in Marmion, unable to brook the chilly air; but the fact is that they are tied to their food plant, which grows upon the sheltered coast. The Apollo, depending on Saxifrage and Sedum, does not descend much below 3,000 feet.

Thus a knowledge of Botany is the key to the study of the Lepidoptera. More numerous and more perfect specimens are obtained by searching for the larva on their proper food plant than by racing about in the burning sun. You may collect caterpillars towards evening, when the heat has abated and the valley is in shade. These larvæ are brought up in cages, carefully protected against ichneumons. When they have pupated, they are transferred to a ventilated case designed for the purpose.

The greatest drawback to Butterfly collecting is that, even when kept in expensive cabinets, the insects are rapidly destroyed by breakage, "grease," and mites. Unless constantly renewed by fresh specimens, a collection soon disappears. Nature-printing has many advantages, of which these are a few:—

1. The collection is imperishable, cannot be broken, or attacked either by "grease," or by mites, an equally destructive plague.
2. A new specimen does not necessitate a re-arrangement, for the pictures are mounted upon separate cards.

3. Half as many insects only are required; for the same individual gives both upper and under side.

4. Specimens may be sent by post without fear of damage. Thus great trouble and expense are avoided in naming and exchanging.

5. The date, name, and locality cannot be separated from the insect. When this happens a Butterfly loses all interest.

6. A collection of hundreds, or even thousands, may be quite easily carried about, whereas even a small boxful of Butterflies, set in the ordinary way, is an encumbrance when travelling. This is an important point; for it is a great advantage, when working in a strange district, to have one's collection at hand for reference. No books can replace the actual specimen, and no book gives a complete series of the variations of each species.

7. We dispense with the complicated apparatus of setting boards, setting pins, body pins, &c.

8. Butterflies may be killed by benzine, or in any way that is convenient; for it matters nothing if they become rigid.

9. No damp-tin is required for collecting, and all the trouble of relaxing is avoided.

10. We escape the great expense of a cabinet or air-tight boxes. These boxes cost five shillings each, and twenty of them are soon filled. A collection stored in any other way does not last many months.

Compared with these advantages, the drawbacks are insignificant. The principal objections to Nature-printing are the following:—

1. The bodies, antennæ, &c., are wanting. These may be drawn in. This is the only objection really worth considering, and it applies only to museums and public collections. For scientific purposes, an insect should be perfect. But a private collector must adopt the simplest and most practical system. A person who has any other occupation in life cannot spare time for the tedious operation of doctoring diseased specimens, nor can ordinary people afford the expense of replacing Butterflies which are damaged or destroyed.

2. Some transparent-winged species, such as Cratægi, cannot be printed.

3. Certain species, especially in the genus Lycæna, lose their brilliancy (but on the upper side only) by having the scales reversed

as they are in the nature-printing process. Other species, however, print so well that it is not possible to tell the copy from the original. 4. It takes rather longer to nature-print a Butterfly than to set it in the ordinary way.

A book on Nature-printing has been published. None of the methods explained in this work are perfectly satisfactory. Doubtless many improvements will be discovered when naturalists turn their attention to this matter.

So rich is the insect fauna of this region that the Butterflies (*Rhopalocera*) are by no means perfectly known. The late M. Millière, of Cannes, did excellent work in his own district. But a great deal remains to be done. As regards the Moths (*Heterocera*), we are still further from a complete knowledge. New species are constantly discovered. M. Wagner, a music master, has lately found a new Burnet (*Zygæna*) on the Mt. Chauve, that is, within a walk of Nice. There are spots near the coast as yet quite unexplored from an entomological point of view. Any beginner who puts a light in his window at nightfall will catch moths which no lepidopterist in Europe, not even Dr. Staudinger, can name.

In this chapter, and in previous ones, I have mentioned a good many of the handsomest insects. A few more may be added. The Eleven-line Podalirius (*Undecimlineata*) occurs near Nice: my wife found the neat, pointed, red-brown pupa on the wall of a cottage, and kept it on the chance of a surprise. A fortunate find! A rare Thais (*T. Medesicaste*) may be taken in places where the *Aristolochia Pistolochia* grows; for instance, in the Esterel, and at Duranus. If you are not afraid of sunstroke, you may easily supply yourself and your friends with the dazzling *P. Gordius*, and many another Butterfly which would seem to have strayed from the tropics. The Looking-glass Skipper (*Cyclopides Morpheus*) is reported from Berthemont. The great hairy larvæ of *Lasiocampa Pini* feed on the Cypress trees of the Nice château. The cocoons are spun up in the twigs of these same trees within easy reach, and are plentiful enough, but it requires sharp eyes to see them. *Plumistraria* swarms among the pines on a certain date not easy to hit off. The smooth, fat caterpillars of *D. Vespertilio* may he picked off the Epilobe. I have often watched the Striped Hawk Moth (*S. Livornica*) laying eggs on the flowers of Dock

PAPILIO ALEXANOR

(*Rumex*). This is not mentioned among its food plants. A number of small larvæ may be beaten off such plants as the shrubby Dorycnium.

At Alassio, Mr. G. H. Bryan found the following just beginning to come out about the 1st of April:—*Machaon, Podalirius, Belia, Cleopatra, Egeria* (continental form), *Baton, Alceæ, Pamphilus* (pale var.). *Edusa* and *Megæra* were abundant. At Mentone a week later the same entomologist found *Daplidice, Rubi, Melanops, Argiolus, Phlæas* (dark var.), *Sinapis* (with vars.), *Egea* (on old walls), *Euphenoides, Orion, Icarus, Alveus, Hyale.* At Hyères, in the third week in April, he found *Ballus* (fairly common), *Melitæa Cinxia* (emerging), *Belia* (also fresh, with var. *Ausonia*), *Cardamines, Helice, Ilicis, Astrarche, Sao, Antiopa* (hibernated), *Polychloros* (also hibernated), *Thais Cassandra* (on April 24th, on the Pic du Fenouillet), and *Lycæna Bœtica.*

Certain butterflies appear to migrate. I have seen *V. Cardui* crossing the Nice valley steadily and swiftly from dawn till dusk for several successive days. They did not fly together, but separately, each one hurrying along as if he wished to overtake those in front. An enormous number must have passed. They seemed to come from the south-west, and to make for the hills; but I could form no conjecture about their origin or their destination.

I give in the Appendix a list of the Butterflies which occur in the Maritime Alps. My son has taken all excepting those marked with M. Millière's name. The Moths are so numerous that even if I knew them, I could not give a list. But I include the beautiful little Burnets (*Zygænas*) which fly by day, and also some of the Sphinxes, on account of the great interest which attaches to them.

A useful book is Kirby's "Manual of European Butterflies."

Notes:

34   Mr. W. T. Kirby tells me that he considers this fact to be remarkable, because the tropical representatives of European or Japanese butterflies are generally smaller. But the fact here stated is confirmed by Mr. G. H. Bryan, Sc. D., F.R.S.: see *Science Gossip*, March, 1899.

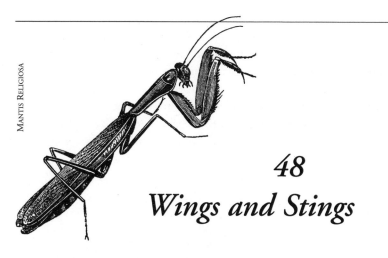

48
Wings and Stings

"An insect of what clime I can't determine,
That lifts its paws most parson-like, and thence
By simple savages—thro' sheer pretence—
Is reckoned quite a saint among the vermin."

TH. HOOD

MANTIS RELIGIOSA.—These curious-looking creatures are sure to attract the attention of strangers. How well they are designed to deceive the eye; how well adapted to seize their unsuspecting prey! Truly the Mantis is the very incarnation of grab, with his prominent eyes and muscular front legs. These last he keeps curiously folded: hence the name "Praying Mantis." Fit emblem of predacious piety!

The green-coloured species lie concealed in the foliage which they closely resemble. The thin, dry, brown sort simulate a withered twig. If they do not chance to move, the sharpest eye will not detect them. These wingless ones are immature. The thorax is elongated, and the small serrated abdomen is turned upward like a tail. The whole attitude and appearance of the creature is so comical that you almost condone its ugliness.

Mantis is a cannibal. If two of them are shut up together, they will fight until the weaker is killed and eaten. Even in the immature stage they will destroy each other. When kept a short time without food, one of these insects will devour its own legs. If irritated or threatened, the head is thrown back so as to bring the sword-like front legs into action, the wings and wing covers are spread out to shield the abdomen, and a rustling sound is heard as when a turkey-cock trails his wings upon the ground.

In its fighting attitude it is rendered still more vicious-looking by a couple of dark spots resembling snake's eyes which appear on the thorax. This refers to the common Riviera species.

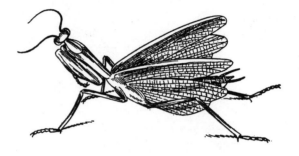

MANTIS IN FIGHTING ATTITUDE

With all its ferocity, the Mantis is said to be abjectly afraid of so small a creature as an ant!

The range of Mantis extends as far north as Vienna, Geneva, and Le Havre.

The papery egg-clusters are common and easy to find. They are attached by the pointed end to a stone. Each one contains many rows of eggs.

These animals are very tenacious of life, and seem to require but little moisture; some species are found in deserts far removed from water. They present a remarkable instance of reflex action. If the first segment, with the head and the powerful front legs, be severed from the body, this latter, raised on the remaining legs, will behave as if still alive. On the other hand, the detached portion of the thorax, which contains a ganglion (nerve centre) will still thrust out the great hooked claws, grasping and grabbing as greedily as ever; and this without the head. An insect Mortmain! I have not tried this experiment, and have no desire to do so. I am content to take Dr. Carpenter's word for the fact.

The Mantis is worshipped by Hottentots and Bushmen: a strange object of veneration; but some of the ideals of polite society are stranger still.

Hornets frequented the Lilac (*Syringa*) bushes in my garden. Although I wished to find out what they were doing, I hesitated at first to approach near enough. One does not care to take any liberties with Hornets. They went to and from a large Lilac so regularly and at such

EGG-CLUSTER OF MANTIS

short intervals that I supposed there must be a nest concealed somewhere there. But I soon discovered that they were perching on the stem, and apparently sucking the sap. They invariably settled on spots where the bark had been removed so as to form a scar. But though I came within less than two feet of the insects at work, I was not able to determine whether they made these wounds on the stem, or only took advantage of those already existing. I found that the Lilacs in other gardens were similarly infested by Hornets. Those which came from the same direction seemed to be friendly, but if a couple coming from opposite quarters met on a Lilac stem one of them became angry. Upon this the other dropped, as if shot, without waiting to be touched. The Hornets in our garden never took any notice of us; and though they are plentiful on the Riviera, I never heard of any one being stung by them. From a note in the Journal of the Selbourne Society, I learn that the ash, an allied plant, is treated in the same way by Hornets in England.

The Scorpion, again, is a creature which is not as black as it is painted. We suppose the insect to be peculiarly venomous, like an adder, an asp, or a cockatrice. We shudder at the vague but terrible words of the rash young king who threatened to chastise his unruly subjects with Scorpions. We are prepared for something dangerous and deadly, and are almost disappointed when we find that the Riviera Scorpions are as harmless as black-beetles. At least, that is my experience of them.

I do not know whether they appear in town houses, as I have fortunately never lived in the town. But they are common enough in the country. I have found them in the chinks of a wooden bedstead, where I would much sooner find Scorpions than certain other insects. Centipedes, again, are much more disgusting. Out of doors you may discover Scorpions under stones in any damp place.

It is believed that these creatures will commit suicide if surrounded by a ring of hot ashes, or placed in any position from which they cannot escape:

> "The mind that broods o'er guilty woes
> Is like the scorpion girt by fire:
> In circle narrowing as it glows,
> The flames around their captive close."
> BYRON

I once saw one of these ugly little lobsters in a bad predicament. He was on a small dry point of rock which rose out of a mountain torrent. As far as I could judge, he showed no signs of dejection or despair; on the contrary, he ran towards my bare foot at a great pace. I left him on his desolate island. To save the life of a Scorpion (or a lawyer) would be to push humanitarian principles to an absurd extreme!

I wonder how the Scorpion gained a place in the Zodiac. If the honour were bestowed on use or beauty, the bee or the butterfly would have been chosen instead. Perhaps he pushed his way up, as some men do, by making everybody afraid of him. "Sic itur ad astra!" But it has been noticed that Scorpions are very plentiful in Egypt when the water of the inundation is subsiding. Thus, the Scorpion would come to be associated with a certain period of the year, as the swallow is a herald of Summer, or the falling leaf a warning that Winter is at hand. The sign of the Scorpion in the Zodiac, therefore, marks the month when the

Nile falls back. This explanation takes it for granted that the science of astronomy originated in Egypt rather than Chaldea.

Those mysterious "Scorpion-men" of the Chaldean mythology show that this creature, like the snake, was regarded as a symbol of evil.

The natives call the insect "Escropion," by metathesis; just as the Crocodile becomes in popular Italian "Coccodrillo." I have used the word "insect," but I do not mean to imply that the Scorpion belongs to the class Insecta. He has eight legs. Some terms are forced upon us. Thus we speak of a "silkworm" and a "black beetle," though we know that Bombyx is no worm, and that Blatta is no beetle.

The Scorpion has as many as four pairs of lungs. There are some persons, alas, who would be quite satisfied to possess one pair moderately sound.

But the worst tormentors in this region are the flies. More to be dreaded are they than Hornets or Scorpions. One insect is particularly troublesome, for it resembles a house-fly so closely that you may easily be stung while off your guard.

SCORPION

CICADA

49
Insect Minstrels

"Nunc cantu crebro rumpunt arbusta Cicadæ;
Nunc etiam in gelida sede lacerta latet."

THE three great performers are the Cicada, the Grasshopper, and the Mole Cricket. Of these, the first holds the palm. The Cigale is a true musician. In vain the Grasshopper rubs and rasps his hard front wings together, and the Mole Cricket sends up from the entrails of the earth his subterranean sounds. Marsyas is no match for Apollo.

There is nothing ethereal about the Grasshopper with his solid body and coarse appetite. He has great ability, perfect command of his instrument, and marvellous execution, but no genius; the divine afflatus is wanting. We listen, but we feel no rapture; for we know we could make as loud a noise ourselves if we worked with sufficient energy.

But we love the *Mole Cricket*: we delight to listen to his song, for he is one of the harbingers of Spring. When we hear towards evening in the Olive grove the merry sound, like the tinkling of an electric bell, but sweeter far, we know that Summer is nigh, that the swallows are due, and that the Quince tree will soon be decked with its porcelain blossoms. There is something mysterious about this music issuing from beneath the earth. So must the strains of Orpheus have echoed forth from the dark caves of Tænarus as he descended to the lower regions to claim the lost Eurydice.

This insect is able to enjoy himself in solitude: like the Greek philosopher, he has learnt the secret of associating with himself. Diogenes may be perfectly happy in his cask, but then he can peep out through the bung-hole and see how the wide world is going on. Whereas Gryllus can see nothing whatever from the bottom of his burrow; nor is it likely that he can hear anything; his own voice is far too loud.

"Que faire dans un gîte, si l'on ne songe?"

says the poet: but the cricket does nothing of the sort. Dream and ponder! Not he. He makes merry in his dark retreat. "Est Ulubris."

Lest any one should take me to task for enjoying the music of the Mole Cricket, I will shelter myself behind an authority which no naturalist will venture to impugn. Says Gilbert White: "Sounds do not always gives us pleasure according to their sweetness and melody: nor do harsh sounds always displease. We are more apt to be captivated or disgusted with the associations which they promote than with the notes themselves. Thus the shrilling of the field Cricket, though sharp and stridulous, yet marvellously delights some hearers, filling their minds with a train of Summer ideas of everything that is rural, verdurous, and joyous."

To dig out a Mole Cricket is an almost hopeless task, but I have heard that they may be captured in this way: You insert into the hole a halm of grass, so as to tickle the Cricket. He loses his temper. Musicians frequently have "la tête très près du bonnet": did not Händel smash his violin on the head of a man who missed an accidental? He catches hold of the straw, and sticks to it so tight that you can draw him out of the hole. My son tells me that after rain he has found the Mole Cricket singing close to the entrance of his burrow. He can then be easily captured. Perhaps he finds the basement of his dwelling damp in rainy weather, and moves to the upper story.[35]

To Mr. W. F. Kirby I am indebted for the following note: "It is said that if you throw water on the ground in the evening, and cover the spot with a board, you will find Mole Crickets underneath next morning, if there are any about."

What a persevering performer is the Cricket! His repertoire is limited, for he knows but one single tune. Indeed, his compass is also small, for he has but one single note. It is said that no insect has more than one note. Most song-birds have two or three: the nightingale alone has four or five notes. The Cricket makes up for these defects by abundant verve and brio. His little score is marked fff, and the pace is fast and furious. Whenever the spirit moves him he strikes up, and he stops when he can hold out no longer. He may be out of tune; he cares not a rap. I have heard a Cricket quite a semitone flat. Up somewhere in the seventh position, so to speak, he shrills his strident solo. The altos may come in where they can. His style is simple; but for staccato and pizzicato who can beat him?

Older than the song of birds is the music of the Cricket. The Palæornis of the Weald, and that strange feathered creature of the Solenhofen States, may seem to us to be incalculably ancient. But they are new-comers on this planet, if we compare them with the great Cricket of the old Devonian age. "The stridulating or musical apparatus of this primeval insect" (says Lyell) "introduces us to the sounds of the Devonian woods, bringing before our imagination the trill and hum of insect life that enlivened the solitudes of these strange old forests."

Thoreau would postpone any business to hear a Cricket sing. Yes, the simple sounds and sights of Nature are a necessity to certain men. The townsman knows not the meaning of this; nor can he understand the painful and paralysing effect of the pandemonium roar of London upon the man who loves the wilds.

Now we come to the Cicada. How to describe her song? I shall not venture to attempt it. Anacreon has called the Tettix "blessed": what further compliment is needed? The Diva of the insect world would scorn our little bouquets. Hers are no modest drawing-room pieces, but a wild, fierce, passionate whirling chant, like that of the sun worshippers of old, as they danced intoxicated round the image of their god. Her melody has no monotony: for touching, as it were, an organ stop, she makes her music rise and swell and pulsate till the air is laden with the sound.

As a sign that they were natives of the soil, the Athenian ladies wore in their hair a golden ornament, which Virgil calls a Cicada:

> *"Aurea solenni comptum quem fibula ritu*
> *Cecropiæ tereti nectebat dente Cicadæ."*

But Virgil is clearly wrong, for the Cicada lives in trees: it is the grasshopper which clings closely to the soil, rising but a short distance on his scarlet wings, and returning quickly to the sod. A golden Locust was doubtless the ornament which nestled in the locks of the Athenian women.

The Cigale is confounded with the grasshopper by persons who have not visited the sunny South, nor heard the insect stridulate. I have a copy of La Fontaine's Fables, with handsome full-page illustrations. The artist, no Provençal evidently, has drawn the Cigale as a Locust or grasshopper. Now, the Cigale, with its long transparent wings and wide-set eyes, has no resemblance to a Locust. Probably the poet knew a Cigale from a grasshopper, but indeed a man who failed to recognise his own son may easily have overlooked the distinction between one insect and another.

The Cicadæ of Brazil are said to be audible at the distance of a mile, if the voice of a man held the same ratio to his size, he could be heard the whole world over!

The song of the Cicada begins to be heard in the last days of June, when the temperature approaches Summer heat, that is 75 Fahrenheit. A species of Cicada is kept by the Japanese in little cages of beautiful construction, just as song-birds are by us. I have seen these cricket-cages for sale in Nice.

It is affirmed that the Cicada occurs in the New Forest, and that the insect has even been captured and identified. There is something incongruous about Cigales in Hampshire: why not fire-flies in Hyde Park, or humming-birds in Hoxton? Mr. Kirby informs me that the Cicada of the New Forest is small, and does not chirp loud.

While I write of insect sounds, one point occurs to me; a point not settled yet. We are all familiar with the soothing murmur of the myriad bees that swarm among the greenish yellow blossoms of a Linden tree. You may hear the same sound if you stand beneath a Judas tree (*Cercis*) in April when the branches are lined with red. By the way, "Judas" is here a corruption of "Judæa." Now this insect buzz is heard at times when no insect can be seen. Resting in a shady spot not far from where I lived, we have listened to this *Summer hum*, and yet completely failed to ascertain the cause of it. The sharpest eye could not discern a winged thing of any sort or size. We might be tempted to suppose that the insects which make this noise are too far off to be seen by the naked eye: but in this case their buzzing could surely not be heard. Nor were they hidden in the sod, for I examined that carefully. I came to the conclusion that a better naturalist might solve this riddle, which is beyond my powers. But Gilbert White also failed to explain this apparently simple matter. Jefferies is here at fault, he touches on the question, but does not seem to be aware of the difficulty. I am inclined to think that these sounds have no connection with insect life, but are similar to those commonly heard in certain valleys of the Rocky Mountains, in the Sinaitic Peninsula, and elsewhere. There seems to be something cosmic about this murmuring of the Summer air; something mysterious: we are tempted to call it a "vibration of the universal lyre."

Humboldt thus vividly describes the phenomenon; but his words leave an impression of vagueness and of mystery:—"If beyond the silence we listen for the faintest undertones, we detect a stifled, continuous hum of insects, which crowd the air close to the earth; a confused murmuring sound which hangs round every bush, in the cracked bark of trees, in the soil undermined by lizards, millipedes, and bees; a voice proclaiming to us that all nature breathes, that under a thousand different forms life swarms in the gaping and dusty earth, as much as in the bosom of the waters, and in the air which wraps us round."

There is a cricket in this region which makes a sound so birdlike that no person would believe himself to be listening to the stridulation of an insect. Being in doubt, I inquired of a peasant, who told me that the sound did not proceed from any bird. And in these mountains there is another insect which utters towards evening a single clear bird-like note. I was deceived for a long time by this sound, but one evening I traced it to a small box bush: striking this with a stick, I found that no bird flew out. This experiment I repeated on several occasions with the same result.

Anacreon's Ode to the Cicada is thus translated by Thomas Moore:

"O thou, of all creation blest,
Sweet insect that delight'st to rest
Upon the wild wood's leafy tops,
To drink the dew that morning drops,
And chirp thy song with such a glee
That happiest kings may envy thee!
Whatever decks the velvet field,
Whate'er the passing seasons yield,

Whatever buds, whatever blows,
For thee it buds, for thee it grows.
Nor yet art thou the peasant's fear,
To him thy friendly notes are dear,
For thou art mild as matin dews,
And ever when the summer hues
Begin to paint the gloomy plain,
We hear thy sweet prophetic strain;
Thy sweet prophetic strain we hear,
And bless the notes, and thee revere.
The Muses love thy shrilly tone,
Apollo calls thee all his own:
'Twas he who gave that voice to thee,
'Tis he who tunes thy minstrelsy.
Unworn by age's dim decline,
The fadeless blooms of youth are thine.
Melodious insect! child of earth!
In wisdom mirthful, wise in mirth;
Exempt from every weak decay
That withers vulgar frames away;
With not a drop of blood to stain
The current of thy purer vein;
So blessed a life is passed by thee,
Thou seem'st a little deity."

MOLE CRICKET

Notes:

35 The Mole Cricket I believe *always* sings close to the entrance of his burrow. My sons capture it with the greatest ease, thus:—Approach on tiptoe with bull's eye lantern; when sure of the position, cut off the retreat into the burrow by plunging a spade into the earth; the cricket is then easily taken.—T. H.

MOSQUITO

50
Mosquitos

SHAKESPEARE says that "Gnats are unnoticed wheresoe'er they fly." But this does not apply to the *Culex pipiens*. This variety of gnat is very much noticed wherever he flies, or rather wherever he perches. Indeed, the new arrivals from England talk about little else.

I do not know whether the Mosquito has hitherto been regarded as a test of character; but it has often occurred to me that the student of human nature might derive both entertainment and instruction from observing the effect of a Mosquito-bite upon persons of different idiosyncrasy, thus:—

The *intrepid* man hears the buzz without quailing.

The *irascible* man slaps his own face, in the vain hope of crushing one.

The *vindictive* man kills a great number and arranges their bodies in a row.

The *fussy* man goes about with a bottle of liquid ammonia.

The *sceptical* man disbelieves in Mosquitos; he says it is all "prickly heat."

The *profane* man wishes that Noah had not allowed any Mosquitos to enter the Ark.

The *credulous* man believes that tobacco smoke will keep them off.

The *malingerer* excites pity by pretending that he has not slept all night.

The *extravagant* man burns half a box of pastilles before going to bed.

The *sensational* man shows you his hand swollen to the size of a pumpkin, and tries to make you believe that a Mosquito has done it.

The *mendacious* man swears that a Mosquito bit him through the sole of his boot!

The *hopeful* man puts his trust in an "Indian recipe" which takes three weeks to prepare, and is not ready yet.

The *vain-glorious* man sucks lemons till he makes his blood so sour that the Mosquitos won't touch him; then he triumphs over every one.

The *eccentric* man sleeps with gloves on, and his head in a bag: he says he has no bites; but ask him to show you his wrists!

The *scientific* man catches one, and examines it under the microscope.

The *audacious* man sleeps without a curtain.

The *awkward* man gets his foot outside the curtain.

The *absent-minded* man forgets to pull his curtain to.

The *unlucky* man has a hole in his curtain.

The *statistical* man calculates how many bites to the square inch.

The *speculative* man wonders what the bite would be like if a Mosquito were the size of a barn-door fowl.

The *taciturn* man scratches persistently, but makes no remark.

The *nonchalant* man pretends that his bites don't itch; but he has a good scratch when no one is looking.

The *mysterious* man has no curtains to his bed; he scorns pyrethrum and pellitory powder; will have nothing to say to elder leaves, "fidibus," or any other remedy; yet he is never bitten.

The *sensible* man does not trouble himself much about Mosquitos; nevertheless he uses a strong expression now and then, when they pitch upon a tender spot.

I may as well mention that these persons were living under one roof in a villa on the Cimiez hill in the year 1882. I had the pleasure of meeting the "vindictive man" quite lately. He is a most good-natured person (when not dealing with mosquitos), and is head of a business firm in the Midlands. The "nonchalant man" has gone to Australia. Others, perhaps, have taken a still longer journey.

Every one is anxious to hear of a remedy for Mosquito bites. Alas! I do not know of any cure; but sufferers may comfort themselves with the hope that medical men, such is their insight into the secrets of Nature, will in due time find out a lymph or virus or pus or putridity of some sort, which, inoculated upon our bodies, may preserve us against Mosquito bites; just as we are now guaranteed against all danger from small-pox, phthisis, rabies, cholera, and many other diseases.

Meanwhile I will mention, *pro bono publico*, a method of prevention which, as the proverb says, is better than any cure. This method was imparted to me by Sir Thomas Hanbury, the esteemed owner of the famous gardens at La Mortola, near Mentone. It is thus: you procure a small fish, the greediest, most gluttonous and guzzling that may be had, and you put him in the tank, pond, or reservoir in your garden. That is all; the rest you leave to the working of natural laws. Now the enemy, the Mosquito that is, has his weak moments like the rest of us. He passes one stage of his existence in the water; here he is condemned to float head downwards, and to breathe through the tip of his tail. In this predicament he can neither buzz nor bite; on the contrary, he is perfectly helpless, and the carp that you have put into the tank, pond, or reservoir, gives him no quarter. In fact, the Mosquitos get fewer and fewer as the carp becomes fatter and fatter.

It is obvious that if there were a carp in every tank, pond, or reservoir, there would be no Mosquitos. The only difficulty is that your neighbour may have a pond devoid of fish; and the Mosquitos which ought to bite him may find their way in at your bed-room window, for the insect is no respecter of persons.[36]

Another method of keeping off Mosquitos, which may be described as humanitarian, is strongly recommended by the same authority. It is very simple: you place a saucerful of honey by your bedside, and the Mosquitos are supposed to regale themselves with this, instead of sucking your blood. With all deference to the opinion of Sir Thomas, I question whether this carnivorous little vampire can be so suddenly converted to a vegetarian diet. These sudden conversions are always more or less dubious. But I leave it to my readers to try the experiment for themselves.

The plan adopted in Brazil is somewhat less refined, but probably a good deal more effective. The people here (says the great naturalist Wallace in his delightful book about the Amazon valley) all use cow-dung, burnt at their doors, to keep away the "plague," as they very truly call the Mosquitos; for this is the only thing that has any effect. In the evening every house and cottage has its pan of burning dung, which gives rather an agreeable odour; and as there are plenty of cattle about, this necessary of life is always to be procured.

It is said that the Castor Oil Plant (*Ricinus*) keeps off Mosquitos, and that it is grown near houses in Egypt for this purpose.

Canon Scott Holland is the inventor of a strategic system. You are supposed to elude the hungry insect by moving furtively from one bed to another. This may be all very well if you have to deal with the more unsophisticated sort, but the Riviera Mosquitos could not be hoodwinked by any such manœuvres; they would soon find out which bed you are in.

W. H. Hudson ("Naturalist in La Plata") states that Mosquitos vanish as if by magic when a dragon-fly appears. It has therefore been suggested that one or two dried dragon-flies suspended from fine silk, under the roof of an open porch infested with Mosquitos, will scare all the little pests away, and they will not come back while the dragon-flies are there.

Scientific investigators have discovered that Mosquito larvæ cannot endure paraffin oil. One drachm poured on the surface of a pool about a square yard in area is sufficient to destroy all the larvæ. As they keep to the surface, I suppose that the depth of the water does not matter.

I propose next to describe a method which is of my own invention. It is known that a water plant called Utricularia devours not only small insects, but even very minute fish just hatched. The plant is covered with little bags or open bladders; if an insect or a fish puts his head into one of these bags, he is lost. Now, the larvæ of gnats, if I do not mistake, are captured among other small fry by the Utricularia. Then, why not supply each tank, pond, cistern, and reservoir with a plant of

Bladderwort? You might put in a carp as well; then if the Mosquito did not come to grief by peeping into a bladder, the carp would be sure to do for him.

The Chinese plait a kind of "creeping jenny" into a rope, which they light at the lower extremity and hang near the bed. This, it appears, smoulders slowly, emitting a pungent, aromatic, not wholly unpleasant odour, very unacceptable to the Mosquitos, which keep at respectful distance.

There is by the Danube mouth a snake which devours Mosquitos. A traveller in the Dobrudsha found one of these creatures by his bed-side, and was about to kill it; but seeing how usefully it was occupied, he spared its life. After a short time this animal became tame enough to take Mosquitos and other insects from his hand. Mr. Barclay does not explain how the snake managed to catch the Mosquitos. As they seldom settle on the floor, it is not easy to see how a reptile could reach them. Why should not some ophiologist introduce this serpent to the Riviera? The hotels might then advertise "Snakes in every bedroom; no extra charge!" Those who object to snakes might try the Chick Chack (*Ptyodactylus*), a common lizard of the Malay Archipelago. It is warranted to keep a house clear of Mosquitos.

The Swedish globe-trotter Sven Hedin was wrought to such a pitch of furious resentment by the attacks of the Lob Nor Mosquitos that he set fire to the whole neighbourhood. Then, as he drew the excellent picture of the conflagration which he gives us in his book, he gloried in the thought that millions of his enemies were being roasted to death. There is certainly a great deal of thoroughness about this method, and it may possibly be found suitable in out-of-the-way places where there are no policemen; but it would never do to set fire to the Grand Hotel in order to get rid of the Mosquitos!

The Arctic explorer, Mr. E. Rae, on the other hand, makes light of Mosquitos. He left Vardö thus equipped: The face smeared with a mixture of oil and tar, in addition to this a coffee-coloured net veil, and a pair of gloves reaching to the elbow, thickened with whalebone and strong enough to turn a sword cut. Protected in this manner, he sarcastically sketches the insect as *Culex pabulator*, *Culex volans*, *Culex repletus*, and *Culex cogitans*.

When Nansen landed on a desolate part of the Greenland coast, he found swarms of Mosquitos ready to receive him. Darwin asks what Mosquitos find to eat in those regions which are not inhabited by human beings. If Darwin does not know, of whom shall we inquire? The question is abstruse. What do spiders live on where there are no flies? lawyers where there are no fools? priests where there are no dupes? These investigations lie beyond the scope of Natural History; they belong to the domain of philosophy. We will therefore dismiss them as too recondite for these humble pages!

Malaria is believed to be caused by a parasitic protozoon which destroys the red corpuscles of the blood; and it is said that the Mosquito is the chief agent in spreading this contagion. "Were there no Mosquitos there would be no ague." On the other hand, a naturalist who has studied this insect in the tropics affirms that its main business in the larval stage is to purify polluted water. Mr. Rodway placed some of the immature Mosquitos in a glass of water which was teeming with the most pestilent microbes and bacteria. Before long the water was absolutely pure and wholesome. But before we accept the Mosquito larva as a scavenger, and take his early virtues as a set-off against the sins of his adult stage, we must be quite certain that the disappearance of the microbes is not due to the larger animalcules which are in their turn devoured by the Mosquito.

It is said that a spider will starve rather than eat a mosquito. Perhaps he fears the malarial infection!

It is the female Mosquitos that treat us so badly. The male is a harmless and well-behaved insect, which never thinks of biting anybody: he is in fact so very abstemious that he eats nothing at all. No ritualist could fast more rigorously: his life is one long Ramadan.

If the note produced by the wings of the Mosquito is imitated, the insects of the other sex will flock to the spot. This note, familiar enough to us, but much less attractive, alters under certain circumstances. If you light a pastille, the Mosquitos, fleeing from the fumes, buzz about close to the ceiling. As soon as ever the pungent odour reaches them, the note made by their wings rises to a higher pitch, as if, rendered desperate by the smell, they were increasing the rapidity of their flight.

Those who take a special interest in Mosquitos should visit the Étang des Pesquiers at Hyères. If the supply of these insects ever ran short on the Riviera, this extraordinary sea-girt swamp could furnish as many myriads as might be required.

Notes:

36 Sir Thomas explains that a single fish is not sufficient to keep down the Mosquitos. "I put three to six," he says, "or in a very big tank, a dozen." The following information on this burning question contains his *ipsissima verba*: "The cesspools of hotels and villas are the worst haunts of the Mosquitos: there the larvæ exist and thrive, no matter how foul the water is. *Remedy*: Metal gauze over the ventilating aperture to prevent the insect passing. *General remedy*: Insist that the landlord provides a proper net, not an ornamental curtain to your bed, and take care to tuck it in thoroughly before retiring to rest."

51
The Tarantula

THE natives call any living creature which they particularly object to a *Tarantula*. In fact, this word is used here much as orthodox people apply the word "heretic"! What is a "heretic"? Any one who says anything the priest does not like: this is Luther's definition. Similarly, a Tarantula is any animal of any sort to which you happen to have an aversion. In Nice the harmless Gecko is a "Tarantula"; and dearly he pays for being called by a bad name. As soon as this lizard appears in any respectable house, the tocsin is sounded, and the miserable little reptile is done to death. But what is his offence? None that I can discover, unless it be that he is really able to walk on the ceiling, a feat which few other creatures can perform successfully.

NEST OF TRAP-DOOR SPIDER

The real genuine Tarantula is not a Gecko, nor any other lizard, but a spider. In order that you may know all about this famous insect, which has prompted so many musical compositions, I translate the following detailed and most accurate description from an old French work on Entomology kindly lent me by Miss S. Rose:—

"The Tarantula is a species of spider, very injurious and venomous. It is a little larger than the spiders which we usually find. It has on each side four feet, each of which has four joints: it has also hooked claws. With the four anterior feet it walks forward, but with the others it retreats. It lives in a concavity of the ground, at a depth of two feet. Into this hole it thrusts itself by the posterior part of its body, so as to preserve the more carefully the food which it is dragging in with the front feet. In order to be the better protected from all external annoyance, it closes the entrance; and for this purpose uses straws rather than any other substance, so that it may be able to draw its breath freely, and not be suffocated for want of air.

"The upper part of the body is of an ashy hue, with red spots on the back. If you turn the insect over, you observe that the belly below is yellowish, and the abdomen is marked with black spots in some places. She has in her mouth two blackish hooks with which she bites and takes her food. She weaves a web also, as do other spiders, and catches in it flies and butterflies and animals of divers species, which she lives upon. She lays about sixty eggs, which she warms and hatches with her breast, and she carries the young ones about until they are large enough to shift for themselves.

"The temperament of the Tarantula is cold, damp, and phlegmatic. This is proved by the fact that she can live a long time without eating, even as much as fifty days. In the second place she is hurtful only in the Summer, that is, in the months of June, July, and August, when the heat is most intense. For the poison is then warmed, and has power to do harm, being liquefied by the sun. But when the weather is cold it is destitute of all energy. It is evident in the third place, from the sticky web which she weaves, that she has a great deal of viscous moisture which she uses in spinning.

"You must also know that if a person has been bitten by this animal, the effect of the poison does not appear at first; but it works slowly, and produces its malign consequences only after the lapse of a year. In six months after the bite, however, certain symptoms are usually noticed, such as lassitude, chill, fever, nausea. As the Summer advances the most extraordinary phenomena are produced in the bodies of those who were stung the year before. For some do nothing but sing and laugh incessantly: others, on the contrary, weep and are silent, as if bereft of speech. Some are overcome by continual slumber, others are perpetually awake. Some are seized by great sadness and a terrible dread, imagining that they are confined in prison; while others, again, conduct themselves like madmen, being possessed by the idea that they are kings and sovereigns, and that they have acquired a universal dominion all over the world.

"Some authorities add that those thoughts which occupied the mind at the time of being stung remain after the poison has worked its way. As a general rule the victims of the Tarantula listen with pleasure to the sounds of musical instruments: and if peradventure one can light upon the note which accords with the evil which they are suffering, they set themselves to dance, observing exactly the cadence of the tune; and by this violent exercise, accompanied by great perspiration, they are gradually cured: for the poison is insensibly dissipated, and quits the body which has been invaded by it. But if, unfortunately, the diapason of the music is not in concert with the nature of the disease, the suffering of the patient is only increased thereby, and he does not set himself to dance. So that we must be careful to employ musicians, who by their experience and skill may be able to discover those harmonies which are best suited to restore the patient to his former health.

"Some of those who are under the influence of this poisonous spider will show a preference for certain colours; green, yellow, red, and so forth. These different effects depend upon the varying constitution of the person who is stung, and also in some measure upon the nature of the particular spider. Similarly we observe that the effect of strong drink varies according to the temperament of the drinker: he may become warlike, or jovial, or sleepy, or witty, or talkative, or liberal, or boastful.

"The Tarantula herself is of such a nature that, when she hears the sound of musical instruments, she begins to dance after her own fashion. Nowhere are the effects of her sting so much to be dreaded as in the province of Pouille. This is due partly to the heat of the climate, and partly to the fact that spiders of this district are peculiarly venomous."

The romance of this quaint old naturalist is not without some elements of fact. The subterranean burrow of his Tarantula may well have been derived from some traveller's account of the Trap Door Spider. The mythical insect is represented as taking care of its young ones. This, again, is founded on fact, for I have seen a large black spider so completely covered with young ones that its body was hidden by them. With regard to the influence of music upon animals, some experiments tried lately by a violinist in the London Zoological Gardens tend to show that many animals, whether they enjoy harmonies or not, are keenly sensitive to discord.

Perhaps there is an allegory concealed in the statement that a person stung by a Tarantula falls under the dominion of the thoughts which occupied him at the time. It may well be that the Angel of Death hands each man over to the complete control of his ruling passion; and that we thus obtain for ever that which we have loved and longed for in this present state.

Galton ("Travels in South Africa") describes the real Tarantula[37] as a poisonous black spider which is an important ingredient in the Bushman poison. It seems to be, for its size, the most venomous of creatures. Death is frequently the consequence of its bite. A young man who was with Galton lingered between life and death for a long time after being bitten by one. Though a quick runner, the Tarantula has short legs. When teased with a twig, it snaps its flippers together, and makes a distinct noise with them. The panacea for all poisonous bites among Mr. Galton's party was the oil from their tobacco pipes.

There is a minute spider considered poisonous by the natives. This insect is of a bright yellow colour, and lives gregariously in a web which radiates from a centre in all directions. When at rest they are gathered together in a dense cluster, but, if you touch the web, an innumerable swarm of little spiders spread themselves like golden beads along the threads. Then they slowly re-assemble. These centrifugal spiders are seen in Spring by the roadside everywhere on the Riviera. I have not often seen them in England.

In the hill district there is a huge hairy creature which tries to walk across the ceiling and falls off. This insect illustrates the derivation of the word "hideous" from the Latin "hispidus," rough, hairy.

Dr. Allen Sturge (my kind and skilful medicine man) found a small bird caught in a spider-web. This web was weighted with a pebble. It would be interesting to know whether this spider regarded the bird as a welcome or unwelcome capture. I think that the insect must have raised the pebble into the air by pulling on a line which he had, as he supposed, made fast to the ground. It is not likely that he carried the stone up the tree, and then hung it from the web.

But the spiders which attract most attention are the remarkable species which close their little burrows with a lid. These Trap-door Spiders are described in a book by Moggridge. They are abundant in the Vallon Obscur, Nice, and common on mossy banks.

Notes:

[37] The Tarantula (*Lycosa tarantula*) derives its name from the city of Taranto in Italy, where this venomous spider abounds. The disease supposed to be occasioned by its bite was known as *Tarantism*, the cure of which by means of music led in the middle ages to the composition of songs and tunes that still survive under the name of *Tarantella.*—T. H.

52

Ligurians

WHEN Hercules was returning from his toilsome journey to the distant west, driving before him the red cattle of the sunset, he passed along this Cornice or ledge of coast: for so the story runs. The natives tried to rob him of the oxen which he had won from King Geryon. The hero defended himself. The natives avoided coming to close quarters with so terrible a foe: they hurled rocks upon him, and showered stones from every eminence. This is the Ligurian method of warfare—

> *"Instare jugis et grandia volvere saxa."*

Had not Jupiter succoured the demigod, he must have had the worst of the encounter. And is not the stony plain called "Crau," between Avignon and Marseilles, a witness of the fact?

The Ligurian still flings stones: does any one offend him, he stoops to pick one up. Even the ancient heroes sometimes fought in this manner. Perseus, attacked while seated at his marriage feast, snatches a log from the hearth and throws it, though girded with the magic sword of Mercury. And the last effort of Turnus was to seize with hurrying hand a mighty stone and fling it at his foe. The resident on the Riviera becomes an adept at avoiding stones!

It cannot be denied that these people are much given to strong language. I lived in a house where the road made a double bend; it was rare that a carter could guide his horses round that corner without an oath. One day the following announcement appeared in a local paper printed in English: "Grand International Cursing Match; first prize 10,000 frs." Some new variety of wickedness, I thought. But no: it was merely a misprint for "Coursing." If ever there were an "International Cursing Match" (which Heaven forbid) there are no people anywhere who could hold their own for a moment against the Niçois. Of course, all this strong language is not to be taken seriously. It is merely used for the sake of emphasis and ornament, and is very different from the coarse profanity of the English proletariat.

The Ligurian has altered little since ancient times. It is doubtful if the population of any district can ever radically change; for a given region produces men of certain character, just as the fauna and flora vary with the nature of the soil and the conditions of the atmosphere. You may plant a country with an alien race; but these strangers will gradually disappear, or else the new-corners will change to the type which they have supplanted. The greater ferocity of the invaders may maintain them for a time; but climate is against them, and diet. Of each generation those only survive who approach nearest to the type that is suited to its environment; until at last the invaders are either absorbed or killed off by disease, and no trace of them remains. How few of the tall blue-eyed, yellow-haired Kelts are left in Ireland! The earlier race of short dark men has swallowed them up. What strain of Gothic blood remains in North Africa; or even in Spain, though the Spaniard may boast himself "Hidalgo" or son of the Goth?

There is a sense in which all peoples may be called autochthonous, for each new inroad from the frozen north or from the dismal plains of Asia is but a new branch grafted, as it were, upon the ancient stock which still persists. It is not without reason that Englishmen delight to call themselves "Britons," and that in France "un bon Gaulois" means "an honest fellow." For the invasion of the fifth century AD has left us "Britons" still; and France, though "Frankish" in name, preserves to this day both the virtues and the vices of the ancient Gaul. Even the brilliant Athenians, the instructors of the world in art and letters, were not ashamed to call themselves "Pelasgi," for they knew that many of their own high qualities were inherited from that earlier race with whom the hard and warlike Aryans had amalgamated.

The original Ligurians extended southward into the peninsula. French ethnologists regard the brachycephalic (short-headed) as the true Ligurian type, but Professor Sergi ("The Mediterranean Race," English version, 1901) includes them, together with the Iberians, Pelasgi, and Libyans, in that dolichocephalic (long-headed) race which occupied in pre-Aryan times the Mediterranean region and also the western countries of Europe. To this same family belonged the long-barrow men

VIEW IN THE FENESTRA VALLEY

of France and Britain. The Rhone was the dividing line between the Ligurians and Iberians. Mr. Hall ("Romans on the Riviera") has an interesting chapter on the ethnology of Liguria.

When the plebeian Marius, having supplanted his former general, Metellus, had taken the command of the Jugurthine war, he was well-nigh frustrated by a rocky fortress which, with all his military skill, he was unable to reduce. The troops were discouraged, and a failure would rob him of that favour of the mob which had raised him into power. His position was critical, and fortune seemed to have deserted him. Now there is no sorrier spectacle than a demagogue who is "down in his luck," who has staked everything upon some venture which he cannot carry through, and is unable to go either back or forward. From this dilemma a Ligurian, a soldier in an auxiliary regiment, saved Marius. This man had left the camp to search for snails; and as he scrambled along the rocky base of the hill on which the stronghold stood, filling his helmet with the molluscs, and stopping now and then to thrust back those which were trying to crawl out again, he found a precipitous path which led up to the top. By this the hill was scaled, and the treasures of the king fell into the hands of Marius.

I said that the Ligurians had altered little since ancient times: here is a proof of it. This soldier was both a snail-eater and a wonderful climber: so are his descendants of the present day. After each shower of rain you may see numbers of people searching the walls and banks and hedgerows, as if intent upon some branch of natural history. They are, in fact, ardent conchologists, but their collection is confined to those specimens which they consider edible. If you have a native servant, she will keep your garden clear of snails.

Virgil (Bk. xi.) is not complimentary to the Ligurians. Their chief is represented as fleeing from that Volscian Virago. When the hostile queen approaches and he hears her dreadful threats, his courage fails him, and he would fain escape. "You shall never again," says she, "feast on Ravioli in the hospitable shade at Villeneuve Loubet, nor join the pious pilgrimage to Laghet: never again shall you celebrate the gay Carnival with cap and bells and parti-coloured domino." In another minute he will be run through the body by this warlike woman, so the wily Ligurian takes refuge in a stratagem. "Would Camilla have any

objection to fight on foot? If she will dismount, he will do the same."
Quite ready to oblige, the amazon springs from her warhorse, and hands
the bridle to a friend. Then the Niçois puts spurs to his steed, and hopes
by hard galloping to escape his fate. But his fair enemy is far too swift:
she can speed o'er the standing corn, and scarce disturb the ripening
ears: she can skim the waters, leaving but a faint ripple on the surface of
the stream. What a strong-minded female was this Virgin Camilla!

As might be expected, in a district overrun by so many races, Greeks,
Romans, Moors, and others from the north, there is a great variety of
features and of type. One ugly kind of brachycephalic skull is far too
common: a misshapen head, narrow in front, and so broad behind as to
give the cranium almost a triangular outline. On the other hand, we not
unfrequently see men of handsome features and of fine physique.

The Ligurians, whatever their failings, are cheerful and good-natured
folk, polite, and for the most part pleasant to deal with: "*poulit e real,*"
as they say themselves.

53
The Sunny South

"La Prouvenço ounte l'oulivo afloco
Sus li pendent de touti il coustiero."

THE natives of these parts are, as a rule, frugal and laborious, but, once their work is over, there are no mortals in this world more festive. They pass their cheerful life, to use Victor Hugo's words:

"Aux rayons d'un ciel sans nuages,
Parmi le myrte et l'aloès."

A lady of the English middle class came in from a walk with the report that there was a great fight going on in an open place near the new Boulevard, and such a crowd! "Did not the police interfere?" some one inquired. "No; why ever should they?" The other next asked how long the fight had been going on. "Well, it began yesterday afternoon, and they tell me that these fights often last two or three days." "Goodness gracious!" exclaimed her friend, "a fight going on for two or three days, and the police don't interfere: how shameful!" Fortunately some one then turned up who understood the Cockney accent, and it became clear that nothing worse than a "fête" was taking place.

These "fights" begin in Spring, and they continue all through the Summer, mostly on Sundays, but often on week days as well. Sometimes there are two or three fêtes going on in different parts of the town at the same time. Each trade and business has its special fête: the tramway men, clerks, printers, and so forth. Then every village and hamlet has its festin, at which all the country side is welcome. There are even fetes which seem to have no pretext whatever. A very small inducement is enough to set these festive people dancing. Haweis says that they dance badly: I hesitate to contradict the great Broad Church divine, but they certainly ought to be proficient, for they have six months' uninterrupted practice every year.

To me it seems that the dancing of these Ligurians is marked by much modesty and by a complete absence of vulgarity.

Canon Hole ("Nice and her Neighbours") is even more uncomplimentary: he denies that a Frenchman can kick! If he only saw the Chasseur Regiment at drill, he would change his opinion.

Our "skirt dancers," and certain ladies of society, boast that they can kick a hat off a peg six feet from the ground: This is doubtless an elegant accomplishment for a lady, and a proof of great activity; but the Chasseur is the champion kicker. To see these men at their military exercises, one would suppose them to be a troupe of acrobats. They "lift a lively leg," as Burns would say, raise one foot to the height of a man's head, and spin round and round like a ballet dancer, kicking the whole time. No Englishman could do it. A kicking match between two of the drill instructors is an extraordinary sight. They spring up and down like grasshoppers: first a box on the ears, then a kick in the face, then a foul stroke with the half-closed fist, for which an English boy would be sent to Coventry, even in the lowest Commercial Academy. There are many things in France which a person of cosmopolitan ideas may view with much complacency, but this military kicking drill is so unmanly, so utterly ungraceful and undignified, that one is amazed to see any men submitting to it. We were always on excellent terms with the polite, good-natured, and well-behaved soldiers of the Chasseur regiment in St. Martin Vesubia.

Two elements make up a native fête, dancing and gambling: there is not much drinking and guzzling. I have seen as many as eight little gaming tables in a row. The variety of systems is infinite, from the lottery or "Tombola," to pure roulette. The simplest and commonest arrangement consists of a circular board which supports a pyramid of cheap crockery. This revolves with a clicking sound which never ceases at these fêtes.

The two great Ligurian games are Mora[38] and Bowls. Of the former a ludicrously inaccurate description is given in one of Howells' books. It is clear that this writer has never played the game, nor even taken the trouble to look on while a couple of mule drivers dashed their knuckles on the table, shouting "three! seven! five! four!"

Bowls, as played here, is a simple and primitive game. Any bit of waste ground will suit, or even the dusty road. Herbert Spencer criticises the attitude of the "Discobolus"; but the statue is absolutely accurate: this is the proper position for a man "pointing" at the game of bowls. Nearly every one can play billiards, for the game is cheap and is not disreputable. The passion for cards is characteristic of the south of Europe; these people are so constituted that they can sit half the day at cards. They will even begin before dinner. To the people of the North there is something incomprehensible about this almost Eastern sluggishness.

On the eastern Riviera the Italian national game of *Pallone* or hand-ball may be seen. It is played here without any regular court on the ciassa or piazza in the middle of the village.

The various *Provençal Dialects* are popularly supposed to be either a corruption of French or else a mixture of French and Italian. They are rather to be regarded as remnants of the old "Langue d'Oc," a Romance language parallel with French, Italian, Spanish, and Portuguese. All these were equally derived from Latin. The "Langue d'Oil," or northern French was spoken by men more warlike and more barbarous; the southern dialect, "sounding of sweet Provençal song and sunburnt mirth," as sings the poet Keats, by a race more refined and more effeminate. In the smiling plains of Provence, says Demogeot, the new language which took the place of Latin was perfumed with the dying odours of Roman art and civilization, and resonant with the soft echo of melodious sounds. Provençal, now a despised patois, was at one time the most polished dialect in Europe, fashionable in courts and made famous by the love songs of the Troubadours.

"The Troubadour—judged by present-day commercial standards—seems a being ill-fitted to deserve the plaudits of posterity; yet the debt we owe to these wandering minstrels of Provence is indeed incalculable. For they kept alive in ages of turmoil, brutality, and lust those ideals of romance and of beauty by which nations are made great."

But we must not forget that this ancient language has other and nobler titles to distinction than the serenades of minstrels; it was used for the hymns and services of the Albigenses, and became in a manner identified with this cruelly persecuted faith. In France, as in England,

St. Martin Vesubia

language followed the fortunes of the people who spoke it. The struggles of Wessex with Mercia and Northumbria caused two of the three English dialects to disappear. Similarly, the decay of the Langue d'Oc is due to the rivalry between the northern and southern provinces of France, which ended in the sanguinary defeat of the Albigenses and their subjugation to the spiritual despotism of Rome. From this date the Langue d'Oc gradually sank.

As Dante called Italian the language of "si," the word for "yes," so the southern French took the name of the Langue d'Oc from the Latin "hoc," used for "yes"; and the northern dialect that of Langue d'Oil from the Latin "illud."

The three great pilgrimage resorts for the Nice district are Laghet, Utelle, and the Madonna di Fenestra. *Laghet is* just behind Turbie, near the head of a valley which opens into the Paillon. The peasants flock to Laghet from a great distance, even from beyond Mentone. *Utelle* is north of Nice, on a commanding mountain top, not far beyond Levens. This "high place" is the rendezvous for the people of the mountain districts, as Laghet is for those of the coast. The *Madonna di Fenestra* stands at the head waters of the Vesubia torrent, beyond the Summer resort of St. Martin Vesubia. This sanctuary is 6,000 feet above sea-level, and 2,000 feet below a col, which is crossed by a mule path into Italy. The Madonna dwelling here presides over the Alpine regions: her title is "Queen of Heaven," "Regina Cœli." The cognomen "Fenestra" is derived from a "window" or hole in the rock through which the souls of her devout adherents fly upwards to the empyrean.

The image in this shrine is supposed to have come down from heaven like that Ephesian one of old.

Under the chapel are caverns, in which they say that the ice never melts. Though she has her home so near to the perpetual snow, this goddess finds the Winter too severe. Accordingly, she is carried down the valley, with much perspiration, by her faithful worshippers to winter-quarters in the shelter of the village. The spot where this Celestial Virgin reigns throned among the snows is indeed worthy of the "Queen of Heaven." The rustling Pine woods form her sacred grove; and stationed round, guarding as it were the portals of her temple, stand rugged peaks, inspiring awe and reverence—

"The Alps,
Those palaces of Nature, whose vast walls
Have pinnacled in clouds their snowy scalps,
And throned Eternity in icy halls
Of cold sublimity."

A religion in such close sympathy with Nature, and so deeply penetrated by the sense of Beauty, may well laugh to scorn the narrow systems bred in the dull brains of unimaginative bigots. Rome may deny progress and proscribe enlightenment, she may plunder the poor and fawn upon the rich, she may sink deeper and deeper into corruption and political intrigue; but she will nevertheless continue to sway the fairest regions of this world so long as her opponents divorce Religion from the love of Nature and the worship of the Beautiful.

Picturesque customs survive in some of the more distant villages. For instance, the young folk celebrate the Summer solstice by leaping through the bonfires which are lighted in each open place. When the weary villagers have gone to rest, St. John, for he is the patron of this day, throws over the smouldering embers his mantle of camel's hair; and the next morning, early, those who search the ashes will find "St. John's Hairs," a precious treasure and talisman to be preserved. I suppose that these "hairs" are thread-like crystals formed by the melting of some substance which has fallen on the flames.

Before the annexation in 1860 the Var formed a line of demarcation between the ignorant and easy-going semi-Italian people to the east, and the more enlightened and energetic French population to the west. This line has now shifted eastward as far as Turbie, for Nice is completely Gallicised: not so Monaco and Mentone. Turbie is the true frontier; it was so in Roman times, and must be so again: "hucusque Italia, dehinc Gallia." When France exacted payment from Italy for her help against the Austrians, she grabbed too much. Mentone must return to Italy.

The natural frontier follows the line of water-parting between the tributaries of the Paillon and of the Vesubia on the west, and those of the Bevera and of the Roya to the east. This line runs almost due north from the Cap d'Ail (or Aglio) close to Monaco, by the Tête de Chien, Turbie, Mts. Agel, Baudon, and Ours, between Escarène and Sospello, to the Carmette and the Aution; thence to the crest of the Alps, leaving to France the head-waters of the Fenestra and Boreon torrents, which in fact can hardly be approached from Italy.

I find this confirmed by Francis Galtoni. It is. well known, he says, that when you cross the high ground between Nice and Mentone, the country to the east is wholly Italian in its colours and its aspect; whereas that to the west of Turbie is unmistakably French. By "French" of course he means "Provençal."

Notes:

38   The game of Mora is one of the most widely spread; it was known to the Ancient Egyptians, and when I lived in China I found the natives there were adepts at it.—T. H.

54

Problems To Solve

THE following Problems connected with Natural History are a few of those which have interested me, and which I commend to the attention of Naturalists on the Riviera:—

Chapter I. Does it benefit a decaying palm-tree to split the trunk vertically?

Chapter II. Can an orange be grafted on a pomegranate?

Chapter III. Will an olive-seed germinate without passing through the body of a bird?

Chapter VI. Are the seeds of the cultivated Fig ever known to germinate?

Of what use, if any, is the Urginea to the Fig?

Is Broussonetia able to ripen its fruits on the Riviera?

Is it the nature of the Celtis to have one branch in full leaf and another equally healthy one quite bare? Or is this due to some defect of soil or climate?

Chapter VII. Has the angle of ramification of a given tree any relation to the average slope of the ground to which that species is adapted?

Chapter VIII. Phyllotaxy of the cone of *Pinus pinaster?*

Chapter IX. Can Jasius larvæ be raised on rose leaves?

Do Arbutus fruits cause paralysis?

Chapter X. Origin of the operculum in the flower of Eucalyptus?

Does Punica possess deciduous staminate flowers?

Chapter XI. Etymology of "Fraxinet"?

Chapter XII. What conditions govern the capricious distribution on the Riviera of *Euphorbia dendroides?*

Purpose of the imitative seed of Ricinus?

Are the fruits of *Euphorbia lathyris* innocuous, the plant being poisonous?

Why are the Conifers confined to the northern slopes of the mountains?

Chapter XIII. Has the flowering of the *Arundo donax* any connection with the weather?

Is it due to the drier air of Nice that Thais is wanting, and that tree-ferns do not flourish as well as at Cannes?

Chapter XIV. Are hermaphrodite (perfect) Maize flowers rare?

Chapter XVII. Does *Capparis spinosa* in this district ever turn the edges of the leaves to the sky? Does the fruit ripen?

Chapter XX. What is the wall-plant which revealed the existence of a ruin?

Chapter XXIII. *Nicotiana glauca* and *Diplotaxis tenuifolia* are conspicuously successful in resisting drought. In virtue of what special adaptation do they thus flourish almost without water?

Wanted, a complete list of Riviera leafless plants.

Chapter XXIV. Is the drooping habit of some Junipers correlated with the fact that the stomata are more numerous on the upper side of the leaf?

From what district are the small fruits and seeds derived which occur frequently in the wool with which mattresses are stuffed?

Chapter XXV. Why should a field be covered with the lobes of Opuntia?

Can certain plants, such as Agave and Urginea, be compelled to flower by cutting off the leaves?

Chapter XXVIII. What can be done to prevent the extermination of such flowers as the wild Peony?

Chapter XXIX. Has the irrigation by the water of the Vesubia canal appreciably affected the climate of Nice?

Why do Latin authors call the Myrtle "bicolor"?

Does my observation on the flowers of *Lilium bulbiferum* hold good for all localities?

Chapter XXXI. Does the prickly collar round the seedling of *Medicago denticulata* keep off snails?

And does this same spinous pod prevent ants from carrying the seed underground and eating it?

Chapter XXXIX. At what time of year did the nativity of Christ take place?

Chapter XL. Is there any germ of truth in the popular belief that Genepie is stored in the body of the chamois for winter consumption?

Chapter XLI. Is the dark-coloured Myoxus of the St. Martin district a variety of *M. glis*, or a different species?

Chapter XLIII. Can a connection be traced between the failure of the olive crop and the persistent destruction of insect-eating birds?

Chapter XLIV. Is any lizard on the Riviera unable to endure the midday sun in Summer?

Is the phenomenon of œstivation observed in many plants beside *Euphorbia dendroides?*

Chapter XLVII. Whence and whither does *V. cardui* migrate?

Chapter XLIX. Has any naturalist given a *definite* explanation of the "Summer hum"?

Chapter LIII. What are "St. John's hairs"?

APPENDIX I

List of Butterflies

BUTTERFLIES of the Riviera and the Maritime Alps, with the more conspicuous species of Sphinx and Burnet.

N.B.—The names are from Staudinger.

MILL. signifies that the species is given on the authority of Millière; M., mountain; L., local; A., alpine; R., rare.

RHOPALOCERA:
Papilio
    Podalirius.
    Alexanor, M. L.
    Machaon.
Thais
    Polyxena, L.
    Medesicaste, L.
Parnassius
    Apollo, M. A.
    Mnemosyne, MILL., A.
Aporia
    Cratægi.
Pieris
    Brassicæ.
    Rapæ.
    Napi.
    Callidice, A.
    Daplidice.
Anthocharis
    Belia.
    v. Ausonia.
    v. Simplonia, M. R.
    Tagis v. Bellezina [?],
    MILL.
    Cardamines.
    Euphenoides, L.
Leucophasia
    Sinapis.
Colias
    Palæno, MILL., A.
    ab. Verdandi, MILL., A.

Phicomone, A. L.
    Hyale.
    Edusa.
    ab. Helice, R.
Rhodocera
    Rhamni, M. R.
    Cleopatra.
Thecla
    Betulæ, M.
    Spini.
    W-album, R.
    Ilicis.
    Acaciæ, MILL., R.
    Roboris, M. L. R.
    Quercus.
    Rubi.
Thestor
    Ballus, R. L.
Polyommatus
    Virgaureæ, M.
    Thersamon v. Omphale
    [?], MILL.
    Hippothoë, M.
    v. Eurybia.
    Alciphron, MILL., M.
    v. Gordius.
    Dorilis, M.
    v. Subalpina, M.
    Phlæas.
Lycæna
    Bœtica, R.
    Telicanus, L.

Aegon.
    Argus, M. A.
    Orion, L.
    Baton, L.
    v. Panoptes [?], MILL.
    Orbitulus, M.
    Astrarche, L.
    Icarus.
    Eumedon, M. R.
    Amanda, M.
    Escheri, M.
    Bellargus.
    Corydon.
    Hylas, M.
    Meleager, M.
    ab. Stevenii, M.
    Dolus [?], MILL.
    Admetus v. Ripartii, M.
    Damon, M.
    Donzelii, MILL.
    Argiolus.
    Sebrus [?], MILL.
    Minima.
    v. Lorquinii.
    Semiargus, M.
    Cælestina [??], MILL.
    Cyllarus, M.
    Melanops, R. L.
    Iolas, MILL.
    Arion, L.
Nemeobius
    Lucina, M.

Libythea
  Celtis, R. L.
Charaxes
  Jasius, R.
Apatura
  Ilia ab. Clytie, M. R.
Limenitis
  Camilla, L.
Vanessa
  Egea.
  ab. J. album.
  C. album, L.
  Polychloros, M. R. L.
  Urticæ
  Io.
  Antiopa.
  Atalanta.
  Cardui.
Melitæa
  Cynthia, A.
  Aurinia v. Iberica v.
  Provincialis, MILL.
  Cinxia, M.
  Phœbe, M.
  Didyma.
  v. Occidentalis, M.
  v. Alpina, M.
  v. Meridionalis, MILL.
  Athalia, M.
  Parthenie, M.
  v. Varia, M.
Argynnis
  Selene.
  Euphrosyne, M.
  Pales, A.
  Dia, L.
  Amathusia, M.
  Daphne, M.
  Hecate [?], MILL.
  Lathonia, M.
  Aglaja, M.
  Niobe [?], MILL.
  v. Eris, M.
  Adippe, M.
  ab. Cleodoxa, R.
  Paphia.
  ab. Valesina.
  Pandora [?], MILL.

Melanargia
  Galathea, MILL.
  ab. Leucomelas, M. R.
  v. Procida, M.
  Syllius, L.
Erebia
  Epiphron, M.
  v. Cassiope.
  Melampus, MILL.
  Manto, MILL.
  v. Pyrrha, MILL.
  Ceto, M.
  Medusa, MILL.
  Stygne, MILL.
  v. Pyrenaica, M.
  Evias, M.
  Epistygne, M. L.
  Tyndarus, A.
  v. Dromus, A.
  Gorge, M.
  Goante, M.
  Neoridas, M.
  Æthiops, M.
  Ligea, M.
  Euryale, M.
Œneis
  Aëllo, A. R.
Satyrus
  Hermione.
  Alcyone.
  Circe.
  Briseis, M.
  Semele, M.
  Arethusa, M. L.
  Statilinus, M.
  Fidia [?], MILL.
  Dryas, M.
  Actæa, M. L.
  Cordula, M.
Pararge
  Mæra.
  Hiera, M.
  Megera.
  Ægeria v. Egerides.
Epinephele
  Lycaon, M.
  Janira.
  v. Hispulla.

  Ida, R.
  Tithonus.
  Pasiphaë, MILL.
  Hyperanthus, M.
Cænonympha
  Iphis, M.
  Arcania, M.
  Dorus, M.
  Pamphilus.
Spilothyrus
  Alceæ.
  Altheæ.
  Lavateræ.
Syrichthus
  Tessellum, MILL.
  Sidæ, MILL.
  Carthami.
  Alveus.
  Calcaliæ.
  Malvæ.
  Sao.
Nisoniades
  Tages.
Hesperia
  Thaumas.
  Lineola.
  Acteon, R.
  Sylvanus.
  Comma.
Cyclopides
  Morpheus, MILL.
Carterocephalus
  Palæmon, MILL.

HETEROCERA:
Acherontia
  Atropos.
Sphinx
  Convolvuli.
  Ligustri.
  Pinastri.
Deilephila
  Vespertilio, M.
  Galii, M.
  Euphorbiæ.
  Nicæa, R.
  Livornica.
  Celerio, MILL., R.

Elpenor.
Porcellus.
Nerii, R.
Smerinthus
Tiliæ.
Quercus, L.
Ocellata.
Populi.
Pterogon
Proserpina, M.
Macroglossa
Stellatarum.
Bombyliformis, R.
Fuciformis, MILL.

Zygæna
Erythrus, MILL.
Pilosellæ, M.
Scabiosæ, M.
Orion, M. R.
Sarpedon, MILL.
Achilleæ.
Exulans, A.
Meliloti, MILL.
Trifolii, MILL.
Loniceræ.
Stœchadis, L.
Filipendulæ.
Transalpina, M.

Ephialtes, ab. Medusa, M.
Lavandulæ.
Rhadamanthus.
Hilaris, M. L.
Fausta, M.
Carniolica, ab.
Berolinensis, M.
Occitanica.

APPENDIX II

Opinions of Distinguished Botanists

I am reading the "Riviera Nature Notes" with great enjoyment. They are full of information, admirably told.

    SIR JOSEPH HOOKER, F.R.S.

An extremely interesting and suggestive book.

    Journal of Botany

The author is a well-grounded botanist, who knows the district and the flora.

    PROFESSOR BOULGER

Fort intéressant.

    M. C. NAUDIN, *Director of the Botanic Gardens at Antibes*

Un rayon de soleil du Midi.

    M. H. CORREVON, *Director of the Alpine Garden, Geneva*

Ihr Werk über die Riviera hat mir ausserordentlich gefallen.

    PROFESSOR O. PENZIG, *Genoa*

FURTHER READING

A selection of general, botanical and horticultural literature spanning a century:

Rambles on the Riviera
Eduard Strasburger, trans O. & B. Comerford Casey, T. Fisher Unwin, 1906

Along the Rivieras of France & Italy
Gordon Home, J. M. Dent, 1908

Common Objects of the Riviera
I. & H. Chamberlain, George Routledge & Sons, 1913

The Englishman's Holiday: A Social History
J. A. R. Pimlott, Faber & Faber, 1947

The First of Trees: The Story of the Olive
Robert Standish, Phoenix House, 1960

The Naturalist's Riviera
A. N. Brangham, Phoenix House, 1962

Flowers of the Mediterranean
Oleg Polunin & Anthony Huxley, Chatto & Windus, 1965

Flowers of Europe
Oleg Polunin, Oxford University Press, 1969

Flowers of South-West Europe
Oleg Polunin & B. E. Smithies, Oxford University Press, 1973

Miss Willmott of Warley Place
Audrey le Lievre, Faber & Faber, 1980

Trees and Timber in the Ancient Mediterranean World
Russell Meiggs, Clarendon Press, 1982

The Mediterranean Gardener
Hugo Latymer, Frances Lincoln, 1990

English-French Dictionary of Building, Property & Gardening
J. Kater Pollock & Lynne Forbes, Flowerpoll, 1990

Mediterranean Gardening: a Practical Handbook
Yves Menzies, John Murray, 1991

Côte d'Azur: Inventing the French Riviera
Mary Blume, Thames & Hudson, 1992

Wildlife Travelling Companion: France
Bob Gibbons & Paul Davies, The Crowood Press, 1992

The English Garden Abroad
Charles Quest-Ritson, Viking, 1992

Mediterranean Wild Flowers
Marjorie Blamey & Christopher Grey-Wilson, HarperCollins, 1993

Gardens of the Riviera
Vivian Russell, Little, Brown & Company, 1993

Gardens of the French Riviera
Louisa Jones, Flammarion, 1994

Mediterranean Gardening: A Waterwise Approach
Heidi Gildemeister, Editorial Moll, 1995

Olives: The Life and Lore of a Noble Fruit
Mort Rosenblum, North Point Press, 1996

Gardens of Italy: A Touring Guide to Over 100 of the Best Gardens
Penelope Hobhouse, Mitchell Beazley, 1998

Gardens of France: A Touring Guide to Over 100 of the Best Gardens
Patrick Taylor, Mitchell Beazley, 1998

Gardens of Provence & the Côte d'Azur
Marie-Françoise Valéry, Taschen, 1998

Create a Mediterranean Garden
Pattie Barron, Aquamarine, 1999

Wildflowers of the Mediterranean
David Burnie, Dorling Kindersley, 2000

Complete Mediterranean Wildlife
Paul Sterry, HarperCollins, 2000

Queen Victoria and the Discovery of the Riviera
Michael Nelson, I. B. Tauris, 2001

Mediterranean Plants and Gardens for Everyone
Vicomte de Noailles and Roy Lancaster, Floramedia, 2001

French Riviera: Living Well Was the Best Revenge
Xavier Girard, Assouline, 2002

Garden Plants for Mediterranean Climates
Graham Payne, The Crowood Press, 2002

France: Travellers' Nature Guide
Bob Gibbons, Oxford University Press, 2003

La Mortola: In the Footsteps of Sir Thomas Hanbury
Alasdair Moore, Cadogan Guides, 2004

Create a Mediterranean Garden
Pattie Barron, Lorenz Books, 1999

Gardening the Mediterranean Way
Heidi Gildemeister, Thames & Hudson, 2004

The Mediterranean Garden Society
www.mediterraneangardensociety.org